THE GEOMETER'S SKETCHPAD®

Windows Quick Reference

Sketch Window with Menus and Toolbox

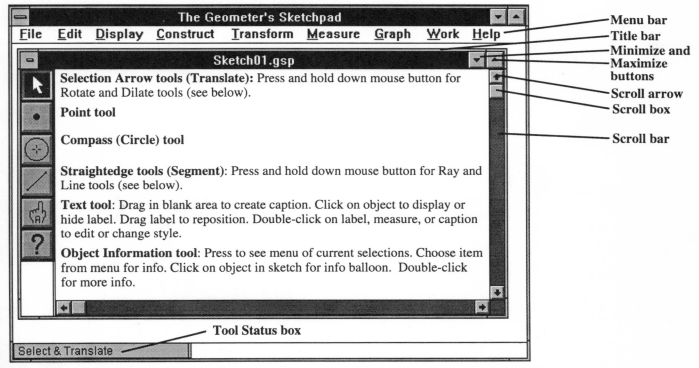

- Menu bar
- Title bar
- Minimize and Maximize buttons
- Scroll arrow
- Scroll box
- Scroll bar

Selection Arrow tools (Translate): Press and hold down mouse button for Rotate and Dilate tools (see below).

Point tool

Compass (Circle) tool

Straightedge tools (Segment): Press and hold down mouse button for Ray and Line tools (see below).

Text tool: Drag in blank area to create caption. Click on object to display or hide label. Drag label to reposition. Double-click on label, measure, or caption to edit or change style.

Object Information tool: Press to see menu of current selections. Choose item from menu for info. Click on object in sketch for info balloon. Double-click for more info.

Tool Status box

Select & Translate

Translate, Rotate, and Dilate Tools

Select and move objects in sketch with Translate tool. Drag right to choose Rotate or Dilate tool. Select a point to Mark as Center in the Transform menu. Select objects in sketch and drag to rotate or dilate.

Segment, Ray, and Line Tools

Drag right to choose Ray or Line tool. Press and hold down mouse button in sketch and drag in desired direction to construct segment, ray, or line.

Selection

Selecting one object	Click on object with any S...
Selecting additional (multiple) objects	Hold down Shift key whil...
Selecting multiple objects with marquee	Press in blank area of ske... ...of selection (marquee), release to select all objects in, or partially in, selection marquee.
Deselecting one or more objects from group	Hold down Shift key while clicking selected objects.
Deselecting all objects	Click in blank area in sketch.

File and Edit Menus, Action Buttons

File

New Sketch	Ctrl+N	Create a new sketch.
Ne**w** Script		Create a new script.
Open...	Ctrl+O	Open saved script or sketch.
Save	Ctrl+S	Save changes to active script or sketch.
Save **A**s...		Save active script or sketch with new name.
Close	Ctrl+F4	Close active window.
Print Preview...		View sketch as it will appear printed (alternates to Print Options for scripts).
Print		Print active sketch or script.
E**x**it	Alt+F4	Leave Sketchpad.

Hint: For full help on any menu command, point mouse to menu command and press F1.

Edit

Undo	Ctrl+Z	Undo last step in sketch (unlimited). Shift+Ctrl+Z undoes to beginning.
Redo	Ctrl+R	Redo last undone step in sketch (unlimited). Shift+Ctrl+R redoes all.
Cu**t**	Ctrl+X	Remove selected objects from sketch and move them to Clipboard.
Copy	Ctrl+C	Copy selected objects to Clipboard.
Paste	Ctrl+V	Paste objects in Clipboard to sketch.
Paste **L**ink		Pastes link to contents of a file copied from some other application.
Cl**e**ar	Ctrl+Del	Clear selected objects from sketch.
Action **B**utton ▶		See cascading menu below.
Select **A**ll	Ctrl+/	Select all objects (varies with active tool).
Select Pare**n**ts	Ctrl+U	Select parents of selected objects.
Select C**h**ildren	Ctrl+D	Select children of selected objects.
Lin**k**s...		Edits link to all files pasted into active sketch.
Insert **O**bject...		Inserts object created by some other application into active sketch.
Hide Toolbo**x**		Alternates to Show Toolbox (alternates to Hide/Show Comment for scripts).
Show Clipboar**d**		Show contents of Clipboard.

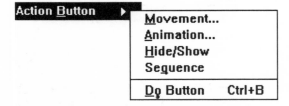

Action Button ▶		
Movement...		Create action button to move first selected point to second selected point.
Animation...		Create button to animate selected points on selected segment or circle paths.
Hide/Show		Create two buttons: one to hide selected objects and the other to show them.
Se**q**uence		Create button to play sequence of selected buttons.
Do Button	Ctrl+B	Perform action of selected button. (Shortcut: Double-click button.)

Action button tips: You can sequence inserted sound and video objects as well as action buttons. If you save your sketch with an action button selected, that button will play automatically when the sketch is next opened. Use action buttons to prepare ready-to-go presentations.

Calculator

To invoke the calculator, choose Calculate in the Measure menu or use the Ctrl-= keyboard shortcut.

The display area shows the expression being built. Click Remove to remove the last-entered quantity or operator. Click OK when expression is as desired.

Three pop-up menus list values, functions, and units you may enter into the expression. (Functions are explained below.)

The keypad has numbers, a decimal point, and operators you can click or type from the keyboard. Operators are addition (+), subtraction (−), multiplication (*), division (/), exponentiation (^) and change sign (±). Use parentheses to determine order of operation.

This is the Functions pop-up menu from the calculator. Choose a function, a quantity, and close parentheses.

sin[cos[tan[	Trigonometric functions
arcsin[arccos[arctan[	Inverse Trigonometric functions
abs[	Absolute value
sqrt[	Square root
ln[	Natural logarithm
log[	Log base 10
round[	Nearest integer
trunc[	Nearest integer toward zero
sgn[	Signum (−1 if argument < 0, 0 if argument = 0, +1 if argument > 0)

Distance[D to focus) Distance[F to Segment directrix)
pi
e

The Values pop-up menu. Choose a measurement or calculated value to enter it into the expression. (Or click on it in the sketch window.) Enter pi (π) or the base of exponential logarithms (e).

Degrees Inches

The Units pop-up menu. Choose the desired unit for a factor in the expression. For example,
Area (polygon) / 1 inch
will have distance units.

Keyboard Shortcuts

F1	Provides on-line help for tool or command pointed to by mouse.
Ctrl	Temporarily invoke Selection Arrow tool.
Up or down arrow	Move up or down to next tool in Toolbox.
Left or right arrow	Cycles current tool (including all Selection Arrow tools and Straightedges).
F4, F5, F6, F7, F8, or F9	Chooses Selection Arrow, Point, Compass, Straightedge, Text, or Info tool.
Shift+(Script name in Work menu)	Fast plays the script.
Shift+Movement (Action Button menu)	Bypass Movement Speed dialog when creating action button.
Shift+Animation (Action Button menu)	Bypass Path Match dialog when creating action button.
Shift+Animate (Display menu)	Bypass Path Match dialog when animating.
Shift+(Display menu items)	Change text formatting, line thickness, and colors without affecting display setting for future text or objects.

Note: Other shortcuts for menu choices are designated in the menus.

KEY CURRICULUM PRESS
Innovators in Mathematics Education
P.O. Box 2304 · Berkeley · California 94702

Display and Construct Menus, Preferences

Line Style	▶	Display selected and new straight objects and circles with thick, thin, or dashed lines.
Color	▶	Display selected and new objects with color.
Text Style	▶	Change text style or size for selected caption or selected objects' labels.
Text Font	▶	Change font of selected caption or selected objects' labels.
Hide Objects	Ctrl+H	Hide selected objects.
Show All Hidden		Show all previously hidden objects.
Show Labels	Ctrl+K	Show labels of selected objects. (Alternates to Hide Labels.)
Relabel Objects...		Change labels for new objects or for selected objects.
Trace Objects	Ctrl+T	Leave trace of selected objects when dragged. (Alternates checked/unchecked.)
Animate...		Animate selected points on selected segment or circle paths.
Preferences...		See below.

Choosing Preferences

Click boxes to show labels for points, straight objects, and circles as they're constructed.

Choose cm, inches, or pixels for distance, length, and area measures. Choose degrees, radians, or directed degrees for angle measures. (Clockwise point selection yields negative degree measures for directed angles.) Display measured precision to nearest unit, tenth, hundredth, or thousandth.

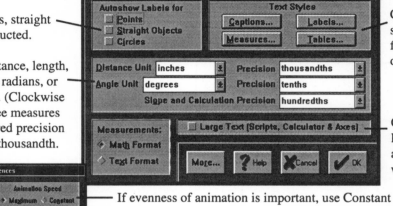

Choose fonts, styles, and sizes for various types of text.

Choose to show larger text in script and calculator windows.

Choose speed at which to play scripts.

Choose which menus appear in the menu bar.

If evenness of animation is important, use Constant (slower) speed.

Set the number of samples in newly constructed locus objects. A larger number yields a smoother locus but slows things down.

Set or clear directory used to store script tools. If set, a Script Tool tool appears in the sketch toolbar under which lie all the scripts stored in the set directory.

Set dots per inch (d.p.i.) or drag inch marker until exactly one inch long to make measurements accurate on your display screen. (These switch to metric if Distance Units are set to centimeters, above.)

Construct

Construct		Selections Required	Hint
Point On Object		One or more objects	Press and hold Object Information
Point At Intersection	Ctrl+I	Two paths	tool to verify that you have the proper
Point At Midpoint	Ctrl+M	One or more segments	selections for a given construction.
Segment	Ctrl+L	Two or more points (Switches to Ray or Line according to current tool.)	
Perpendicular Line		One straight object and one or more points (or vice versa)	
Parallel Line		One straight object and one or more points (or vice versa)	
Angle Bisector		Three points (point, vertex, point), in order	
Circle By Center And Point		Two points (center and radius endpoint), in order	
Circle By Center And Radius		One point (defining center) and one segment (defining radius)	
Arc On Circle		Three points (center and two points on circle) or circle and two points on it	
Arc By Three Points		Three points	
Interior	Ctrl+P	Three to 30 points (vertices), in order; or a set of circles or arcs	
Locus		An object and a point on a path	
Construction Help...		Lists required selections for Construct commands.	

Transform, Measure, and Work Menus

Transform

Translate...	Translate selection by fixed or dynamic polar or rectangular vector
Rotate...	Rotate selection by fixed angle or dynamic angle around point marked as center.
Dilate...	Shrink or stretch selection by fixed or dynamic marked ratio about point marked as center.
Reflect	Reflect selection across line, ray, segment, or axis marked as mirror.
Mark **C**enter "G" Ctrl+F	Mark last selected point as center for rotation or dilation (Shortcut: Double-click a point.)
Mark **M**irror "k" Ctrl+G	Mark last selected segment, ray, or line as mirror for reflection. (Shortcut: Double-click a straight object.)
Mark **V**ector	Mark last two selected points as inital and terminal points for dynamic translation vector.
Mark D**i**stance	Mark selected measurement as a distance for dynamic translation. (See more below.)
Mark **A**ngle	Mark last three selected points or measurement as angle for dynamic rotation. (See more below.)
Mark R**a**tio	Mark last two selected segments or measurement as ratio for dynamic dilation. (See more below)
Defi**n**e Transform...	Define multi-step custom transformation that created selected image from selected pre-image. Custom transformations are added to bottom of Transform menu. When custom transformations exist, use Remove Transform command to delete them.

More on Marking Dynamic Transformation Quantities

Marked vectors, angles, and ratios allow you to perform transformations based on dynamic objects in your sketch. Angles are marked in clockwise (negative) and counterclockwise (positive) order: point, vertex, point. Ratios are marked in scale factor order: numerator over denominator. Select a shorter segment then longer segment to mark a ratio that shrinks objects. Measured distances, angles, and ratios may also be marked as dynamic transformation quantities.

Measure

Selections Required

Distance	Two points, or one point and one straight object
Length	One or more segments
Slope	One or more straight objects
Radius	One or more circles, circle interiors, arcs, arc segments or sectors
Circum**f**erence	One or more circles or circle interiors
Area	One or more circles, circle interiors, polygon interiors, sectors, or arc segments
Perimeter	One or more polygon interiors, sectors, or arc segments
A**n**gle	Three points (point, vertex, point), in order (See Preferences for more on signed angles.)
ArcAngle	One or more arcs, sectors, or arc segments. Or, a circle and two or three points on the circle
ArcLeng**th**	One or more arcs, sectors, or arc segments. Or, a circle and two or three points on the circle
R**a**tio	Two segments (or three points if the Option key is held down)
Coordi**nates	One or more points
Equation	One or more lines or circles
Calculate...	No selection required. Selected measurements will appear in Values pop-up menu.
Tabulate	One or more measures
Add **E**ntry	Table (Double-clicking on table also adds entry.)

Using the Work Menu

Choose a document name from the menu to make it active.

Choosing a script while holding down the Shift key plays it (fast) in the active sketch.

Work

Make **S**cript	Make a new script describing selected objects.
Tile Shift+F5	Tile all open windows.
Cascade Shift+F4	Cascade all open windows.
Arrange **I**cons	Arrange icons of minimized windows.
Close **A**ll	Close all open windows.
1 Script01.gss	List of open windows, broken down into scripts and sketches.
√ 2 Sketch01.gsp	

Graph Menu

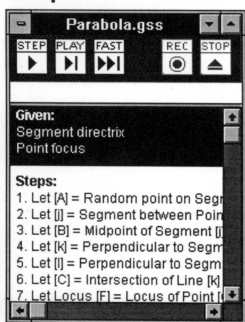

Create a coordinate system with origin at window center and unit equal to current distance unit.
Show (or hide) a grid using current unit
Toggle whether new and dragged points snap to grid
Choose between rectangular or polar grid

Plot a rectangular or polar value or point
Type or paste coordinates for points to plot

Choose rectangular or polar coordinate measurements
Choose form for selected, and new line and circle equations

More on Create Axes
With a circle selected, the command is Define Unit Circle. With a segment or distance measurement selected it is Define Unit Length. With a single point selected it is Define Origin. With a point (origin) and segment or distance (unit length) selected it is Define Axes.

Script Window

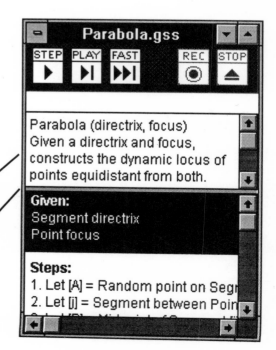

Step: Plays one step of script. (Click again to play next step.)

Play: Plays entire script, one step at a time. (Set speed in Preferences.)

Fast: Plays entire script instantly, without showing hidden objects.

Record: Starts recording construction in sketch. (Script moves behind sketch.)

Stop: Stops recording construction in sketch. Also stops and resets script during playback (Step or Play).

Given and Steps: Select objects in sketch (in order) to correspond with objects listed as Givens before attempting to play script steps.

Script objects with brackets [ ] around their labels correspond to sketch objects whose labels can vary. Double-click a step to change its label. Descriptive labels are useful in Givens to make it easier to create/select objects for playback. Any objects labeled in script steps without brackets will be given that label when the script is played.

While playing or recording script, move pointer over given or step text and press and hold mouse button to see object in sketch corresponding to given or step.

Comment: The script on the right is displaying a text comment. Drag the comment bar down to add or edit the script's comment. Comment bar appears white on scripts without comments, shaded on scripts with comments. Drag the comment bar up again to hide the comment from view. Also use Show Comment/Hide Comment in Edit menu to control script comment. The first line of a comment determines the name of the script when used as a script tool.

Text comment

Comment bar

The Geometer's Sketchpad

Exploring Geometry

With

THE
GEOMETER'S
SKETCHPAD.

Dynamic Geometry™
for the 21st Century

KEY CURRICULUM PRESS
Innovators in Mathematics Education

Exploring Geometry
with *The Geometer's Sketchpad*

Author: Dan Bennett

Editors: David Rasmussen, Steven Rasmussen, Dan Bennett

Production: Ann Rothenbuhler

Sketchpad Design and Implementation: Nicholas Jackiw

Project Direction: Steven Rasmussen

Special Thanks: Dan Chazan, Lew Douglas, Judi Mathis, David Rasmussen, Tamara Rasmussen, all the teachers who provided feedback on these activities

The Geometer's Sketchpad is a product of the Visual Geometry Project at Swarthmore College. Portions of this work were funded by the National Science Foundation. The Visual Geometry Project was directed by Drs. Eugene Klotz and Doris Schattschneider.

Research leading to the development of *Exploring Geometry* was funded by the Small Business Innovation Research Program of the National Science Foundation.

10 9 8 7 6 5 4   99 98 97 96 95

Key Curriculum Press
P.O. Box 2304
Berkeley, California 94702
510-548-2304

Exploring Geometry Sketches and Scripts Disks

Key Curriculum Press guarantees that the Sketches and Scripts Disks that accompany this book are free of defects in materials and workmanship. A defective disk will be replaced free of charge if returned within 90 days of the purchase date. After 90 days, there is a $10.00 replacement fee.

Limited Reproduction Permission

Contents

Exploring Geometry with The Geometer's Sketchpad.................................1
    The Geometer's Sketchpad and Change in Mathematics Teaching.......1
    Where Sketchpad Came From 2
    Where Exploring Geometry Came From..................................2
    Using Exploring Geometry Activities and Disks.......................3
    Using Sketchpad in Different Classroom Settings.....................8
    Exploring Geometry and Your Geometry Text 9

Four Guided Tours: Learning to Use Sketchpad 18
    Guided Tour I (Macintosh): The Freehand Tools...................... 19
    Guided Tour II (Macintosh): The Centroid of a Triangle 22
    Guided Tour III (Macintosh): Constructing a Rhombus 26
    Guided Tour IV (Macintosh): Dynamic and Custom Transformations... 30
    Guided Tour I (Windows): The Freehand Tools 34
    Guided Tour II (Windows): The Centroid of a Triangle.............. 37
    Guided Tour III (Windows): Constructing a Rhombus................. 41
    Guided Tour IV (Windows): Dynamic and Custom Transformations..... 45

Chapter 1: Lines and Angles 49
    Construction: Euclid's Proposition 1—An Equilateral Triangle......... 51
    Art: Daisy Designs 53
    Construction: Duplicating a Line Segment........................... 55
    Construction: Duplicating an Angle 57
    Investigation: Building an Electronic Protractor................... 59
    Investigation: Angles Formed by Intersecting Lines 61
    Investigation: Properties of Parallel Lines 63
    Investigation: Perpendicular Bisectors 65
    Investigation: Slopes of Parallel and Perpendicular Lines......... 67
    Investigation: Distance from a Point to a Line.................... 69
    Construction: Angle Bisectors 71
    Construction: Angle Trisector..................................... 73
    Art: Drawing a Box with Two-Point Perspective..................... 75

Chapter 2: Transformations, Symmetry, and Tessellations........................... 79
    Investigation: Introduction to Transformations................... 81
    Investigation: Properties of Reflection 85
    Investigation: More Properties of Reflections..................... 87
    Investigation: Reflections in the Coordinate Plane 89
    Investigation: Poolroom Math...................................... 91
    Problem: Feed and Water or Water and Feed? 93
    Investigation: Reflections Across Intersecting Lines............. 95
    Investigation: Reflections Across Parallel Lines 97
    Investigation: Glide Reflections.................................. 99
    Exploration: Symmetry in Regular Polygons 101
    Investigation: Tessellating with Regular Polygons 103
    Art: A Tumbling Block Design 105
    Investigation: Tessellating with Triangles 109
    Art: A Translation Tessellation...................................111

Chapter 3: Triangles 115
    Investigation: Angle Bisectors in a Triangle.................................117
    Demonstration: Excircles of a Triangle.......................................119
    Investigation: Circumscribing a Triangle 121
    Problem: A Tricky Telescope 123
    Investigation: Altitudes in a Triangle 125
    Investigation: The Centroid of a Triangle...................................127
    Modeling a Problem: The Surfer and the Spotter....................129
    Investigation: Midsegments of a Triangle 131
    Investigation: Triangle Sum...133
    Investigation: Exterior Angles in a Triangle..............................135
    Investigation: Triangle Inequalities..137
    Investigation: Properties of Isosceles Triangles.........................139
    Exploration: Constructing Isosceles Triangles............................141
    Investigation: Napoleon's Theorem...143
    Investigation: Morley's Theorem...145
    Demonstration: Triangle Congruence—SSS?...............................147
    Demonstration: Triangle Congruence—AAA?..............................149
    Demonstration: Triangle Congruence—SAS?..............................151
    Demonstration: Triangle Congruence—SSA?..............................153
    Demonstration: Triangle Congruence—ASA?..............................155

Chapter 4: Quadrilaterals 157
    Investigation: Defining Special Quadrilaterals 159
    Exploration: Properties of Quadrilaterals...................................161
    Investigation: Properties of Parallelograms 163
    Investigation: Properties of Rectangles......................................165
    Investigation: Properties of Rhombuses 167
    Investigation: Midpoints in a Quadrilateral 169
    Exploration: Special Midpoint Quadrilaterals............................171
    Exploration: Using Properties of Rectangles...............................173
    Exploration: Using Properties of Rhombuses 175
    Investigation: Properties of Isosceles Trapezoids 177
    Puzzle: Dissecting a Special Isosceles Trapezoid.........................179
    Investigation: The Midsegment of a Trapezoid 181

Chapter 5: Polygons 183
    Investigation: Exterior Angles in a Polygon...............................185
    Investigation: Inscribed Stars..187
    Construction: The Regular Pentagon..189
    Construction: Templates for the Platonic Solids.........................191

Chapter 6: Circles...193
    Exploration: Chords in a Circle...195
    Investigation: Congruent Chords in a Circle...............................197
    Investigation: Tangents to a Circle 199
    Investigation: Tangent Segments 201
    Investigation: Circles and Angles..203
    Investigation: More on Circles, Angles, and Arcs 205
    Investigation: The Circumference/Diameter Ratio 207
    Investigation: Arc Length 209
    Problem: Distance in a Circle 211
    Investigation: Tracing a Cycloid Curve......................................213

Chapter 7: Area...**215**
 Investigation: Area of Parallelograms....................217
 Investigation: Area of Triangles...............................219
 Investigation: A Triangle Area Problem................221
 Exploration: Triangle Area/Perimeter....................223
 Investigation: A Square Within a Square...............225
 Investigation: A Triangle Within a Triangle...........227
 Investigation: Maximum Area Rectangles...............229
 Investigation: The Area of a Trapezoid..................233
 Problem: Dividing Land...235
 Investigation: Area of Regular Polygons................237
 Problem: Boarding Up the Bathroom Window..............241
 Demonstration: The Area of a Circle.....................243
 Investigation: New Area Formulas........................245
 Investigation: Archimedes' Tombstone..................247

Chapter 8: The Pythagorean Theorem..............................**249**
 Investigation: The Pythagorean Theorem...............251
 Demonstration: Visual Proof of the Pythagorean Theorem................255
 Investigation: Dissection Proof of the Pythagorean Theorem............257
 Investigation: Pythagorean Triples.......................259
 Investigation: The Isosceles Right Triangle............261
 Investigation: A Special Right Triangle—30-60-90........................263
 Construction: The Square Root Spiral...................265

Chapter 9: Similarity..**267**
 Investigation: The Golden Rectangle......................269
 Investigation: Similar Polygons.............................273
 Investigation: Similar Triangles—AA Similarity...........................275
 Investigation: Similar Triangles—SSS Similarity........................277
 Investigation: Similar Triangles—SAS Similarity........................279
 Investigation: The Geometric Mean.......................281
 Investigation: Intersecting Chords........................283
 Investigation: Secant Segments............................285
 Problem: Modeling a Similar Triangle Problem.......................287
 Problem: Modeling a Similar Triangles/Mirror Problem................289
 Construction: Subdividing a Segment....................291
 Art: Spacing Fenceposts in Perspective.................293
 Investigation: Proportions with an Angle Bisector in a Triangle.......297
 Investigation: Parallel Lines in a Triangle.............299
 Construction: A Pantograph.................................301
 Investigation: Proportions with Area....................305

Chapter 10: Trigonometry...**309**
 Investigation: Trigonometric Ratios......................311
 Exploration: A Sine Wave Tracer..........................315
 Investigation: Modeling a Ladder Problem............317
 Construction: Creating a Fractal...........................319

Exploring Geometry with The Geometer's Sketchpad

If you just obtained The Geometer's Sketchpad along with this book you're no doubt excited to get started with the program and introduce it to your students as soon as possible. But take a little time first to read this introduction. It offers some background on Sketchpad and different ways to use it (some of which may be familiar from *Teaching Geometry with the Geometer's Sketchpad* which comes with the program) and some explanation of ideas we had in mind when we created these activities. The better you understand the organization, approach, and intent of the activities, the more effectively you'll be able to use them.

The Geometer's Sketchpad and Change in Mathematics Teaching

The way we teach mathematics—geometry in particular—is beginning to change, thanks to a few important developments in recent years. The deductive approach to teaching geometry is finally being seriously challenged, and alternatives are available after more than a century of failing to reach a majority of students. (The National Assessment of Educational Progress found in 1982 that doing proofs was the least liked mathematics topic of 17-year-olds, and less then 50% of them rated the topic as important.) First, in 1985, Judah Schwartz and Michal Yerushalmy of the Education Development Center developed a landmark piece of instructional software that enabled teachers and students to use computers as teaching and learning tools rather than just as drillmasters. The Geometric Supposers, for Apple II computers, encouraged students to invent their own mathematics by making it easy to create simple geometric figures and make conjectures about their properties. Learning geometry could become a series of open-ended explorations of relationships in geometric figures rather than a rehashing of proofs of theorems that students tend to take for granted anyway.

By publishing Michael Serra's *Discovering Geometry: An Inductive Approach* in 1989, Key Curriculum Press joined the forces of change. *Discovering Geometry*, a high school geometry textbook, takes much the same approach that the creators of The Geometric Supposers espoused: students should create their own geometric constructions and themselves formulate the mathematics to describe relationships they discover. With *Discovering Geometry*, students working in cooperative groups do investigations, often using compass and straightedge constructions, to discover properties. Students look for patterns and use inductive reasoning to make conjectures. Proof is left until the end of the book, after students have mastered geometry concepts and can appreciate the significance of proof.

The approach of The Geometric Supposers, *Discovering Geometry*, and now The Geometer's Sketchpad, is consistent with research done by the Dutch mathematics educators Pierre van Hiele and Dina van Hiele-Geldof. From classroom observations, the van Hieles learned that students pass through a series of levels of geometric thinking: Visualization, Analysis, Informal Deduction, Formal Deduction, and Rigor. Standard geometry texts expect students to employ formal deduction from the beginning. Little is done to enable students to visualize or to encourage them to make conjectures. A main goal of The Supposers, *Discovering Geometry*, and The Geometer's Sketchpad is to bring students through the first three levels, encouraging a process of discovery that more closely reflects how mathematics is invented: a mathematician first visualizes and analyzes a problem, making conjectures before attempting a proof.

In the meantime, in 1988, the National Council of Teachers of Mathematics (NCTM) published *Curriculum and Evaluation Standards for School Mathematics* (the *Standards*) which call for significant changes in the way mathematics is taught. In the teaching of geometry, the *Standards* call for decreased emphasis on the presentation of geometry as a complete deductive system and a decreased emphasis on two-column proofs. The *Standards* call for an increase in open exploration and conjecturing and increased attention to topics in transformational geometry. In their call for change, the *Standards* recognize the impact that technology tools, including The Geometric Supposers, can have on the way mathematics is taught by freeing students from time-consuming, mundane tasks and allowing them the time and means to see and explore interesting relationships.

The Geometer's Sketchpad is among the first in the next generation of educational software that will add to the momentum of change begun by The Geometric Supposers and spurred on by publications like *Discovering Geometry* and the NCTM *Standards*. Sketchpad brings geometry exploration tools to state-of-the-art hardware, enabling students to explore relationships dynamically so that they can see change in geometric figures as they manipulate them. Sketchpad combines this breakthrough with complete construction and transformation capabilities and the extensibility offered by scripting, broadening the scope of what it's possible to do with geometry software to an extent never seen before.

Where Sketchpad Came From

The Geometer's Sketchpad was developed as part of the Visual Geometry Project, a National Science Foundation-funded project under the direction of Dr. Eugene Klotz at Swarthmore College and Dr. Doris Schattschneider at Moravian College in Pennsylvania. In addition to Sketchpad, the Visual Geometry Project has produced The Stella Octangula and The Platonic Solids: videos, activity books and manipulative materials also published by Key Curriculum Press. Sketchpad creator and programmer Nicholas Jackiw joined the VGP in the summer of 1987. He began serious programming work a year later. Sketchpad for Macintosh was developed in an open, academic environment in which many teachers and other users experimented with early versions of the program and provided input to its design. Nicholas came to work for Key Curriculum Press in 1990 to produce the "beta" version of the software tested in classrooms. A core of thirty schools soon grew to a group of over fifty sites as word spread and more people heard of Sketchpad or saw it demonstrated at conferences. The openness with which Sketchpad was developed generated incredible enthusiasm for the program. By the time of its release in the spring of 1991 it had been used by hundreds of teachers, students, and other geometry lovers and was already the most talked about and awaited piece of school mathematics software in recent memory.

In Sketchpad's first year, Key Curriculum began to study how the program was being used effectively in schools. Funded in part by a grant for small businesses from the National Science Foundation, this research is reflected in this book and in new versions of Sketchpad. Classroom research will continue to form the basis for further development of the software and accompanying materials. Sketchpad for Windows was released in March, 1993.

Where Exploring Geometry Came From

From the time teachers and students first used Sketchpad, we've been soliciting feedback on what types of activities can be used most effectively in the classroom. Funding from the National Science Foundation's Small Business Innovation Research Program enabled us to visit classrooms and interview teachers and students. In this way, we could directly observe what kinds of activities work best. Two important messages came through in our research:

1. Sketchpad's ease-of-use can best be taken advantage of if initial activities require only simple constructions. With experience, Sketchpad's power enables students to create figures of arbitrary complexity. But students who are beginners using the program best grasp concepts when their thinking is directed towards relationships, and not constructions. For this reason, teacher comments to these activities name a level of proficiency required (beginner, experienced user, and power user), and the bulk of the activities are designed for beginners.

2. Sketchpad can integrate different geometry topics in ways textbooks don't. For example, in a single Sketchpad triangle investigation, students might investigate line and angle relationships, area, and transformations, and symmetry. The consequence of this finding is that, with few exceptions, the activities in this book don't follow a linear sequence. It's important to know that the organizational scheme chosen in no way dictates a proper order in which to use the activities.

Ideas for these activities come from a variety of sources. We started with *Discovering Geometry*. We knew we'd find good ideas there for discovery lessons that would be easily adaptable to computer-based exploration. We also collected ideas from teachers we had contact with in our research who were using Sketchpad. Finally, we studied other geometry books for ideas for problems that would make good Sketchpad investigations. *Geometry*, by Harold Jacobs (W. H. Freeman and Co., 1974), and *Geometry, An Investigative Approach*, by Don Chakerien et. al. (Sunburst Communications, 1987), were good sources for problems that we adapted here.

Using Exploring Geometry Activities and Disks

The Geometer's Sketchpad was designed primarily for use in high school geometry classes. Testing has shown, though, that its ease of use makes it possible for younger students to use Sketchpad successfully, and the power of its features has made it attractive to teachers of college-level mathematics and teacher education courses. *Exploring Geometry* was also designed primarily for high school geometry. Other volumes will address the specific needs of younger and older students. You will find, however, that many of these activities will be useful if you teach middle school or college.

The activities in this book cover the core content of a typical geometry course (with the exception of some three-dimensional topics like volume). Courses using an inductive approach could use Sketchpad virtually every day to discover geometry properties. Students in courses using a deductive approach could use Sketchpad to discover theorems they would then prove, or to confirm and develop understanding of theorems after they prove them. Even in a deductive course, Sketchpad could become an everyday tool. But we urge you to use Sketchpad in moderation. We believe students learn best when exposed to a variety of different learning opportunities. And more of your students will succeed in geometry if you combine approaches to address a variety of learning styles. Any one type of learning experience can become routine and boring if it's used again and again to the exclusion of other experiences. Don't be tempted to structure your course around doing all these activities. They're here for when you need them—for when you think a particular lesson is just right for exploration on the computer, for when your students start lobbying for a trip to the computer lab, for that day when the lab is free and you want an activity to fit that week's lesson plans. Use what you consider to be the best activities at the most opportune times.

The sketches and scripts on the disks that come with this book are, for the most part, examples of what students are expected to produce themselves in the activity. See page 7 for more about these disks.

How Exploring Geometry is Organized

The order of the activities in this book follow, more or less, the order of investigations in the text *Discovering Geometry: An Inductive Approach*, by Michael Serra. As publishers of the text, we obviously believe this is a sensible order in which to address these topics. And we wanted it to be convenient for users of *Discovering Geometry* to use these activities. One important difference in the topics' order is that the Transformations chapter is found early in this volume. Sketchpad makes it easy to construct figures using transformations and to investigate symmetry. We recommend you get students started early using Sketchpad's transformation capabilities so they can take advantage of them in their constructions.

But don't be misled by the organization of this book into thinking that activities need to be done in any particular order. Every activity is self-contained. None rely on students having done another activity. (The teacher comments reference related activities that might be helpful to do first.)

Preceding the activities in this book are two versions of four Guided Tours: one version for Macintosh users and another for users of IBM or IBM-compatible machines running Windows. The Tours are different from the activities in that their intent is to help students learn how to use the software—not to help them learn geometry. If your students are unfamiliar with the program, use these before you use the activities. If your students are unfamiliar with using the computer, allow one class period for each tour. This will give students plenty of time to explore the software and the computer at their own pace. If students are already well-oriented to using computers, you can probable do two tours in a class period. Even if you don't use the tours with students, read through them yourself so that you'll be aware of some of the conventions we use to describe constructions in the activities.

Exploring Geometry activities fall under seven headings: Investigation, Exploration, Demonstration, Construction, Problem, Art, and Puzzle (though there's only one puzzle). The greatest number of activities are Investigations. Investigations guide students toward discovering a specific property or small set of properties. There are more of these because we felt explicit instructions were most needed for carefully guided investigations. Explorations are more open-ended. In Explorations, students are asked to discover as much as they can about a figure or figures, and are not expected to come up with uniform findings. By their nature, open-ended explorations require little explanation, and thus are not the main subject of as many activities. A great number of open-ended questions can be found as extensions to Investigations in a section with the heading Explore More. A Demonstration relies on a pre-made sketch whose complexity makes it impractical for students to do the construction in a class period. The approach in the other four categories should be clear when you look at the activities. Here we'll look more closely to the first three approaches: an Investigation, an Exploration, and a Demonstration.

A Guided Investigation: The Centroid of a Triangle

This investigation guides students to make some specific conjectures. They are given instructions to create a construction with certain specifically defined relationships, in this case, a triangle and its medians. Students then measure and manipulate their construction to see what relationships they can find that can be generalized for all triangles. After this experimentation, students are asked to write conjectures.

Each activity is introduced by describing what it is students will be investigating. Necessary vocabulary is defined, and students are given a preview of what they'll be doing and why.

The steps for creating the construction needed for the investigation appear under the **Sketch** heading. These steps are described geometrically—not in terms of specific keyboard and mouse actions.

Students then **Investigate** their figures. They often measure things and look for relationships that hold as their figures are manipulated.

Investigation: The Centroid of a Triangle

In this investigation you'll discover properties of the medians in a triangle. Record a script of your construction so that when you finish you can demonstrate what you did.

Sketch

Step 1: Construct triangle *ABC*.

Step 2: Construct midpoints on each side.

Step 3: Construct two medians, $\overline{AD}$ and $\overline{BF}$, and their point of intersection *G*.

Step 4: Construct the third median.

Step 5: Measure the distances from *B* to *G* and from *F* to *G*.

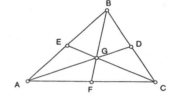

Investigate

When you constructed the third median did it pass through the point of intersection of the other two medians? Drag any vertex or side of your triangle. Do the three medians always intersect in a single point? Perform some calculations on *BG* and *GF* and see if you can build an expression that remains constant as you manipulate the triangle. Build similar expressions for *CG* and *GE* and for *AG* and *GD*.

The point of concurrency of the three medians is called the **centroid**.

Conjecture: Write your conjectures below.

_____
_____
_____
_____
_____

Present Your Findings

Discuss your results with your partner or group. To present your findings you could:

1. Add comments to your script so that you can use it to present your findings to your classmates. Then play or step through your script and explain to someone how you arrived at your conjectures.

2. In your sketch, change the label of *G* to Centroid. Add captions to your sketch, print it out, and write an explanation of your investigation and conjectures.

Explore More

1. Construct interiors of the small triangles like *AFG*, and investigate relationships among areas.

2. Investigate special cases (equilateral, isosceles triangles, etc.). Do medians have any special properties in these special cases? Write your conjectures on the back of this sheet.

From this investigation, students are asked to **Conjecture**. The activity sheet provides space for students to write a few lines describing their findings.

Present Your Findings suggests ways students can use Sketchpad to articulate their findings, usually in the form of commented sketches or scripts.

Assuming students will finish the guided part of an investigation at different rates, activities suggest ways students can **Explore More**. These suggestions are usually more open-ended, and allow students to pursue extensions to an investigation in creative ways.

An important aspect of this—and, in fact, any—Sketchpad investigation is that by manipulating a single figure students can potentially see every case of that figure. Here they have compelling visual evidence that the medians continue to intersect in a single point even as the triangle changes from acute to right to obtuse, from scalene to isosceles to equilateral. And the ratio into which the centroid divides the medians remains constant for all triangles. These generalizations can be made by manipulating one simple construction which can be made and measured in a matter of a few minutes by students experienced with just the basics of using Sketchpad. Students are encouraged to communicate their findings and explore extensions to the investigation. After students have discussed their findings in pairs or small groups, it's important to discuss them as a large group. Ask students to share any special cases they've discovered, and use your questions to emphasize which relationships can be generalized for all triangles: "Did your medians continue to intersect in a single point even as you changed your triangle from being acute to being obtuse? Was the ratio constant no matter what shape triangle you had?"

An Open-Ended Exploration: Properties of Quadrilaterals

In an open-ended exploration there is not a specific set of properties that students are expected to discover as outcomes of the lesson. A question or problem is posed with a few suggestions as to how to use Sketchpad to explore the problem. Different students will discover different relationships and write their findings in their own words. There are minimal instructions for creating a construction.

In this example, students are asked to come up with as many properties of different types of quadrilaterals as they can.

Again, various discoveries should be discussed in small groups, then with the whole class. To bring closure to the lesson you might want to compile on the chalkboard a list of all the properties your students discovered.

Exploration: Properties of Quadrilaterals

Use the Segment tool to construct any quadrilateral and its diagonals. Measure the lengths of the sides, diagonals, and angles. (Measure any other distances you think might be important.) Manipulate the quadrilateral to make it approximate a rectangle, then a parallelogram, rhombus, square, kite, and finally, a trapezoid. List any properties you discover below or on a separate piece of paper:

Quadrilateral: _____

Rectangle: _____

Parallelogram: _____

Rhombus: _____

Square: _____

Kite: _____

Trapezoid: _____

start with this

drag top

drag side until sides are equal

drag top

drag vertex

A Demonstration: A Visual Proof of the Pythagorean Theorem

A teacher (or student) can use Sketchpad to prepare a demonstration for others. Sometimes a complex construction can nicely show a property, but it would be impractical to have students do the construction themselves. In that case, teachers might use a demonstration sketch accompanied by an activity sheet.

Before using this demonstration, students can actually discover the Pythagorean Theorem themselves in a guided investigation. The purpose of the this lesson, though, is as a demonstration of a visual "proof" of the theorem. The sketch used in the lesson is a pre-made sketch of some complexity. Students aren't expected to create this construction themselves to discover the Pythagorean Theorem. They may already be familiar with the Pythagorean Theorem but have a chance with this demonstration to look at it in a new and interesting way.

This demonstration might be done most efficiently as a whole-class demonstration with you or a student working at an overhead projector. Alternatively, you could reproduce the activity master for students to use on their own time or at the end of a lab period in which they've been doing other investigations related to the Pythagorean Theorem.

With appropriate system software, you can conduct the demonstration over a network in a computer lab. On networked Macintoshes with System 7, choose Demonstrate To in the Display menu to send the sketch to other computers running Sketchpad. Viewers will see what you do to the sketch, but will not be able to alter it themselves until you stop the demonstration. Manipulate the figure incrementally (viewers of a demonstration only see the end result of a movement). Stop the demonstration. Students will now have access to tools and menus and can explore the sketch themselves. Suggest they manipulate the original triangle and try the experiment again to confirm that it works for any right triangle. Under an IBM ICLAS network, you can send images of your sketches to other computers on the network for demonstrations, though students will not be able to continue working on those sketches.

Demonstration: Visual Proof of the Pythagorean Theorem

In this activity you'll do a visual demonstration of the Pythagorean Theorem based on Euclid's proof. By **shearing** the squares on the sides of a right triangle you'll create congruent shapes without changing the areas of your original squares.

Sketch

Step 1: Open the sketch **Shear Pythagoras** (Mac) or **8pythag\shear.gsp** (Windows). You'll see a right triangle with squares on the sides.

Step 2: Measure the areas of the squares.

Step 3: Drag point *A*, then point *B*, onto the line that's perpendicular to the hypotenuse. Note that as the squares become parallelograms their areas don't change.

Step 4: Drag point *C* so that the large square deforms to fill in the triangle. The area of this shape doesn't change either. It should appear congruent to the shape you made with the two smaller parallelograms.

Step 5: Change the shape of the triangle and try the experiment again.

Investigate

You should now have two shapes. One shape was formed from the two squares on the legs of the right triangle. The other shape was formed from the square on the hypotenuse. What can you say about these shapes?

Conjecture: Write your conjectures below.

_____
_____
_____
_____
_____
_____
_____
_____
_____

Explore More

Once you've manipulated the squares so that you have congruent shapes, you can Copy and Paste the shape that's on the hypotenuse. Drag the copy over the shape on the legs and see that it fits perfectly.

Teacher Comments for Activities

Teacher comments are found on the back of the first page of each activity. In these comments we offer more information about the level of student for which the activity is appropriate, what prerequisite geometry facts and terms are assumed, what Sketchpad proficiency is required, how much class time to allow, tips for doing the construction, commentary about the investigation and possible conjectures, and suggestions for extensions to the activity. A description of these categories of comments follows:

Student Audience: Middle School (grades 6-8), High School (standard geometry course: grades 9-12), College/Teacher Education

Student audience categories will naturally overlap, and you shouldn't hesitate to try activities designated for different levels if you think they're appropriate to what you're doing with your students. In most cases, activities for more advanced students assume more proficiency using Sketchpad.

Prerequisites: Under this heading are listed terms and concepts students should be familiar with before undertaking the activity. In many cases these prerequisites can be introduced as students begin the activity.

Sketchpad Proficiency: Beginner, Experienced User, Power User. All the activities, including those designated Beginner, assume very basic knowledge of how to use a computer in general and Sketchpad in particular: clicking and dragging (creating objects using the Toolbox), selecting (including multiple objects), using menus (for constructing and measuring), opening and closing documents (sketches and scripts).

Experienced users should be able to do more complex constructions with hidden objects, record and play basic scripts, use animation, and perform transformations using the transformation tools and the Transform menu. Activities designated for experienced users are not necessarily difficult; you probably just don't want to use them with students who've never used Sketchpad. Users might be considered "experienced" after just a few sessions with the program.

Power users know nearly every feature of Sketchpad and can do complex constructions that require precise mouse manipulations, advanced selection techniques, advanced scripting experience, custom transformations, and keyboard shortcuts. Students needn't be power users to try an activity so designated, but they may find it takes a long time or seems tedious because they lack the experience needed to do it efficiently.

Example Sketches/Scripts: Example sketches and scripts accompany nearly every activity and can be found on two disks: one for Macintosh and one for IBM and compatible computers running Windows. You'll use only the disk appropriate for your machine. (Don't worry, if the computer doesn't like your disk it will tell you.) The intent of these examples is to help you, the teacher, quickly see a finished construction like that which students are asked to make. Only in the Demonstration activities are the sketches intended to actually be used by students as part of the activity. Some of the example sketches are "presentation sketches" that you or your students might use to demonstrate or review an investigation. In many cases, you may be tempted to use the pre-made sketch to speed up an investigation. That's fine, but **don't** get the mistaken impression that the examples form the basis for the investigations. Students should do their own constructions to get full benefit of an interactive learning experience. Encourage students to create and save their own utility scripts to be used in future investigations. Students will take ownership of scripts and sketches that illustrate their own mathematical endeavors.

Macintosh sketches and scripts are given descriptive names and can be found in the folders for their respective chapters. Windows sketches and scripts are listed by their full names so that it's clear what directories they can be found in. So, for example, the example sketch for the first activity in this book is listed as: **Equilateral Triangle** (Mac) or **1lineang\equitri.gss** (Windows).

Class Time: How much class time your students spend on an activity depends largely on how much time you want them to spend writing about, talking about, or presenting their findings. None of the activities are designed to take longer than one 50-minute class period on the computer, but you might choose to spend days talking about one investigation. On the other hand, you might be able to do two or three activities in a single class period. The class time suggested in these comments includes time to do the construction, manipulate it, make some observations, think, and write down one or more conjectures. It does not include time for extended discussion, presentations, or extensions to the activity.

Construction Tips: Very specific instructions for performing constructions are, for the most part, left to the documentation and are not given in the activities. Tips are given in the teacher comments for construction steps where users might get hung up or for shortcuts that can make the construction quicker.

Investigate/Conjecture: Some conjectures that students might make are given. In the case of Investigations, students are led by the activity to make one or two specific conjectures. In Explorations, the list of possible conjectures is longer and more nebulous. In any case, students may not make all the conjectures listed here, nor should the lists here be considered complete.

Explore More: Some extensions are suggested briefly in the activities themselves. In the teacher comments these and other extensions are described in more detail.

Using Sketchpad in Different Classroom Settings

Different schools have a variety of different classroom settings in which computers are used. Sketchpad was designed with this in mind, and its display features can be optimized for these different settings. Teaching strategies also need to be adapted to available resources. What follows are some suggestions for using and teaching with Sketchpad if you're in a classroom with one computer, one computer and an overhead display device, a handful of computers, or a computer lab.

One Classroom with One Computer

Perhaps the best use of a single computer is to have small groups of students take turns using the computer. Each group can investigate or confirm conjectures they have made while working at their desks or tables using standard geometry tools like compass and straightedge. In that case, each group would have an opportunity during a class period to use the computer for a short time. Alternatively, you can give each group a day on which to do an investigation on the computer while other groups are doing the same or different investigations at their desks. A single computer without an overhead projection device or large screen monitor has limited use as a demonstration tool. While Preferences can be set in Sketchpad for any size or style of type, a large class will have difficulty seeing what's going on on a small computer screen.

One Computer and an Overhead Projection Display

A variety of devices are available that plug into computers so that screen output can be displayed using an overhead projector. The Geometer's Sketchpad was designed to work well with overhead projection displays. This increases your options considerably for classroom uses. You or a student can act as a sort of emcee to an investigation, asking the class as a whole things like, "What should we try next? Where should I construct a segment? Which objects should I reflect? What do you notice as I move this point?" With an overhead projection display, you and your students can prepare demonstrations, or students can make presentations of findings that they made using the computer or other means. Sketchpad becomes a "dynamic chalkboard" on which you or your students can draw more precise, more complex figures which, best of all, can be distorted and transformed in an infinite variety of ways without having to erase and redraw. Watching a teacher use Sketchpad as a demonstration tool is a good way for students to learn some fundamentals of using the program before they go to the computer lab. Teachers can also model good Sketchpad presentation techniques for students. Set Preferences to display text in a large and bold style and use thick lines to make text and figures clearly visible from all corners of a classroom.

A Classroom with a Handful of Computers

If you can divide your class into groups of three or four students so that each group has access to a computer, you can plan whole lessons around doing investigations with the computers. Make sure of the following:

- That you introduce to the whole class what it is they're expected to do.
- That students have some kind of written explanation of the investigation or problem they're to work on. It's often useful for that explanation to be on a piece of paper on which students have room to record some of their findings, but for some open-ended explorations the problem or question could simply be written on the chalkboard or typed into a sketch itself. Likewise, students' "written" work could be captioned and commented sketches and scripts.
- That students understand that everybody in a group needs the chance to actually operate the computer.

- That students in a group who are not actually operating the computer are expected to contribute to the group discussion and give input to the student operating the computer.
- That you move among groups posing questions, giving help if needed, and keeping students on task.
- That students' findings are summarized in a whole class discussion to bring closure to the lesson.

A Computer Lab

The experience of teachers in using Sketchpad in the classroom (as well as the experience of teachers using The Geometric Supposers) suggests that even if enough computers are available for students to work individually, it's perhaps best to have students work in pairs. Students learn best when they communicate about what they're learning, and students working together can better stimulate ideas and lend help to one another. If you do have students working at their own computers, encourage them to talk about what they're doing and to compare their findings with those of their nearest neighbor—they should peek over each others' shoulders. If they're working in a Macintosh System 7 networked lab, they should demonstrate to one another using Demonstrate To to collaborate on investigations and share findings. The suggestions above for students working in small groups apply to students working in pairs, as well.

If your laboratory setting has both Macintoshes and computers running Windows, your students can read sketches created on one type of machine with the other. Use a program like Apple File Exchange (a utility program that comes with the Macintosh) to translate the file to the proper disk format. Once you've translated the file, simply use Sketchpad's Open command to open it on the other computer.

Exploring Geometry and Your Geometry Text

You already have some idea of the flexibility Sketchpad offers as a teaching tool. The variety of ways it can be used makes it the ideal tool for exploring geometry, regardless of what text you're using. Use Sketchpad to demonstrate concepts or example problems that are presented in the text. Or have students use Sketchpad to explore problems given as exercises. If your text presents theorems and proves them (or asks students to prove them) along the way, give your students an opportunity to explore the concepts with Sketchpad before you require them to do a proof. Working out constructions using Sketchpad will deepen students' understanding of geometry concepts and will make proof more relevant than it would be otherwise. The descriptive titles of activities in *Exploring Geometry* should make it easy to identify activities that are appropriate for the concepts your classes are studying.

Sketchpad is ideally suited for use with books that take a discovery approach to teaching and learning geometry. In Michael Serra's *Discovering Geometry*, for example, students working in small groups do investigations and discover geometry concepts for themselves, before they attempt proof. Many of these investigations call for compass and straightedge constructions, any of which could be done with Sketchpad. Many other investigations involving measurements, calculations, or transformations can also be done effectively and efficiently with Sketchpad. In fact, the first step in creating *Exploring Geometry* was to do nearly every investigation in *Discovering Geometry* using Sketchpad.

We stress again, however, that we don't advocate that you abandon all other teaching methods in favor of using the computer. Students need a variety of different learning experiences like hands-on manipulatives, compass and straightedge constructions, drawing, paper and pencil work, and discussions. And some students learn better in some ways than others, so you'll reach more students by offering a variety of opportunities. Students need to apply geometry to real-life situations and see where it is used in art and architecture and where it can be found in nature. While Sketchpad can serve as a medium for many of these experiences, its potential will be reached only when students can apply what they learn with it to different situations. As engaging as using Sketchpad can be, it's important that students don't get the mistaken impression that geometry exists only in their books and on their computer screens.

The Geometer's Sketchpad and *Exploring Geometry* are particularly well-suited for use with *Discovering Geometry: An Inductive Approach*. Clearly, Sketchpad and *Exploring Geometry* can be used with any text. But to offer an idea of how these activities can be used with *Discovering Geometry*, we've included a correlation with the text.

Correlation of Exploring Geometry with Discovering Geometry

Discovering Geometry Chapter 0

Discovering Geometry Investigation, Problems/Page	Topic/Conjecture	Exploring Geometry Activity/Suggestions for Using The Geometer's Sketchpad
Example A, Exercise 1 *Page 4*	Line art	Sample sketch **Graph Paper (Cartesian)** (Mac) or **samples\misc\grafcart** (Windows) provides a grid on which students can create line designs.
Exercise Set *Page 7*	Daisy Designs	Art: Daisy Designs, *Page 53*.
Example C *Page 9*	Op Art	Art: A Tumbling Block Design, *Page 105*.
Example *Page 16*	Islamic Designs	Art: Daisy Designs, *Page 53*. **6-Hexagon (By Edge)** (Mac) or **1lineang\6byedge.gss** (Windows) and other scripts can be used as starting points for creating Islamic Designs with Sketchpad.
Examples *Pages 24, 26*	Perspective Drawing	Art: Drawing a Box with Two-Point Perspective, *Page 75*.
Example *Page 33*	Perspective View of a Tiled Floor	See sample script **Chessboard** (Mac) or **samples\scrpts\nifty\chess.gss** (Windows).
Special Project: Spacing Fenceposts in Perspective *Page 34*	Advanced Perspective	Art: Spacing Fenceposts in Perspective, *Page 293*

Discovering Geometry Chapter 2

Discovering Geometry Investigation, Problems/Page	Topic/Conjecture	Exploring Geometry Activity/Suggestions for Using The Geometer's Sketchpad
Exercise Set B *Pages 78 to 79*	Poolroom Math (Incoming and Outgoing Angles)	Investigation: Poolroom Math, *Page 91* (This activity approaches the topic from a transformations perspective.)
Exercises 4, 5 *Pages 86 to 87*	Defining Midpoints and Angle Bisectors	Good place to introduce students to Midpoint and Angle Bisector in Sketchpad's Construct menu.
Exercises 3, 4 *Page 89*	Defining Parallel and Perpendicular Lines	Good place to introduce students to Parallel and Perpendicular in Sketchpad's Construct menu.
Exercise Set *Page 101*	Defining Special Quadrilaterals	Investigation: Defining Special Quadrilaterals, *Page 159*

Exploring Geometry

Discovering Geometry Investigation, Problems/Page	Topic/Conjecture	*Exploring Geometry* Activity/Suggestions for Using The Geometer's Sketchpad
Investigation 3.1.1 *Page 125*	Duplicating a Line Segment	Construction: Duplicating a Line Segment, *Page 55.*
Exercise 10 *Page 127*	Constructing an Equilateral Triangle	Construction: Euclid's Proposition 1—An Equilateral Triangle, *Page 51.*
Investigation 3.1.2 *Page 126*	Duplicating an Angle	Construction: Duplicating an Angle, *Page 57.*
Investigations 3.2.1 to 3.2.2 *Pages 128 to 130*	Constructing Perpendicular Bisector	Investigation: Perpendicular Bisectors, *Page 65.*
Investigation 3.3.2 *Page 132*	Distance from a Point to a Line	Investigation: Distance from a Point to a Line, *Page 69.*
Investigation 3.4.1 to 3.4.2 *Pages 135 to 136*	Properties of an Angle bisector	Construction: Angle Bisectors, *Page 71.*
Investigation 3.4.3 *Page 136*	Angles in an Equilateral Triangle	Construction: Euclid's Proposition 1—An Equilateral Triangle, *Page 51.*
Exercise Set *Pages 140 to 141*	Constructing Triangles and Quadrilaterals	Problems 1 to 4 can be investigated with the example sketches **SSS, SAS, ASA, SSA** (Mac) or **3triangl\congrnce\sss.gsp**, etc. (Windows).
Lesson 3.6 *Pages 142 to 143*	Constructing Parallel Lines	Sketchpad constructs parallels automatically, but try these constructions using freehand tools only.
Exercise Set *Pages 145 to 146*	Construction Problems	Make sure students construct givens separately in sketch. (Or set up beforehand.)
Investigation 3.8.1 *Page 147*	Angle Bisectors in a Triangle	Investigation: Angle Bisectors in a Triangle, *Page 117.*
Investigation 3.8.2 *Page 147*	Perpendicular Bisectors in a Triangle	Investigation: Circumscribing a Triangle, *Page 121.* Problem: A Tricky Telescope, *Page 123.*
Investigation 3.8.3 *Page 147*	Altitudes in a Triangle	Investigation: Altitudes in a Triangle, *Page 125.*
Investigations 3.9.1, 3.9.2 *Pages 151 to 152*	The Centroid	Investigation: The Centroid in a Triangle, *Page 127.*
Special Project *Page 155*	Constructing the Nine-Point Circle	Easy with Sketchpad. Tough on paper! See example script **9-Point Circle** (Mac) or **3triangl\9ptcircl.gss** (Windows).

Discovering Geometry Chapter 4

Discovering Geometry Investigation, Problems/Page	Topic/Conjecture	Exploring Geometry Activity/Suggestions for Using The Geometer's Sketchpad
Investigation 4.1.1 Page 161	Vertical Angles Conjecture: C-1	Investigation: Angles Formed by Intersecting Lines, Page 61.
Investigation 4.1.2 Page 162	Linear Pair Conjecture: C-2	Investigation: Angles Formed by Intersecting Lines, Page 61.
Investigation 4.2.1 Page 164	Triangle Sum Conjecture: C-4	Investigation: Triangle Sum, Page 133.
Investigations 4.3.1 to 4.3.3 Pages 168 to 170	Polygon Sum Conjectures: C-6 to C-8	Do investigations as described in book, then use Sketchpad to confirm findings.
Investigation 4.4.1 Page 172	Exterior Angles of a Polygon: C-9	Investigation: Exterior Angles of a Polygon, Page 185.
Investigation 4.4.2 Page 173	Exterior Angle Conjecture: C-10	Investigation: Exterior Angles of a Triangle, Page 135.
Investigation 4.5.1 to 4.52 Pages 180 to 181	Triangle Inequality Conjectures: C-11 to C-12	Investigation: Triangle Inequalities, Page 137.
Investigation 4.6.1 Page 182	Isosceles Δ Conjecture and Converse: C-13, C-14	Investigation: Properties of Isosceles Triangles, Page 139.
Paragraph Proof Page 184	Equilateral Triangle Conjecture: C-15	Construction: Euclid's Proposition 1—An Equilateral Triangle, Page 51. Investigation: Properties of Isosceles Triangles, Page 139.
Investigations 4.7.1, 4.7.2 Pages 186 to 188	Angles Formed by Parallel Lines and Transversal: C-16 to C-18	Investigation: Properties of parallel Lines, Page 63.
Investigation 4.7.3 Page 189	Constructing Parallels Using Alternate Interior Angles	Try constructing parallel lines by duplicating alternate interior angles, without using Construct Parallel.
Investigation 4.8.1 Page 192	Isosceles Trapezoid Conjecture: C-19	Investigation: Properties of Isosceles Trapezoids, Page 177.
Investigation 4.9.1 Page 194	Triangle Midsegment Conjecture: C-20	Investigation: Midsegments of a Triangle, Page 131.
Investigations 4.9.2 to 4.9.3 Pages 195 to 196	Trapezoid Midsegment Conjecture: C-21	Investigation: The Midsegment in a Trapezoid, Page 181.
Exercise 3B Page 197	Midpoints of the Sides of a Quadrilateral	Investigation: Midpoints in a Quadrilateral, Page 169.

Exploring Geometry

Discovering Geometry Investigation, Problems/Page	Topic/Conjecture	Exploring Geometry Activity/Suggestions for Using The Geometer's Sketchpad
Inv. 4.10.1 to 4.10.3, Pages 198 to 199	Properties of Parallelograms: Conjectures C-22 to C-25	Exploration: Properties of Quadrilaterals, Page 161. Investigation: Properties of Parallelograms, Page 163.
Investigation 4.1.1, Page 201	Properties of Rhombuses: C-26 to C-27	Exploration: Properties of Quadrilaterals, Page 161. Investigation: Properties of Rhombuses, Page 167.
Investigation 4.1.1, Pages 201 to 202	Properties of Rectangles: C-28 to C-29	Exploration: Properties of Quadrilaterals, Page 161. Investigation: Properties of Rectangles, Page 165.
Lesson 4.14, Pages 209 to 210	Slopes of Parallel and Perpendicular Lines: C-31 to C-32	Investigation: Slopes of Parallel and Perpendicular Lines, Page 67.

Discovering Geometry Chapter 5

Discovering Geometry Investigation, Problems/Page	Topic/Conjecture	Exploring Geometry Activity/Suggestions for Using The Geometer's Sketchpad
Investigation 5.2.1, Page 226	SSS Congruence Conjecture: C-33	Demonstration: Triangle Congruence—SSS? Page 147.
Investigation 5.2.1, Page 227	AAA Congruence Test	Demonstration: Triangle Congruence—AAA? Page 149.
Investigation 5.3.1, Page 230	SAS Congruence Conjecture: C-34	Demonstration: Triangle Congruence—SAS? Page 151.
Investigation 5.3.2, Page 232	SSA Shortcut?	Demonstration: Triangle Congruence—SSA? Page 153.
Investigation 5.4.1, Page 234	ASA Congruence Conjecture: C-35	Demonstration: Triangle Congruence—ASA? Page 155.
Investigation 5.4.2, Page 236	SAA Congruence Conjecture: C-36	After using Demonstration: Triangle Congruence—ASA?, discuss how SAA follows from ASA as long as congruent parts correspond.
Investigation 5.7.1, Page 250	Parts of Isosceles Triangles: C-37	Investigation: Properties of Isosceles Triangles, Page 139.

Discovering Geometry Chapter 6

Discovering Geometry Investigation, Problems/Page	Topic/Conjecture	Exploring Geometry Activity/Suggestions for Using The Geometer's Sketchpad
Exercise Set C, Page 265	Introductory Circle Constructions	Use Circle by Center + Radius from Construct menu. Measure AB/PQ in Problem 4. What is this constant?
Lesson 6.2, Page 266	Circle Properties: C-38 to C-40	Investigation: Congruent Chords in a Circle, Page 197. Exploration, Chords in a Circle, Page 195.
Exercise Set B: 1, 3, 4, 5, Page 268	More Circle Properties	Problem 1 is found in Exploration: Chords in a Circle, Page 195. Other problems are easily done on using Sketchpad.

Discovering Geometry Investigation, Problems/Page	Topic/Conjecture	Exploring Geometry Activity/Suggestions for Using The Geometer's Sketchpad
Investigation 6.3.1 *Page 270*	Tangent Conjecture: C-42	Investigation: Tangents to a Circle, *Page 199.*
Investigation 6.3.2 *Page 271*	Tangent Segments Conjecture: C-43	Investigation: Tangent Segments, *Page 201.*
Exercise Set B: 1 to 6 *Page 273*	Constructions with Tangents	Investigation: Tangent Segments, *Page 201.*
Investigation 6.4.1 to 6.4.3 *Pages 274 to 273*	Arcs and Angles: C-44 to C-46	Investigation: Circles and Angles, *Page 203.*
Investigation 6.4.3 *Page 275*	Angles Inscribed in a Semicircle: C-46	Investigation: Circumscribing a Triangle, *Page 121.* Problem: A Tricky Telescope, *Page 123.*
Investigation 6.4.4 *Page 276*	Quadrilateral Inscribed in a Circle: C-47	Exploration, Chords in a Circle, *Page 195.*
Investigation 6.4.5 *Page 276*	Parallel Lines Through a Circle: C-48	Investigation: More on Circles, Angles, Arcs, *Page 205.*
Exercise 11 *Page 277*	Angles in an Inscribed Star	Investigation: Inscribed Stars, *Page 187.*
Investigation 6.5.1 *Page 279*	Circumference/Diameter Ratio (π): C-49	Investigation: The Circle/Diameter Ratio, *Page 207.*
Investigation 6.7.2 *Page 283*	Arc Length Conjecture: C-50	Investigation: Arc Length, *Page 209.*

Discovering Geometry Chapter 7

Discovering Geometry Investigation, Problems/Page	Topic/Conjecture	Exploring Geometry Activity/Suggestions for Using The Geometer's Sketchpad
Lesson 7.2 *Page 300*	Properties of Isometries	Investigation: Introduction to Transformations, *Page 81.* Other Investigations in Chapter 2: Transformations.
Special Project *Page 303*	Creating a Frieze	Translate by marked vectors. It might help to show a grid (Graph menu).
Investigation 7.4.1 *Pages 311 to 312*	Symmetries of Regular Polygons: C-51	Investigation: Symmetry in Regular Polygons, *Page 101.*
Exercises 1 to 6 *Page 312*	Sketching Figures with Symmetry	Many of these questions are addressed in investigations about these figures. Students can hand in sketches produced with Sketchpad.
Lesson 7.5 *Pages 317 to 320*	Tessellations with Regular Polygons: C-52	Investigation: Tessellating with Regular Polygons, *Page 103.*

| Lesson 7.6 Pages 321 to 323 | Tessellations with Non-Regular Polygons: C-53 to C-54 | Investigation: Tessellating with Triangles, Page 109. Exercise 1 on Page 323 in Discovering Geometry can also be done with Sketchpad. |

Discovering Geometry Chapter 8

Discovering Geometry Investigation, Problems/Page	Topic/Conjecture	*Exploring Geometry* Activity/Suggestions for Using The Geometer's Sketchpad
Investigation 8.1.2 Page 345	Parallelogram Area Conjecture: C-56	Investigation: Area of Parallelograms, Page 217.
Investigation 8.2.1 Page 347	Triangle Area Conjecture: C-57	Investigation: Area of Triangles, Page 219.
Investigation 8.2.2 Page 348	Trapezoid Area Conjecture: C-58	Investigation: The Area of a Trapezoid, Page 233.
Investigation 8.5.1 Page 357	Regular Polygon Area Conjecture: C-59	Investigation: Area of Regular Polygons, Page 237.
Investigation 8.6.1 Page 360	Circle Area Conjecture: C-60	Demonstration: The Area of a Circle, Page 243.

Discovering Geometry Chapter 9

Discovering Geometry Investigation, Problems/Page	Topic/Conjecture	*Exploring Geometry* Activity/Suggestions for Using The Geometer's Sketchpad
Investigation 9.2.1 Page 384	Pythagorean Theorem: C-61	Investigation: The Pythagorean Theorem, *Page 251*. Investigation: Dissection Proof of the Pythagorean Theorem, *Page 257*. Demonstration: Visual Proof of the Pythagorean Theorem, *Page 255*. Dissections like those on Page 382 in *DG* can also be done with Sketchpad.
Investigation 9.3.1 Page 386	Converse of Pythagorean Theorem: C-62	Investigation: Pythagorean Triples, *Page 259*. Alternative: Construct squares on the sides of a non-right triangle. Show that the sum of the areas on the legs approaches the area on the hypotenuse only as one angle approaches 90°.
Investigation 9.71 Page 397	Isosceles Right Triangles: C-65	Investigation: The Isosceles Right Triangle, *Page 261*.
Investigations 9.7.2 to 9.7.3 Page 398	30-60 Right Triangle Conjecture: C-66	Investigation: A Special Right Triangle—30-60-90, *Page 263*.
Lesson 9.8 Page 402	The Equilateral Triangle	These problems can be explored as an extension to Investigation: The 30-60 Right Triangle, *Page 263*.
Investigation 9.11.1 Page 411	Midpoint of a Hypotenuse: C-68	In addition to measuring, students can construct the circumscribing circle.
Exercise Sets A and B Pages 411 to 412	Constructions with the Pythagorean Theorem	All of Exercise Set A can be done with Sketchpad. For Set B, have students use Sketchpad to check their work.

Discovering Geometry Chapter 10

Discovering Geometry Investigation, Problems/Page	Topic/Conjecture	Exploring Geometry Activity/Suggestions for Using The Geometer's Sketchpad
Special Project Pages 448 to 449	Constructing the Platonic Solids	Construction: Templates for the Platonic Solids, Page 191.

Discovering Geometry Chapter 11

Discovering Geometry Investigation, Problems/Page	Topic/Conjecture	Exploring Geometry Activity/Suggestions for Using The Geometer's Sketchpad
Special Project Page 480	The Golden Ratio	Investigation: The Golden Rectangle, Page 269.
Lesson 11.2 Page 481	Similarity	Investigation: Similar Polygons, Page 273.
Exercise Set D Page 488	Constructing Similar Figures	Do constructions as described in book, then Mark Center on point P and use Dilation tool to confirm similarity.
Investigation 11.3.1 Page 491	SSS Similarity Conjecture: C-72	Investigation: SSS Similarity, Page 277.
Investigation 11.3.2 Page 491	AA Similarity Conjecture: C-73	Investigation: AA Similarity, Page 275.
Exercises 3 and 4 Page 494	Solving Problems with Similar Triangles	Problem: Modeling a Similar Triangles Problem, Page 287.
Investigation 11.4.1 Page 495	SAS and SSA Similarity Tests: C-74	Investigation: SAS Similarity, Page 279.
Lesson 11.5 Pages 496 to 497	Indirect Measurement with Similar Triangles	Problem: Modeling a Similar Triangles/Mirror Problem, Page 289.
Investigation 11.6.1 Page 501	Proportional Parts of Similar Triangles: C-75	Construct similar triangles, then construct and measure altitudes, medians, angle bisectors.
Inv. 11.6.2, 11.6.3 Pages 502 to 503	Proportions and Angle Bisectors in Triangles: C-76	Investigation: Proportions with an Angle Bisector in a Triangle, Page 297.
Exercise Set B: 1 to 3 Page 505	Dividing Segments into Given Ratios	Investigation: Proportions with an Angle Bisector in a Triangle, Page 297.
Lesson 11.7 Page 506	Proportions with Area: C-77	Investigation: Proportions with Area, Page 305.
Lesson 11.9 Pages 515 to 516	Parallel Proportionality: C-79	Investigation: Parallel Lines in a Triangle, Page 299.

Exploring Geometry

	Dividing a Segment into Equal Parts	Construction: Subdividing a Segment, *Page 291.*
Exercise Set B *Page 521*		
Special Project *Page 522*	The Golden Ratio II, Constructing Golden Rectangles	Investigation: The Golden Rectangle, *Page 269.*

Discovering Geometry Chapter 12

Discovering Geometry Investigation, Problems/Page	Topic/Conjecture	*Exploring Geometry* Activity/Suggestions for Using The Geometer's Sketchpad
Investigation 12.2.1 *Page 535*	Trigonometric Tables	Investigation: Trigonometric Ratios, *Page 311.*
Computer Activity *Page 547*	Fractals	Construction: Creating a Fractal, *Page 319.*

Discovering Geometry Chapter 15

Discovering Geometry Investigation, Problems/Page	Topic/Conjecture	*Exploring Geometry* Activity/Suggestions for Using The Geometer's Sketchpad
Lesson 15.1 *Pages 657, 659*	Proving Your Own Conjectures	The example and Problems 1, 3, and 4 illustrate how Sketchpad can be used for investigations and to make conjectures that can then be proved.
Inv. 15.3.1, 15.3.2 *Pages 663 to 664*	Intersecting Chords, Intersecting Secants: C-81 and C-82	If students do these investigations with Sketchpad, make sure they see the relationship to the Inscribed and Exterior Angle Theorems.
Investigation 15.5.2 *Page 672*	Intersecting Chords: C-84	Investigation: Intersecting Chords, *Page 283.*
Investigation 15.5.3 *Pages 673 to 674*	Intersecting Secants: C-85	Investigation: Secant Segments, *Page 285.*
Lesson 15.8 *Pages 685 to 687*	More Midsegment Theorems	Investigation: Midpoints in a Quadrilateral, *Page 169.*

Four Guided Tours: Learning to Use Sketchpad

The following instructions are designed to introduce students to as many Sketchpad features in as short a time as possible. The first set of four tours is for students using Macintoshes. The second set is comprised of the same four tours for users of IBM and compatible computers running Windows. These tours are an accelerated course through the features covered by the Guided Tours in the *User Manual*. Even the simplest activities in *Exploring Geometry* require basic Sketchpad skills. Instructions in the activities describe what to do, but not how to do it. Computer-and-mouse-savvy students can probably pick up these skills along the way, but if you start with these tours, your students will already be experienced users by the time they start doing investigations.

The tours are designed to be reproduced and handed out to students, just like the activities. Every step of a construction is described in detail, and most steps are illustrated with what students will see if they've performed the step successfully. Steps themselves are identified with "bullets" (the • symbol). These are instructions that students should follow exactly. Other paragraphs (usually indented to the right) offer commentary. It's a fair amount of reading and many students will skim to the next step. Students who take the time to read will learn more about Sketchpad, but don't worry too much if students don't absorb everything that's written. Most of what they need to learn, they'll learn by doing.

If students are unfamiliar with using computers and a mouse, you should probably do one tour in a class period. This will give students time to experiment with the program and computer at their own pace. Students who are already well-oriented to using computers can probably do two tours in a class period.

Guided Tour I (Macintosh): The Freehand Tools

In this tour you'll learn how to draw and construct geometric figures using Sketchpad's freehand construction tools. You'll also learn how to "undo" your actions in a sketch, some basics about labeling Sketchpad figures, and how dynamic Sketchpad figures are defined by geometric relationships.

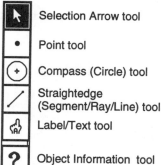

Selection Arrow tool

Point tool

Compass (Circle) tool

Straightedge
(Segment/Ray/Line) tool

Label/Text tool

Object Information tool

On its most basic level Sketchpad provides electronic versions of the tools Euclid used: a tool for creating points, a compass for constructing circles, and a straightedge for constructing segments, rays, or lines.

- Choose the Point tool by clicking and letting go.

  You'll see the Point tool is highlighted, meaning you've chosen it as your active tool.

- Move the pointer into the sketch and click to create several points.

  ○   ◉
  Unselected Point   **Selected Point**

  Note that the last point you created has a bold outline. This shows that the point is selected. Selection is an important concept we'll come back to in a later tour.

- Choose the Segment tool (click on it and let go), then move the pointer into the sketch and press and drag (hold the mouse button down) to create a segment.

  You might have used points already in your sketch for the segment's endpoints or you might not have. If you didn't, Sketchpad supplied the endpoints for free! (You don't need to have points in your sketch already to construct segments.)

- Choose the Selection Arrow tool at the top of the Toolbox.

  This is the tool you'll come back to most often to select and move objects.

- Position the tip of the arrow over one of the segment's endpoints, press, and drag the point. Drag the other endpoint. Drag the segment itself.

You should observe that dragging an endpoint changes the segment's length and direction. If you drag the segment itself, you preserve its length and direction. (Notice that the Selection Arrow changes to horizontal to indicate that it's positioned over an object that can be dragged more or less freely.)

- Experiment with the Point tool, Segment tool, and Circle tool. Make sure you try dragging all these objects and the points that define them to see how they behave.

If at any time you're unhappy with what you've done, even if it's something you did many steps ago, you can reverse your action as follows:

- Position the pointer over the word Edit in the menu bar at the top of your screen. Press and drag down to choose Undo (whatever your last step was).

Your last step was probably just to move, or "translate," a point. Sketchpad is unique in that it has unlimited Undo capabilities.

- Choose Undo again and again to undo your last several steps.

The keyboard shortcut for Undo is ⌘Z.

If you ever just want a blank sketch for a clean start, perform the following steps:

- Click the Close box in the upper left corner of your sketch.

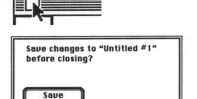

This will get rid of the sketch window you've been working in.

You'll be asked if you want to save the work you've done in this sketch.

- Unless you've done something you wish to keep for later, click "Don't Save."
- Press the File menu and choose New Sketch. You should now have a nice, new, clean sketch in which you can start from scratch.
- Choose the Segment tool and construct a triangle in your sketch.

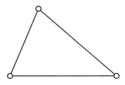

You might have noticed that when you constructed your third side the pointer "snapped" to the point you were aiming for when you got close to it. If you missed, you can always Undo and try again. The snapping behavior makes it easier to hit the points you're trying to use in a construction and with practice, you'll rarely miss.

- Choose the Selection Arrow tool and experiment dragging different vertices and sides of the triangle.

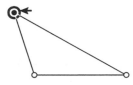

Note that you can drag this triangle into any shape (acute, right, obtuse, etc.) or size. Your triangle doesn't have any constraints at all. It can be any type of triangle and, in fact, can represent *all* triangles. This is the power of Sketchpad's dynamic figures. In the following steps, you'll construct a more constrained triangle—a special case.

- Use the Segment tool to construct a segment.
- Choose the Circle tool. Press on one of the segment's endpoints and drag until the pointer is directly over the other endpoint. Use the Selection Arrow tool to drag each point to confirm that the segment's endpoints really define the circle.

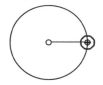

You've used the segment's endpoints to define the center and radius of your circle. You might have constructed your circle so that it "just happened to pass through" the segment's endpoint. In that case, a third point defines the radius of the circle, and the segment will not stay a radius. If that happens, Undo until the circle's gone, then carefully construct the circle again making sure you start *and finish* your circle construction directly over the segment's endpoints.

- Use the Segment tool to construct a second radius. (Start at the center, drag, and release when the pointer is positioned anywhere on the circle.)
- Connect the endpoints of these radii to complete a triangle.

What special kind of triangle is this? How do you know? Use the Selection Arrow tool to drag the different vertices of the triangle. Does it always stay isosceles? Note how the different points behave differently to change the size and shape of the triangle. Which point won't change the length of the legs of the triangle when you drag it? Why?

- Click on the circumference of the circle with the Selection Arrow tool to select it. (Little black squares at top, bottom, left, and right indicate that a circle is selected.)
- Choose Hide Circle in the Display menu.

Now drag the vertices of the triangle. Note that even though the circle is hidden, it still participates in the geometry of your construction. The hidden circle continues to constrain your triangle to be isosceles.

Everything you construct in Sketchpad is automatically given a label. Objects' labels can be displayed individually with the Label/Text tool. (In another tour you'll learn how to display labels automatically using Preferences in the Display menu.)

• Click the hand icon to choose the Label/Text tool.

• Move the hand in your sketch so that the tip of the finger is centered over a point. (The hand will reverse color when correctly positioned.) Click the point.

 A ○ The point's label is displayed as an uppercase letter. If it's a letter followed by a number, like *B1*, that just means you've been sketching for awhile and have run out of alphabet. Whenever you open a new sketch, you start again from *A*.

• If the label is in an inconvenient place, you can press the label and drag it somewhere else.

  When the finger is positioned directly over a label, the letter A appears inside the hand. When you press on a label, a box appears around it to indicate you are acting on the label. Sketchpad won't let you drag a label too far from its object. To hide the label, click the object (not the label) again.

• Press the Segment tool and hold down the mouse button.

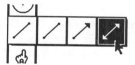 When you hold down the mouse button, segment, ray, and line icons pop out to the right. (You might have noticed this already.) The Segment tool is currently chosen in the Toolbox, but if you drag to the right and release, you can reconfigure your straightedge to create rays or full lines.

• Experiment with creating rays and lines in your sketch.

Rays and lines also come with two points, the first where you press the mouse button and the second where you release after dragging in the direction desired for the ray or line. As with segments, previously constructed points can be used to define rays and lines.

One thing (among many) that sets Sketchpad apart from graphics programs is that objects you construct with Sketchpad are mathematically related by the definitions you give them when you construct them. You've seen that already in your isosceles triangle.

• Experiment more with the freehand tools in the Toolbox. Pay attention to how you construct objects so that they're related to one another. Try some of these freehand constructions. Make sure to manipulate them to see how they behave:

1. A segment and a point on the segment.
2. A segment with one endpoint on another segment.
3. A circle and a segment with one endpoint on the circle.
4. Two segments that intersect and a third that has an endpoint at the intersection.
5. A ray and a line that always goes through the ray's control point. (A ray is defined by two points: an endpoint and a control point that determines its direction.)

Challenge: Construct an equilateral triangle using only the freehand tools. Make sure to drag each vertex to confirm it stays equilateral. If you succeed, congratulations, you've completed Euclid's first postulate in the *Elements*. In fact, you've done it with a strictly Euclidean, collapsible compass!

Guided Tour II (Macintosh): The Centroid of a Triangle

Because Sketchpad keeps track of mathematical relationships, you can create a single construction with certain mathematical definitions, then manipulate that construction and make generalizations for all figures that share the same definitions. In this tutorial, you'll experiment with more Sketchpad features while you investigate and make generalizations about the centroid of a triangle.

- Use the Segment tool to construct a triangle.

- Use the Selection Arrow tool and drag any vertex.

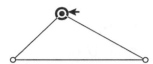

By dragging a single vertex, you can create any shape triangle that can exist. Drag any vertex or side to make your triangle appear acute, obtuse, or right.

- Click one of the sides of the triangle to select it.

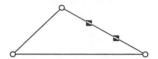

Selection indicators (little black squares) appear on the segment.

- Press Construct in the main menu.

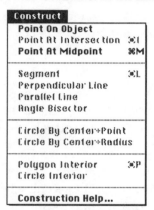

Note that only two choices (besides Help) are available: Point On Object and Point At Midpoint. Lots of other interesting choices are "grayed-out," meaning they're not things you can do to your selection. (Construction Help lists each construction with its prerequisite selections.) If the choice you want isn't available, you either have too little or too much selected. In this case, you should have only a segment selected. If you ever don't have the desired selection or selections, try again by clicking in any blank area of the sketch with the Selection Arrow tool (this deselects everything) and carefully selecting objects to act upon.

- Choose Point At Midpoint.

Now wiggle your triangle around again and appreciate the fact that your midpoint stays a midpoint.

To speed things up a bit, it would be helpful to construct the remaining two midpoints simultaneously. This requires you to select more than on object at a time—a job for the Shift key:

- Click one segment with the Selection Arrow, hold down Shift, and click the other segment.

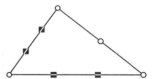

Both segments should show selection indicators.

- Choose Point At Midpoint from the Construct menu.

Again, if the choice isn't available, you may have too much selected. Deselect everything by clicking in a blank area of your sketch with the Selection Arrow tool and try again. You should now have midpoints on all three sides of your triangle.

- Use the Segment tool to construct **just two** of the triangle's three medians (connect two vertices with the midpoints on the opposite sides).

- Choose the Point tool or the Selection Arrow and click the intersection of the two medians.

   Exploring Geometry

This constructs the point of intersection.

Hold on! Did you get ahead of yourself and construct all three medians before you constructed the point of intersection? Sketchpad wouldn't construct their point of intersection. Why not? Think about it: Three segments intersecting in a single point is unusual. In general, three intersecting segments don't define a single point of intersection. So Sketchpad won't give you one. If you already have three medians, you need to select **two** of them with the Selection Arrow tool and choose Point at Intersection in the Construct menu.

- Click this point with the finger of the Label/Text tool (the hand) to display its label.

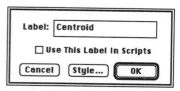

When the tip of the finger is positioned directly over an object the hand becomes highlighted (turns black).

- Double-click the label (not the point) with the Label/Text tool.

The letter A appears in the hand when it's positioned over a label. Double-clicking invokes a dialog box in which you can edit the label.

> **Label:** Centroid
>
> ☐ Use This Label In Scripts
>
> (Cancel) (Style...) **OK**

- Type "Centroid" for the point's new label.
- Click the Style button.

> **Font:** B Helvetica Bold ▾
> **Size:** 9 ▾
> ☐ Bold   ☐ Condense
> ☐ Italic   ☐ Extend
> ☐ Outline ☐ Underline
> (Cancel)   (OK)

You'll be presented with menus for fonts and font sizes and check boxes for style attributes. Choose a font, font style, and size that you think you'll like. Click OK (or press Return) to dismiss the Style dialog box. Click OK again to dismiss the label edit dialog. Your centroid should now be labeled as such.

- Construct the third median.

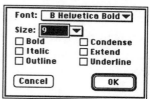

You're ready to make your first conjecture: the three medians in a triangle intersect in a single point. But is that true in all triangles?

- Drag any vertex or side of your triangle.

Drag the triangle into different types: obtuse, right, acute, scalene, isosceles, equilateral. The medians always intersect in a single point. From one construction you can generalize for all triangles. This is the way you'll typically arrive at conjectures with Sketchpad: by distorting a figure and discovering properties that hold for all instances of that figure.

You may also notice that the centroid divides the medians in an interesting way. You'll now take some measurements to investigate this.

- Use the Label tool to display the labels of the endpoints of one of your medians.

- Select the labeled vertex and the centroid (hold down Shift to select more than one object).

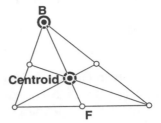

- Press Measure in the main menu.

Again, most choices are grayed-out. Like the Construct menu, the Measure menu makes choices available based on what makes sense for the selections. With two points selected, you can measure the distance between them. It's a little easier in this case to select two points and measure distance. An alternative would be to construct segments from B to Centroid and from Centroid to F and measure length. But those segments cannot be measured unless you construct them separately, on top of the already constructed segment from B to F.

- Choose Distance from the menu.

The distance is displayed in whatever units are currently chosen under Preferences in the Display menu—inches, cm, or pixels. You can edit the text part of this measurement by double-clicking on it with the Label/Text tool (the hand). You can move it like any other object with the Selection Arrow tool.

- Measure the distance from the centroid to the median's other endpoint.

Distance(Centroid to B) = 0.82 inches
Distance(F to Centroid) = 0.41 inches

Do you notice a relationship between these distances? To confirm your conjecture you can perform a simple calculation with these measurements.

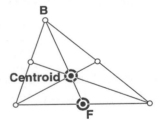

- Use the Selection Arrow tool to select the two measures. Make sure nothing but the measures is selected.

(Did you remember to hold down the Shift key to select more than one object?)

- Choose Calculate in the Measure menu.

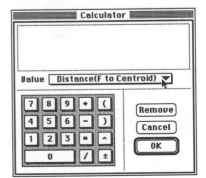

You see a dialog box that looks like a calculator. Near the center of the box is a pop-up menu showing one of your selected measurements. Press this and you'll see your other selected measurement and π. You can choose these measurements, numbers from the keypad, and operators to build expressions that Sketchpad will calculate and display. In this case we want a fairly simple expression.

- Build an expression like this: Distance(Centroid to B)/Distance(F to Centroid)

Your points may have different labels, but don't worry about that.

- When the expression is as you want it in the top part of the Calculate dialog box, click OK.

The ratio will be displayed in your sketch.

Ready to make another conjecture? Don't be hasty though. Better confirm it for all triangles. As you drag parts of your triangle, the measured distances will change, but the ratio will remain a constant 2 (or .5 if you calculated the reciprocal).

If you've finished this investigation early, look around you and see if classmates nearby could use your help. If not, you can carry the investigation further. What can you say about those six little triangles formed by the three medians?

- Select the three vertices of one of the little triangles.

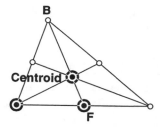

- Choose Polygon Interior in the Construct menu.

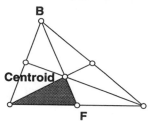

A shaded interior appears, flashing to indicate that it's selected. While it's selected, you can change its appearance using Color (if you have a color monitor) and Shade in the Display menu.

- Construct the interior of another of the little triangles. Give it a different shade or color.

- Select one of the triangle interiors by clicking on it (if it's not already selected) and choose Area from the Measure menu. Now measure the area of the other triangle interior. (If measures are piling up in inconvenient places you can move them with the Selection Arrow tool, just like other objects.)

Area(Polygon 2) = 0.17 square inches
Area(Polygon 1) = 0.17 square inches

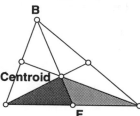

Surprised? It may be easy to prove that two small triangles whose bases are on the same side of the big triangle will have equal areas, but proving that all six triangles have equal areas is more of a challenge. (Confirm that all six do have equal areas, if you're so inclined. And don't forget to drag parts of the large triangle so that you can generalize for all triangles.)

Guided Tour III (Macintosh): Constructing a Rhombus

With Sketchpad, you can use the Segment tool to construct a quadrilateral that looks like a rhombus by simply drawing four connected segments and dragging the vertices until it looks right. But that quadrilateral won't stay a rhombus when you drag its vertices. Why? Because nothing in your drawing *defines* it as a rhombus. All you've told Sketchpad is to connect four segments at their endpoints. In this tutorial, you'll *construct* a rhombus so that it remains a rhombus no matter how you drag it.

If you're studying properties of a rhombus, for example, you need to construct a rhombus with the necessary constraints, not just draw a quadrilateral that looks like a rhombus. Figuring out how to construct a figure with the necessary constraints helps reinforce the defining characteristics of that figure.

In the activities in this book, usually only point labels are shown. In this tour you'll learn how to display point labels automatically. If you follow the steps in an activity exactly, your figure will match up with the figure shown in the activity. But if you undo something , your labels might no longer match those shown in the activity, and it could get confusing. Just remember, the parts and relationships in the figure are important—the labels are not. You probably don't want to spend a lot of time relabeling your sketches to match the activities. You may even prefer *not* to show point labels in your sketch.

Activities almost always begin with an introduction followed by a section titled "Sketch." The Sketch section gives all the steps for a construction. But unlike this guided tour, the steps given in an activity assume you know how to carry out those steps. Below you'll see what the Sketch section of an activity looks like. Don't attempt to follow these steps unless you know what you're doing. Detailed instructions for each step follow in this tutorial.

- Press Display in the menu bar and drag to Preferences. You'll see the dialog shown below right.

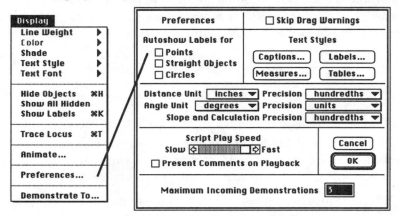

- Click the box to Autoshow Labels for Points. Click OK. Now you're ready for the construction steps.

Again, the steps you see in the following box are shown the way steps are shown in sample activities: they describe geometric constructions, but they don't tell you exactly what to do with Sketchpad. You can try them now, or read on for more specific instructions.

©1996 by Key Curriculum Press   Exploring Geometry

Sketch

Step 1: Construct $\overline{AB}$.

Step 2: Construct circle AB.

Step 3: Construct $\overline{AC}$, where C is any point on the circle.

Step 4: Construct a line through C, parallel to $\overline{AB}$.

Step 5: Construct a line through B, parallel to $\overline{AC}$.

Step 6: Construct $\overline{CD}$, where D is the inter-section of the lines through B and C.

Step 7: Hide the circle and the lines.

Step 8: Construct $\overline{BD}$.

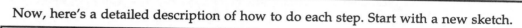

Now, here's a detailed description of how to do each step. Start with a new sketch.

Step 1: Construct $\overline{AB}$.

- Choose the Segment tool and press and drag to create a segment with endpoints A and B.

Sketchpad has given this segment a label (probably *j*) but you've chosen not to display it. To keep things simple, the activities will name all objects after points that define them, so this segment will be called $\overline{AB}$.

Step 2: Construct circle AB.

- Choose the Circle tool. Move the pointer over point A, press, drag so the pointer is directly over point B, and release.

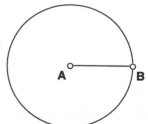

Your circle is defined by two points: center A, where you pressed the mouse button, and radius point B, where you released. For this reason, we adopt an unusual convention in activities for naming Sketchpad circles. Instead of just naming them after their centers, we name circles after the two points that define them. (Sketchpad labels circles with numbers.)

Step 3: Construct $\overline{AC}$, where C is any point on the circle.

- Choose the Segment tool. Press on A and drag until the pointer is somewhere on the circle. Release to construct the segment's endpoint C constrained to lie on the circle.

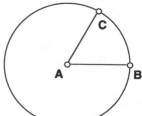

Whenever you release directly over a straight object or circle with any construction tool, the point constructed will be constrained to lie on the straight object or circle.

Step 4: Construct a line through C, parallel to $\overline{AB}$.

- Click the Selection Arrow tool and select point C and segment AB. (Remember to hold down Shift to select both objects.) Choose Parallel Line in the Construct menu.

> **Step 5:** Construct a line through B, parallel to $\overline{AC}$.

- Select point B and segment AC. Choose Parallel Line in the Construct menu.

> **Step 6:** Construct $\overline{CD}$, where D is the intersection of the lines through B and C.

- In this step you'll construct a segment over an existing line. Choose the Segment tool. Press on C and drag until the pointer is over the intersection of the two lines. Release to construct the segment's endpoint D at the intersection.

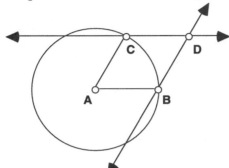

Whenever you release directly over an intersection of two objects with any construction tool, the point constructed will be the point of intersection.

You've constructed all the essentials for your rhombus. But your figure consists of more than just a rhombus—it includes all the objects that define its construction. You want to show only the rhombus. To do this, you'll hide the circle and lines. They'll still be there defining the geometry, you just won't see them.

> **Step 7:** Hide the circle and the lines.

- Select the circle. Choose Hide Circle in the Display menu.
- Press the Segment tool and drag to choose the Line tool. Choose Select All Lines in the Edit menu.

The Select All command changes depending on what tool you're using. In this case it selected all the lines. If you'd chosen the Selection Arrow tool, this command would have selected all the objects in your sketch.

- Choose Hide Lines in the Display menu.

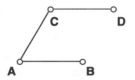

Your rhombus is just about complete now.

> **Step 8:** Construct $\overline{BD}$.

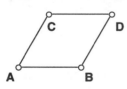

Congratulations. You now have a Sketchpad rhombus. Unlike a rhombus you might draw using only the Segment tool, this rhombus stays a rhombus when you manipulate it. See what happens when you drag any of its vertices. Why do you think dragging A, B, or C gives a different result than dragging D? See if you can drag a part of your rhombus so that it appears square.

You may want to measure some quantities in your rhombus to confirm that it is, in fact, a rhombus. Measurement will also help you explore some angle properties of a rhombus. Instructions to measure something in a sample activity may say simply "Measure AB." In the activities, when we name a segment without a segment symbol, we're referring to the length of the segment or the distance between the points. It can be measured in two different ways.

- First, select segment $\overline{AB}$. Press Measure in the menu bar and choose Length from the menu.

Note that Length and Slope are the only choices that are not grayed-out. The Measure menu, like the Construct menu, requires appropriate selections to make the commands work. The measure Sketchpad displays looks like this: Length(Segment j) = 2.10 inches. Unfortunately, you're not showing the segment label, so unless you do (or unless you can remember that $\overline{AB}$ is segment j) you're unlikely to keep track of which segment that measure refers to. There's a way around this problem:

- Select points A and C. (Remember to hold down Shift.) Choose Distance in the Measure menu.

This time your measure is more helpful. It should say something like: Distance(C to A) = 2.10 inches. In general, if you're displaying point labels, it's easier to measure distances instead of segment lengths, even though distances require two selections. You can also edit labels to be simpler, or more meaningful.

- Double-click on the measure text in your sketch with the Text tool.

The text shown white on black is selected and can be replaced by typing. Or you can click in that box and edit the text. Edit the text to read **CA =** . Click OK.

To finish confirming that the figure is a rhombus, measure the remaining two side lengths.

What about the rhombus' angles? Let's see if there is a relationship between angles.

- Select, in order, points C, A, and B. Choose Angle in the Measure menu.

To identify an angle to Sketchpad, you must select three points, with the vertex the middle selection. (This is the same way most geometry books name angles using three points.)

- Measure other angles, including whatever you need to determine the relationship between angles in the rhombus. (The Calculate command may help you make these relationships clearer.)
- Try different commands in the Construct menu. Can you figure out the selections required to make them work? (If you get stumped, Construction Help lists commands with the prerequisite selections.)
- Answer the following questions:
    1. What can you construct if you have a segment selected?
    2. What do you need to select to enable the command Circle By Center+Radius?
    3. What do you need to select to construct an angle bisector?
    4. What can you construct if you have any combination of two segments, lines, rays, or circles?
    5. What can you construct if you have two points selected? Three points? Four or more points?
- If you have extra time, select your entire rhombus, choose Copy in the Edit menu, and choose Paste to Script in the Edit menu. This creates a script that can be played on any two points to construct a rhombus.

Guided Tour IV (Macintosh): Dynamic and Custom Transformations

In this tour you will create a spiral design using a two-step transformation you define yourself. You can manipulate this design easily because you'll perform your transformations using a dynamic angle of rotation and ratio of dilation. Before you start, you might want to skim to the end to see a picture of what you will create in this tour.

- Close all open sketches and open a new sketch.
- Construct a small angle by using the Segment tool to construct two segments with a common endpoint.
- Select the three angle points in order: bottom endpoint, angle vertex, top endpoint.

If you'd selected the points in the opposite order, you would have marked the angle for a *clockwise* rotation.

- Press the Transform menu and choose Mark Angle.

A brief animation shows the angle has been marked to act as a *counterclockwise* angle of rotation.

- Use the Segment tool to construct two segments, one shorter than the other.
- Select the short segment, then the long one.

By selecting the shorter segment first, you told Sketchpad you want a scale factor less than one. A scale factor comprised of a smaller quantity over a larger quantity will *shrink* objects dilated by it.

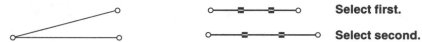

Select first.

Select second.

- Press the Transform menu and choose Mark Ratio.

A brief animation shows that the two segments have been marked to serve as a ratio for dilation.

- Construct a point and while it's selected choose Mark Center in the Transform menu.

At this point you've constructed an angle for rotation, a ratio for a dilation, and a center about which to rotate and dilate any object.

- Construct a polygon interior by holding down the Shift key and using the Point tool to create several selected points.

If you carefully locate points in the correct order, you can create an interesting figure for your polygon interior.

- Choose Polygon Interior from the Construct menu.

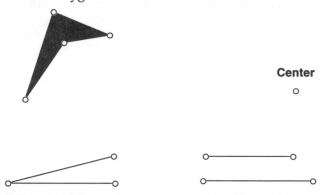

Center

- Select the polygon interior and choose Rotate from the Transform menu.

This dialog box appears:

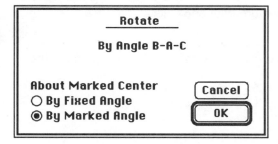

Rotate
_____
By Angle B-A-C

About Marked Center
○ By Fixed Angle   [Cancel]
● By Marked Angle   [OK   ]

- Click By Marked Angle and click OK (or press Return).

Sketchpad constructs a rotated image of your original polygon.

- Select the image and choose a different shade and/or color in the Display menu.

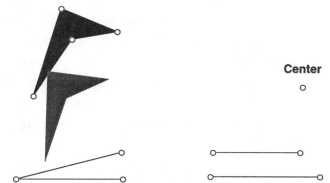

Drag the points on your angle to see how this affects the rotated image.

Center

- Select the rotated polygon interior and choose Dilate from the Transform menu.

This dialog box appears.

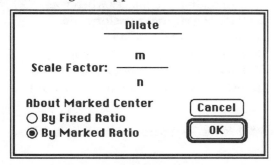

Dilate
_____

Scale Factor: $\dfrac{m}{n}$

About Marked Center
○ By Fixed Ratio   [Cancel]
● By Marked Ratio   [OK   ]

- Click By Marked Ratio and click OK (or press Return).

Sketchpad constructs a dilated image of your rotated image of your original polygon.

- Select the image and choose a shade and/or color in the Display menu that's different from your original and the first rotated image.

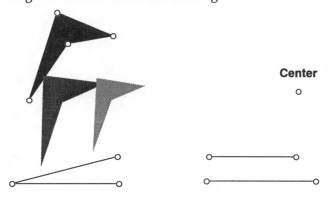

Drag the endpoints of the segments that define the marked ratio and observe how that affects the dilated image.

Center

- To define a custom transformation for the rotation-dilation sequence, select the original polygon (darkest in the illustration above) and the second image (the rotated/dilated figure—lightest in the illustration above). Make sure you hold down Shift to select more than one object.

- Choose Define Transform in the Transform menu.

You'll see this dialog box listing the two transformation steps that constructed the second image from the original.

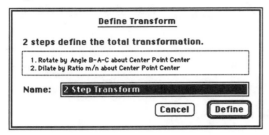

- Type in a descriptive name like "Twist 'n Shrink," and click Define (or press Return).

You've now defined a custom transformation of a rotation followed by a dilation. This two-step transformation, Twist 'n Shrink, now appears in the Transform menu, ready to be applied to any object.

- To apply Twist 'n Shrink to the rotated-dilated image several times, select the rotated-dilated polygon interior and choose Twist 'n Shrink from the Transform menu.

Sketchpad constructs a rotated image and a rotated-dilated image. The new rotated-dilated image is selected, ready to have the transformation applied to it again.

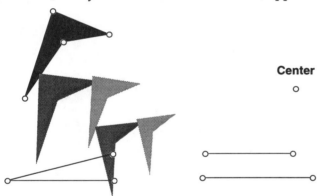

Note that the polygon resulting from the two-step transformation and the intermediate polygon have the same shade and/or color you gave their corresponding pre-images when you defined the custom transformation. Likewise, if you'd hidden the intermediate polygon before you'd defined the transformation, the custom transformation would have hidden it too.

- Press ⌘1 several times to create a spiral towards the center. (⌘1 is the keyboard shortcut for the first custom transformation you define.)

Adjust the angle and ratio to manipulate the spiral. Also, move the original polygon and center point.

Try other combinations of transformations:

- Define as a custom transformation a reflection followed by a translation. Apply it to some polygon interior several times. What's the result?

- Define as a custom transformation two reflections across intersecting lines. What's the result?
- Define as a custom transformation two reflections across parallel lines. What's the result?
- Try a translation followed by a dilation.
- Experiment with translation by marked vector.

Answer the following questions:

- How do you mark an angle of rotation?
- How do you mark a ratio of dilation?
- What else do you need to mark in order to rotate or dilate an object?
- What do you need to select in order to define a custom transformation?
- What's the keyboard shortcut to apply a custom transformation?

Guided Tour I (Windows): The Freehand Tools

In this tour you'll learn how to draw and construct geometric figures using Sketchpad's freehand construction tools. You'll also learn how to "undo" your actions in a sketch, some basics about labeling Sketchpad figures, and how dynamic Sketchpad figures are defined by geometric relationships.

Selection Arrow tools (Translate, Dilate, Rotate)

Point tool

Compass (Circle) tool

Straightedge tools (Segment, Ray, Line)

Label/Text tool

Object Information tool

On its most basic level Sketchpad provides electronic versions of the tools Euclid used: a tool for creating points, a compass for constructing circles, and a straightedge for constructing segments, rays, or lines.

- Choose the Point tool by clicking and letting go.

You'll see the Point tool is highlighted, meaning you've chosen it as your active tool.

- Move the pointer into the sketch and click to create several points.

Unselected Point   Selected Point

Note that the last point you created has a bold outline. This shows that the point is selected. Selection is an important concept we'll come back to in a later tour.

- Choose the Segment tool (click on it and let go), then move the pointer into the sketch and press and drag (hold the mouse button down) to create a segment.

You might have used points already in your sketch for the segment's endpoints or you might not have. If you didn't, Sketchpad supplied the endpoints for free! (You don't need to have points in your sketch already to construct segments.)

- Choose the Selection Arrow tool at the top of the Toolbox.

This is the tool you'll come back to most often to select and move objects.

- Position the tip of the arrow over one of the segment's endpoints, press, and drag the point. Drag the other endpoint. Drag the segment itself.

You should observe that dragging an endpoint changes the segment's length and direction. If you drag the segment itself, you preserve its length and direction. (Notice that the Selection Arrow changes to horizontal to indicate that it's positioned over an object that can be dragged more or less freely.)

- Experiment with the Point tool, Segment tool, and Circle tool. Make sure you try dragging all these objects and the points that define them to see how they behave.

If at any time you're unhappy with what you've done, even if it's something you did many steps ago, you can reverse your action as follows:

- Position the pointer over the word Edit in the menu bar at the top of your screen. Press and drag down to choose Undo (whatever your last step was).

Your last step was probably just to move, or "translate," a point. Sketchpad is unique in that it has unlimited Undo capabilities.

- Choose Undo again and again to undo your last several steps.

The keyboard shortcut for Undo is Ctrl+Z.

If you ever just want a blank sketch for a clean start, perform the following steps:

- Click the Close box in the upper left corner of your sketch.

This will get rid of the sketch window you've been working in.

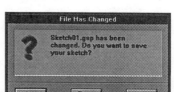

You'll be asked if you want to save the work you've done in this sketch.

- Unless you've done something you wish to keep for later, click "Don't Save."
- Press the File menu and choose New Sketch. You should now have a nice, new, clean sketch in which you can start from scratch.
- Choose the Segment tool and construct a triangle in your sketch.

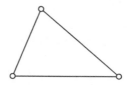

You might have noticed that when you constructed your third side the pointer "snapped" to the point you were aiming for when you got close to it. If you missed, you can always Undo and try again. The snapping behavior makes it easier to hit the points you're trying to use in a construction and with practice, you'll rarely miss.

- Choose the Selection Arrow tool and experiment dragging different vertices and sides of the triangle.

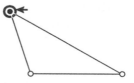

Note that you can drag this triangle into any shape (acute, right, obtuse, etc.) or size. Your triangle doesn't have any constraints at all. It can be any type of triangle and, in fact, can represent *all* triangles. This is the power of Sketchpad's dynamic figures. In the following steps, you'll construct a more constrained triangle—a special case.

- Use the Segment tool to construct a segment.
- Choose the Circle tool. Press on one of the segment's endpoints and drag until the pointer is directly over the other endpoint. Use the Selection Arrow tool to drag each point to confirm that the segment's endpoints really define the circle.

You've used the segment's endpoints to define the center and radius of your circle. You might have constructed your circle so that it "just happened to pass through" the segment's endpoint. In that case, a third point defines the radius of the circle, and the segment will not stay a radius. If that happens, Undo until the circle's gone, then carefully construct the circle again making sure you start *and finish* your circle construction directly over the segment's endpoints.

- Use the Segment tool to construct a second radius. (Start at the center, drag, and release when the pointer is positioned anywhere on the circle.)
- Connect the endpoints of these radii to complete a triangle.

What special kind of triangle is this? How do you know? Use the Selection Arrow tool to drag the different vertices of the triangle. Does it always stay isosceles? Note how the different points behave differently to change the size and shape of the triangle. Which point won't change the length of the legs of the triangle when you drag it? Why?

- Click on the circumference of the circle with the Selection Arrow tool to select it. (Little black squares at top, bottom, left, and right indicate that a circle is selected.)
- Choose Hide Circle in the Display menu.

Now drag the vertices of the triangle. Note that even though the circle is hidden, it still participates in the geometry of your construction. The hidden circle continues to constrain your triangle to be isosceles.

Everything you construct in Sketchpad is automatically given a label. Objects' labels can be displayed individually with the Label/Text tool. (In another tour you'll learn how to display labels automatically using Preferences in the Display menu.)

- Click the hand icon to choose the Label/Text tool.

- Move the hand in your sketch so that the tip of the finger is centered over a point. (The hand will reverse color when correctly positioned.) Click the point.

 A ○   The point's label is displayed as an uppercase letter. If it's a letter followed by a number, like *B1*, that just means you've been sketching for awhile and have run out of alphabet. Whenever you open a new sketch, you start again from *A*.

- If the label is in an inconvenient place, you can press the label and drag it somewhere else.

    When the finger is positioned directly over a label, the letter A appears inside the hand. When you press on a label, a box appears around it to indicate you are acting on the label. Sketchpad won't let you drag a label too far from its object. To hide the label, click the object (not the label) again.

- Press the Segment tool and hold down the mouse button.

   When you hold down the mouse button, segment, ray, and line icons pop out to the right. (You might have noticed this already.) The Segment tool is currently chosen in the Toolbox, but if you drag to the right and release, you can reconfigure your straightedge to create rays or full lines.

- Experiment with creating rays and lines in your sketch.

Rays and lines also come with two points, the first where you press the mouse button and the second where you release after dragging in the direction desired for the ray or line. As with segments, previously constructed points can be used to define rays and lines.

One thing (among many) that sets Sketchpad apart from graphics programs is that objects you construct with Sketchpad are mathematically related by the definitions you give them when you construct them. You've seen that already in your isosceles triangle.

- Experiment more with the freehand tools in the Toolbox. Pay attention to how you construct objects so that they're related to one another. Try some of these freehand constructions. Make sure to manipulate them to see how they behave:

  1. A segment and a point on the segment.
  2. A segment with one endpoint on another segment.
  3. A circle and a segment with one endpoint on the circle.
  4. Two segments that intersect, and a third that has an endpoint at the intersection.
  5. A ray and a line that always goes through the ray's control point. (A ray is defined by two points: an endpoint and a control point that determines its direction.)

Challenge: Construct an equilateral triangle using only the freehand tools. Make sure to drag each vertex to confirm it stays equilateral. If you succeed, congratulations, you've completed Euclid's first proposition in the *Elements*. In fact, you've done it with a strictly Euclidean, collapsible compass!

Because Sketchpad keeps track of mathematical relationships, you can create a single construction with certain mathematical definitions, then manipulate that construction and make generalizations for all figures that share the same definitions. In this tutorial, you'll experiment with more Sketchpad features while you investigate and make generalizations about the centroid of a triangle.

- Use the Segment tool to construct a triangle.
- Use the Selection Arrow tool and drag any vertex.

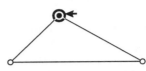 By dragging a single vertex, you can create any shape triangle that can exist. Drag any vertex or side to make your triangle appear acute, obtuse, or right.

- Click one of the sides of the triangle to select it.

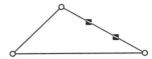 Selection indicators (little black squares) appear on the segment.

- Press Construct in the main menu.

Construct	
Point On Object	
Point At Intersection	Ctrl+I
Point At Midpoint	**Ctrl+M**
Segment	Ctrl+L
Perpendicular Line	
Parallel Line	
Angle Bisector	
Circle By Center And Point	
Circle By Center And Radius	
Polygon Interior	Ctrl+P
Circle Interior	
Construction Help...	

Note that only two choices (besides Help) are available: Point On Object and Point At Midpoint. Lots of other interesting choices are "grayed-out," meaning they're not things you can do to your selection. (Construction Help lists each construction with its prerequisite selections.) If the choice you want isn't available, you either have too little or too much selected. In this case, you should have only a segment selected. If you ever don't have the desired selection or selections, try again by clicking in any blank area of the sketch with the Selection Arrow tool (this deselects everything) and carefully selecting objects to act upon.

- Choose Point At Midpoint.

Now wiggle your triangle around again and appreciate the fact that your midpoint stays a midpoint.

To speed things up a bit, it would be helpful to construct the remaining two midpoints simultaneously. This requires you to select more than on object at a time—a job for the Shift key:

- Click one segment with the Selection Arrow, hold down Shift, and click the other segment.

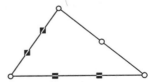 Both segments should show selection indicators.

- Choose Point At Midpoint from the Construct menu.

Again, if the choice isn't available, you may have too much selected. Deselect everything by clicking in a blank area of your sketch with the Selection Arrow tool and try again. You should now have midpoints on all three sides of your triangle.

- Use the Segment tool to construct **just two** of the triangle's three medians (connect two vertices with the midpoints on the opposite sides).
- Choose the Point tool or the Selection Arrow and click the intersection of the two medians.

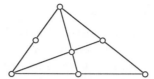

This constructs the point of intersection.

Hold on! Did you get ahead of yourself and construct all three medians before you constructed the point of intersection? Sketchpad wouldn't construct their point of intersection. Why not? Think about it: Three segments intersecting in a single point is unusual. In general, three intersecting segments don't define a single point of intersection. So Sketchpad won't give you one. If you already have three medians, you need to select **two** of them with the Selection Arrow tool and choose Point at Intersection in the Construct menu.

• Click this point with the finger of the Label/Text tool (the hand) to display its label.

When the tip of the finger is positioned directly over an object the hand becomes highlighted (turns black).

• Double-click the label (not the point) with the Label/Text tool.

The letter A appears in the hand when it's positioned over a label. Double-clicking invokes a dialog box in which you can edit the label.

• Type "Centroid" for the point's new label.
• Click the Style button.

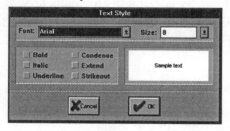

You'll be presented with menus for fonts and font sizes and check boxes for style attributes. Choose a font, font style, and size that you think you'll like. Click OK (or press Enter) to dismiss the Style dialog box. Click OK again to dismiss the label edit dialog. Your centroid should now be labeled as such.

• Construct the third median.

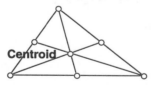

You're ready to make your first conjecture: the three medians in a triangle intersect in a single point. But is that true in all triangles?

• Drag any vertex or side of your triangle.

Drag the triangle into different types: obtuse, right, acute, scalene, isosceles, equilateral. The medians always intersect in a single point. From one construction you can generalize for all triangles. This is the way you'll typically arrive at conjectures with Sketchpad: by distorting a figure and discovering properties that hold for all instances of that figure.

You may also notice that the centroid divides the medians in an interesting way. You'll now take some measurements to investigate this.

• Use the Label tool to display the labels of the endpoints of one of your medians.

- Select the labeled vertex and the centroid (hold down Shift to select more than one object).

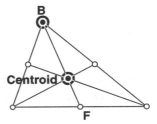

- Press Measure in the main menu.

Again, most choices are grayed-out. Like the Construct menu, the Measure menu makes choices available based on what makes sense for the selections. With two points selected, you can measure the distance between them. It's a little easier in this case to select two points and measure distance. An alternative would be to construct segments from *B* to Centroid and from Centroid to *F* and measure length. But those segments cannot be measured unless you construct them separately, on top of the already constructed segment from *B* to *F*.

- Choose Distance from the menu.

The distance is displayed in whatever units are currently chosen under Preferences in the Display menu— inches, cm, or pixels. You can edit the text part of this measurement by double-clicking on it with the Label/Text tool (the hand). You can move it like any other object with the Selection Arrow tool.

- Measure the distance from the centroid to the median's other endpoint.

Distance(Centroid to B) = 0.82 inches
Distance(F to Centroid) = 0.41 inches

Do you notice a relationship between these distances? To confirm your conjecture you can perform a simple calculation with these measurements.

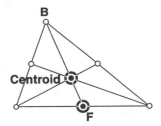

- Use the Selection Arrow tool to select the two measures. Make sure nothing but the measures is selected.

Distance(Centroid to B) = 0.82 inches
Distance(F to Centroid) = 0.41 inches

(Did you remember to hold down the Shift key to select more than one object?)

- Choose Calculate in the Measure menu.

You see a dialog box that looks like a calculator. Near the center of the box is a pop-up menu showing one of your selected measurements. Press this and you'll see your other selected measurement and pi. You can choose these measurements, numbers from the keypad, and operators to build expressions that Sketchpad will calculate and display. In this case we want a fairly simple expression.

- Build an expression like this: Distance(Centroid to B)/**Distance(F to Centroid)**

Your points may have different labels, but don't worry about that.

- When the expression is as you want it in the top part of the Calculate dialog box, click OK.

The ratio will be displayed in your sketch.

Ready to make another conjecture? Don't be hasty though. Better confirm it for all triangles. As you drag parts of your triangle, the measured distances will change, but the ratio will remain a constant 2 (or .5 if you calculated the reciprocal).

If you've finished this investigation early, look around you and see if classmates nearby could use your help. If not, you can carry the investigation further. What can you say about those six little triangles formed by the three medians?

- Select the three vertices of one of the little triangles.

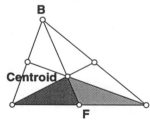

- Choose Polygon Interior in the Construct menu.

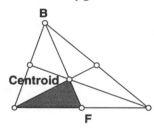   A shaded interior appears, flashing to indicate that it's selected. While it's selected, you can change its appearance using Color in the Display menu.

- Construct the interior of another of the little triangles. Give it a different shade or color.

- Select one of the triangle interiors by clicking on it (if it's not already selected) and choose Area from the Measure menu. Now measure the area of the other triangle interior. (If measures are piling up in inconvenient places you can move them with the Selection Arrow tool, just like other objects.)

Area(Polygon 2) = 0.17 square inches
Area(Polygon 1) = 0.17 square inches

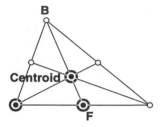

Surprised? It may be easy to prove that two small triangles whose bases are on the same side of the big triangle will have equal areas, but proving that all six triangles have equal areas is more of a challenge. (Confirm that all six do have equal areas, if you're so inclined. And don't forget to drag parts of the large triangle so that you can generalize for all triangles.)

Guided Tour III (Windows): Constructing a Rhombus

With Sketchpad, you can use the Segment tool to construct a quadrilateral that looks like a rhombus by simply drawing four connected segments and dragging the vertices until it looks right. But that quadrilateral won't stay a rhombus when you drag its vertices. Why? Because nothing in your drawing *defines* it as a rhombus. All you've told Sketchpad is to connect four segments at their endpoints. In this tutorial, you'll *construct* a rhombus so that it remains a rhombus no matter how you drag it.

If you're studying properties of a rhombus, for example, you need to construct a rhombus with the necessary constraints, not just draw a quadrilateral that looks like a rhombus. Figuring out how to construct a figure with the necessary constraints helps reinforce the defining characteristics of that figure.

In the activities in this book, usually only point labels are shown. In this tour you'll learn how to display point labels automatically. If you follow the steps in an activity exactly, your figure will match up with the figure shown in the activity. But if you undo something , your labels might no longer match those shown in the activity, and it could get confusing. Just remember, the parts and relationships in the figure are important—the labels are not. You probably don't want to spend a lot of time relabeling your sketches to match the activities. You may even prefer *not* to show point labels in your sketch.

Activities almost always begin with an introduction followed by a section titled "Sketch." The Sketch section gives all the steps for a construction. But unlike this guided tour, the steps given in an activity assume you know how to carry out those steps. Below you'll see what the Sketch section of an activity looks like. Don't attempt to follow these steps unless you know what you're doing. Detailed instructions for each step follow in this tutorial.

- Press Display in the menu bar and drag to Preferences. You'll see the dialog shown below right.

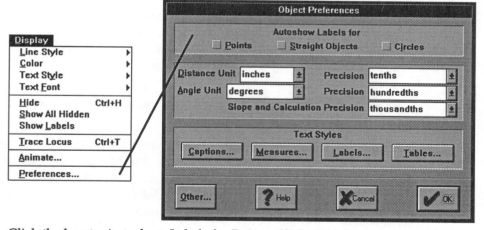

- Click the box to Autoshow Labels for Points. Click OK. Now you're ready for the construction steps.

Again, the steps you see in the following box are shown the way steps are shown in sample activities: they describe geometric constructions, but they don't tell you exactly what to do with Sketchpad. You can try them now, or read on for more specific instructions.

©1996 by Key Curriculum Press

Sketch

Step 1:   Construct $\overline{AB}$.

Step 2:   Construct circle AB.

Step 3:   Construct $\overline{AC}$, where C is any point on the circle.

Step 4:   Construct a line through C, parallel to $\overleftrightarrow{AB}$.

Step 5:   Construct a line through B, parallel to $\overleftrightarrow{AC}$.

Step 6:   Construct $\overline{CD}$, where D is the intersection of the lines through B and C.

Step 7:   Hide the circle and the lines.

Step 8:   Construct $\overline{BD}$.

Now, here's a detailed description of how to do each step. Start with a new sketch.

Step 1:   Construct $\overline{AB}$.

• Choose the Segment tool and press and drag to create a segment with endpoints A and B.

Sketchpad has given this segment a label (probably *j*) but you've chosen not to display it. To keep things simple, the activities will name all objects after points that define them, so this segment will be referred to as $\overline{AB}$.

Step 2:   Construct circle AB.

• Choose the Circle tool. Move the pointer over point A, press, drag so the pointer is directly over point B, and release.

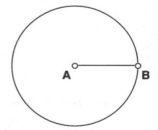

Your circle is defined by two points: center A, where you pressed the mouse button, and radius point B, where you released. For this reason, we adopt an unusual convention in activities for naming Sketchpad circles. Instead of just naming them after their centers, we name circles after the two points that define them. (Sketchpad labels circles with numbers.)

Step 3:   Construct $\overline{AC}$, where C is any point on the circle.

• Choose the Segment tool. Press on A and drag until the pointer is somewhere on the circle. Release to construct the segment's endpoint C constrained to lie on the circle.

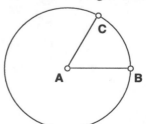

Whenever you release directly over a straight object or circle with any construction tool, the point constructed will be constrained to lie on the straight object or circle.

Step 4:   Construct a line through C, parallel to $\overleftrightarrow{AB}$.

- Click the Selection Arrow tool and select point C and segment AB. (Remember to hold down Shift to select both objects.) Choose Parallel Line in the Construct menu.

> **Step 5:** Construct a line through B, parallel to $\overline{AC}$.

- Select point B and segment AC. Choose Parallel Line in the Construct menu.

> **Step 6:** Construct $\overline{CD}$, where D is the intersection of the lines through B and C.

- In this step you'll construct a segment over an existing line. Choose the Segment tool. Press on C and drag until the pointer is over the intersection of the two lines. Release to construct the segment's endpoint D at the intersection.

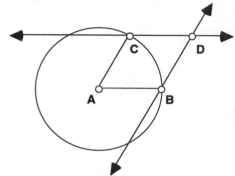

Whenever you release directly over an intersection of two objects with any construction tool, the point constructed will be the point of intersection.

You've constructed all the essentials for your rhombus. But your figure consists of more than just a rhombus—it includes all the objects that define its construction. You want to show only the rhombus. To do this, you'll hide the circle and lines. They'll still be there defining the geometry, you just won't see them.

> **Step 7:** Hide the circle and the lines.

- Select the circle. Choose Hide Circle in the Display menu.
- Press the Segment tool and drag to choose the Line tool. Choose Select All Lines in the Edit menu.

The Select All command changes depending on what tool you're using. In this case it selected all the lines. If you'd chosen the Selection Arrow tool, this command would have selected all the objects in your sketch.

- Choose Hide Lines in the Display menu.

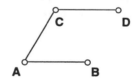

Your rhombus is just about complete now.

> **Step 8:** Construct $\overline{BD}$.

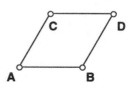

Congratulations. You now have a Sketchpad rhombus. Unlike a rhombus you might draw using only the Segment tool, this rhombus stays a rhombus when you manipulate it. See what happens when you drag any of its vertices. Why do you think dragging A, B, or C gives a different result than dragging D? See if you can drag a part of your rhombus so that it appears square.

You may want to measure some quantities in your rhombus to confirm that it is, in fact, a rhombus. Measurement will also help you explore some angle properties of a rhombus. Instructions to measure something in a sample activity may say simply "Measure AB." In the activities, when we name a segment without a segment symbol, we're referring to the length of the segment or the distance between the points. It can be measured in two different ways.

- First, select segment $\overline{AB}$. Press Measure in the menu bar and choose Length from the menu.

Note that Length and Slope are the only choices that are not grayed-out. The Measure menu, like the Construct menu, requires appropriate selections to make the commands work. The measure Sketchpad displays looks like this: Length(Segment j) = 2.10 inches. Unfortunately, you're not showing the segment label, so unless you do (or unless you can remember that $\overline{AB}$ is segment j) you're unlikely to keep track of which segment that measure refers to. There's a way around this problem:

- Select points A and C. (Remember to hold down Shift.) Choose Distance in the Measure menu.

This time your measure is more helpful. It should say something like: Distance(C to A) = 2.10 inches. In general, if you're displaying point labels, it's easier to measure distances instead of segment lengths, even though distances require two selections. You can also edit labels to be simpler, or more meaningful.

- Double-click on the measure text in your sketch with the Text tool.

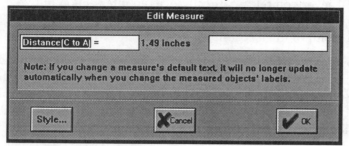

The text shown white on black is selected and can be replaced by typing. Or you can click in that box and edit the text. Edit the text to read **CA** = . Click OK.

To finish confirming that the figure is a rhombus, measure the remaining two side lengths.

What about the rhombus' angles? Let's see if there is a relationship between angles.

- Select, in order, points C, A, and B. Choose Angle in the Measure menu.

To identify an angle to Sketchpad, you must select three points, with the vertex the middle selection. (This is the same way most geometry books name angles using three points.)

- Measure other angles, including whatever you need to determine the relationship between angles in the rhombus. (The Calculate command may help you make these relationships clearer.)
- Try different commands in the Construct menu. Can you figure out the selections required to make them work? (If you get stumped, Construction Help lists commands with the prerequisite selections.)
- Answer the following questions:
  1. What can you construct if you have a segment selected?
  2. What do you need to select to enable the command Circle By Center+Radius?
  3. What do you need to select to construct an angle bisector?
  4. What can you construct if you have any combination of two segments, lines, rays, or circles?
  5. What can you construct if you have two points selected? Three points? Four or more points?
- If you have extra time, select your entire rhombus and choose Make Script in the Work menu. This creates a script that can be played on any two points to construct a rhombus.

©1996 by Key Curriculum Press

Guided Tour IV (Windows): Dynamic and Custom Transformations

In this tour you will create a spiral design using a two-step transformation you define yourself. You can manipulate this design easily because you'll perform your transformations using a dynamic angle of rotation and ratio of dilation. Before you start, you might want to skim to the end to see a picture of what you will create in this tour.

- Close all open sketches and open a new sketch.
- Construct a small angle by using the Segment tool to construct two segments with a common endpoint.
- Select the three angle points in order: bottom endpoint, angle vertex, top endpoint.

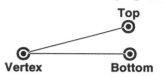

If you'd selected the points in the opposite order, you would have marked the angle for a *clockwise* rotation.

- Press the Transform menu and choose Mark Angle.

A brief animation shows the angle has been marked to act as a *counterclockwise* angle of rotation.

- Use the Segment tool to construct two segments, one shorter than the other.
- Select the short segment, then the long one.

By selecting the shorter segment first, you told Sketchpad you want a scale factor less than one. A scale factor comprised of a smaller quantity over a larger quantity will *shrink* objects dilated by it.

    **Select first.**

Select second.

- Press the Transform menu and choose Mark Ratio.

A brief animation shows that the two segments have been marked to serve as a ratio for dilation.

- Construct a point and while it's selected choose Mark Center in the Transform menu.

At this point you've constructed an angle for rotation, a ratio for a dilation, and a center about which to rotate and dilate any object.

- Construct a polygon interior by holding down the Shift key and using the Point tool to create several selected points.

If you carefully locate points in the correct order, you can create an interesting figure for your polygon interior.

- Choose Polygon Interior from the Construct menu.

Center

○

- Select the polygon interior and choose Rotate from the Transform menu.

This dialog box appears:

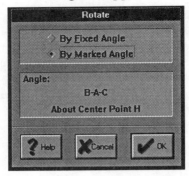

- Click By Marked Angle and click OK.

Sketchpad constructs a rotated image of your original polygon.

- Select the image and choose a different shade and/or color in the Display menu.

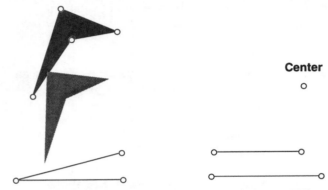

Drag the points on your angle to see how this affects the rotated image.

Center

○

- Select the rotated polygon interior and choose Dilate from the Transform menu.

This dialog box appears.

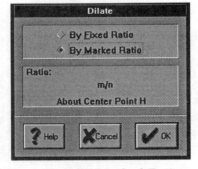

- Click By Marked Ratio and click OK.

Sketchpad constructs a dilated image of your rotated image of your original polygon.

- Select the image and choose a shade and/or color in the Display menu that's different from your original and the first rotated image.

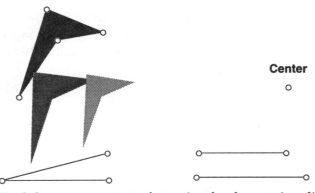

Drag the endpoints of the segments that define the marked ratio and observe how that affects the dilated image.

Center

- To define a custom transformation for the rotation-dilation sequence, select the original polygon (darkest in the illustration above) and the second image (the rotated/dilated figure—lightest in the illustration above). Make sure you hold down Shift to select more than one object.

- Choose Define Transform in the Transform menu.

You'll see this dialog box listing the two transformation steps that constructed the second image from the original.

Define Transform

Name: 2 Step Transform

2 steps define the total transformation.
1. Rotate by Angle B-A-C about Center Point H
2. Dilate by Ratio m/n about Center Point H

? Help   X Cancel   ✓ OK

- Type in a descriptive name like "Twist 'n Shrink," and click Define.

You've now defined a custom transformation of a rotation followed by a dilation. This two-step transformation, Twist 'n Shrink, now appears in the Transform menu, ready to be applied to any object.

- To apply Twist 'n Shrink to the rotated-dilated image several times, select the rotated-dilated polygon interior and choose Twist 'n Shrink from the Transform menu.

Sketchpad constructs a rotated image and a rotated-dilated image. The new rotated-dilated image is selected, ready to have the transformation applied to it again.

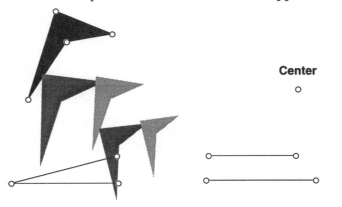

Center

Note that the polygon resulting from the two-step transformation and the intermediate polygon have the same shade and/or color you gave their corresponding pre-images when you defined the custom transformation. Likewise, if you'd hidden the intermediate polygon before you'd defined the transformation, the custom transformation would have hidden it too.

- Press Shift+Ctrl+1 several times to create a spiral towards the center. (Shift+Ctrl+1 is the keyboard shortcut for the first custom transformation you define.)

Adjust the angle and ratio to manipulate the spiral. Also, move the original polygon and center point.

Center

Try other combinations of transformations:

- Define as a custom transformation a reflection followed by a translation. Apply it to some polygon interior several times. What's the result?
- Define as a custom transformation two reflections across intersecting lines. What's the result?
- Define as a custom transformation two reflections across parallel lines. What's the result?
- Try a translation followed by a dilation.
- Experiment with translation by marked vector.

Answer the following questions:

- How do you mark an angle of rotation?
- How do you mark a ratio of dilation?
- What else do you need to mark in order to rotate or dilate an object?
- What do you need to select in order to define a custom transformation?
- What's the keyboard shortcut to apply a custom transformation?

Chapter 1
Lines and Angles

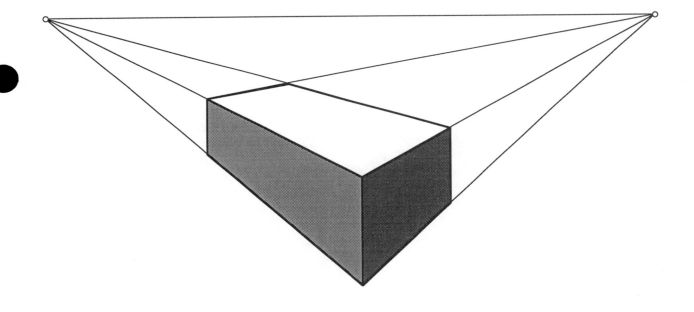

Construction: Euclid's Proposition 1—An Equilateral Triangle

Euclid's *Elements* sequentially builds all of what students typically learn in geometry from a few simple constructions and postulates. Every new property that Euclid presents or figure he constructs is based on properties that were demonstrated previously. The construction that starts it all is the equilateral triangle. Countless other constructions in the *Elements* depend on being able to construct an equilateral triangle with compass and straightedge. In this activity, you'll construct an equilateral triangle using only Sketchpad's freehand tools, the equivalent of Euclid's collapsible compass and straightedge.

Sketch

Step 1: Construct $\overline{AB}$.

Step 2: Construct circle *AB*. (Make sure you use *A* for the center and *B* for the radius-defining point.)

Step 3: Construct circle *BA*. (Use *B* for the center and *A* for the radius point this time.)

Step 4: Construct $\overline{AC}$ and $\overline{CB}$, where *C* is a point of intersection of the two circles.

Step 5: Hide the circles.

Investigate

Drag point *A* or point *B*. What happens to your triangle? Does it appear to stay equilateral? What guarantees that this will always be an equilateral triangle? Hints: What roles do the circles play in your construction? How are the two circles related to one another? How are the sides of the triangle related to the circles? The sides are all equal in length. What about the angles? Measure the three angles.

Conjecture

In the space below, write a description of the construction, including your explanation of what guarantees that the triangle will be equilateral. Also, write a conjecture about the angles in an equilateral triangle.

_____

_____

_____

_____

Present Your Findings

Compare and discuss your construction with your partner or group. To present your sketch you could record a script of your construction and add a comment that describes the steps and why they work.

Explore More

Record a script for this construction, then play it on two vertices of the triangle other than your original two points. (If nothing happens, try selecting the points in the opposite order and play the script again.) Keep playing the script on different pairs of vertices. What can you discover about equilateral triangles?

Construction: Euclid's Proposition 1—An Equilateral Triangle

Student Audience: Middle School/High School

Prerequisites: Students should know, or be introduced to, the term **equilateral**. A discussion of Euclid's tools and how they differ from modern compass and straightedge should interest students. You can explain that Euclid's compass rules stipulate that whenever you pick up the compass point, you lose the radius setting of your compass. Given two points A and B, you could draw the circle with center A, containing B, but you could not use the compass to mark a segment congruent to $\overline{AB}$ on a ray $\overrightarrow{CD}$. This is true of Sketchpad's Circle tool as well. The command Circle By Center+Radius in the Construct menu is Sketchpad's version of the modern, non-collapsible compass.

Sketchpad Proficiency: Beginner

Class Time: 15-30 minutes

Example Script: **Equilateral Triangle** (Mac) or **1lineang\equitri.gss** (Windows)

Construction Tips

The most common mistake students will make will be to construct circles in steps 2 and 3 that merely pass through B and A but aren't defined by these points. Make sure students understand that to construct circle AB, they must press the mouse on A and release when the pointer is directly over B.

Step 4: Segment $\overline{AC}$ and point C can be created in the same step. Use the Segment tool, press the mouse on A and drag to where the circles intersect. Releasing here will create the point at the intersection, C.

Encourage students to record a script for this construction to be included in their own folder of utility scripts. Having an equilateral triangle script will come in handy in later investigations.

Investigate

As students drag points A and B, the triangle will change in size, but will remain equilateral. Dragging $\overline{AB}$ will move the entire triangle without changing its size. All the sides of the triangle are radii of two congruent circles, hence they're all equal. You may want students to manipulate the triangle with the circles still showing to emphasize the role they play in the construction. This is a good opportunity to discuss the role played by hidden objects in a Sketchpad sketch: though not visible, hidden objects (unlike deleted objects) continue to play a role in the geometry of a sketch.

Conjecture

Students should come up with one or more of the following conjectures:

An equilateral triangle is also equiangular.

The measures of the angles in an equilateral triangle are all 60°.

Explore More

By playing an equilateral triangle script on different vertices, students can tessellate (fill the sketch plane without gaps or overlap) with equilateral triangles. (If students play the script on two vertices of an existing equilateral triangle and nothing happens, that means the script merely created the triangle that already existed. Selecting the points in the opposite order will cause the script to create a triangle going in the other direction.)

Art: Daisy Designs

A daisy design is a simple design that can be created using only a compass. From the basic daisy, you can create more complex designs based on the regular hexagon. This activity will give you practice using the freehand tools to construct objects to points of intersection.

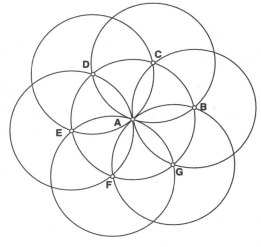

Sketch

Step 1: Construct circle *AB*.

Step 2: Construct circle *BA*.

Step 3: From the points of intersection of these circles, continue constructing circles to existing points. (All these circles should have equal radii.) Points labeled here show one possible order for constructing these circles: *CB*, *DC*, *ED*, then *FG* and *GF*. Construct *FG* instead of *FE* to avoid having three intersecting circles without an intersection point.

Step 4: If your last circle refuses to be constructed, you're probably releasing the mouse on the intersection of three circles. In this case, select two circles and construct their intersection with the Construct menu. Then use this point to construct your final circle.

At this point, you may wish to use the Segment tool to add some lines to your design. You could construct circle and polygon interiors and experiment with shading, but you can probably get better results by printing out the basic design and adding color and shading by hand.

The six points of your daisy define six vertices of a regular hexagon. You can use these points as the basis for hexagon or star designs like these shown below. Once you have all the lines and polygon interiors you want, you can hide unneeded points. You probably don't want to hide your original two points though, as you can use these points to manipulate your figure.

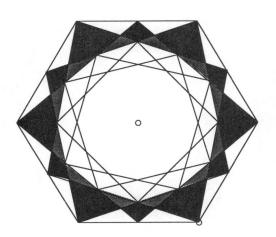

Art: Daisy Designs

Student Audience: Any

Prerequisites: Students should know, or be introduced to, the terms regular and hexagon.

Sketchpad Proficiency: Beginner, though you'll see many missed points of intersection that will cause constructions to fall apart when manipulated. Beginners may experience frustration if they attempt too complicated designs, but this activity will provide good practice at using freehand tools and constructing to points of intersection.

Class Time: 20-45 minutes, depending on how much time you allow students to create more complex designs

Example Sketch/Script: **Hex Designs** (Mac sketch) **Daisy** (Mac script) or **1lineang\hexdes.gsp** (Windows sketch), or **1lineang\daisy.gss** (Windows script)

Construction Tips

Step 2: Make sure students use points *B* and *A* to define the second circle. Some may use *B* for the center of a circle that merely passes through *A* but whose radius is defined by a third point.

Step 3: Students must press the mouse with the pointer positioned directly over two circles' intersection and release directly over *B* to create circle *CB*. If they miss, the design won't hold together when manipulated.

Step 4: The reason for constructing circle *FG* instead of *FE* is that constructing *FE* will cause three circles to intersect at *G* before *G* is constructed. Sketchpad will not allow the construction of an intersection of three objects, as such an intersection is not usually defined by a single point. To construct an intersection of three objects, you must select two of them and use the Construct menu. This can complicate a daisy design by constructing the *two* points of intersection of two circles, creating double points somewhere that can affect dragging.

Point out that by using the Segment tool to connect the outside points of the daisy students can construct a regular hexagon. A six-pointed star can be constructed by connecting alternate points to create intersecting equilateral triangles. Midpoints can be useful in creating more complex designs. Encourage students to experiment and practice using different tools.

Exploring Geometry

Construction: Duplicating a Line Segment

This method for duplicating a line segment with Sketchpad is equivalent to the standard compass and straightedge construction. However, Sketchpad's compass (the Circle tool) is collapsible, like Euclid's compass. Duplicating a segment using only Sketchpad's freehand tools (i.e. Euclid's tools) is more complicated than you'd expect. We'll get around this by using the Construct menu. This construction is a building block for many more complex constructions. For this reason, you may want to record and save a script for duplicating a line segment.

Sketch

Step 1: Construct $\overline{AB}$. This is your given segment.

Step 2: Construct point C. This is one endpoint of your new segment.

Step 3: Select $\overline{AB}$ and C and choose Circle By Center+Radius in the Construct menu.

Step 4: Construct $\overline{CD}$, where D is on the circle.

Step 5: Hide the circle.

Investigate

Move points C and D. Do they behave as you would expect them too? Move point A or B. What effect does changing the length of $\overline{AB}$ have on $\overline{CD}$? In the space below, write a paragraph describing why this construction works. Compare it to how you would duplicate a segment using a compass and straightedge. Why is the command Circle By Center+Radius necessary? (What can you do with an actual compass that you can't do with Sketchpad's compass?)

_____

_____

_____

_____

_____

Present Your Findings

Discuss your construction with your partner or group. To present your findings you could create a script that duplicates a line segment, commented to explain why it works. Save this as a utility script for duplicating a segment.

Explore More

1. Construct three unconnected segments. Now try to construct a triangle whose sides have the same lengths as the three segments. Are all the triangles you can construct with these given lengths congruent? Change the lengths of the segments. Can any three segments make a triangle?

2. Find a copy of Euclid's *Elements*, Book 1, and use Sketchpad to try to do Euclid's Proposition 2: Duplicating a Segment, using only freehand tools.

Construction: Duplicating a Line Segment

Student Audience: Middle School/High School

Prerequisites: None

Sketchpad Proficiency: Beginner

Class Time: 15-20 minutes

Example Script: **Duplicate Segment** (Mac) or **1lineang\dupseg.gss** (Windows)

Construction Tips

This is a very simple construction. The purpose of this activity is to familiarize students with a useful Sketchpad construction technique and connect to experience they may have with compass and straightedge. Students can also create a utility script for duplicating a segment. Even though it only takes four steps to duplicate a segment using the Construct menu, a script could come in handy for this very useful construction.

Investigate/Conjecture

CD is equal to *AB* because it's a radius of a circle with radius *AB*, and all radii of a circle are equal. When you duplicate a segment with compass and straightedge, you open your compass to the length of the given segment, then transfer that distance to the given endpoint of a new segment. You usually make a little arc and draw a segment from the given point to the arc. You could, however, draw an entire circle and draw a segment from the given point to any point on the circle. That's equivalent to this method of duplicating a segment with Sketchpad. The command Circle By Center+Radius is necessary because Sketchpad's compass (the Circle tool) is collapsible. That is, once you make a circle with it, you can't just transfer that radius to another place in the sketch. Each time you make a circle with the Circle tool, you must define its radius by dragging.

Explore More

1. Students can continue this investigation to discover that three sides uniquely determine a triangle (SSS). They can also discover triangle inequality: no side of a triangle can have length greater than the sum of the lengths of the other two sides.

2. Euclid's Proposition 2, duplicating a segment, is complex, but do-able with Sketchpad.

Construction: Duplicating an Angle

In this activity, you'll learn how to duplicate a given angle. The method described is equivalent to the method you would use with a compass and straightedge. You might want to follow the first few steps then try to figure out the rest on your own. This construction is a building block for many other, more complex constructions. You may want to record and save a script for duplicating an angle.

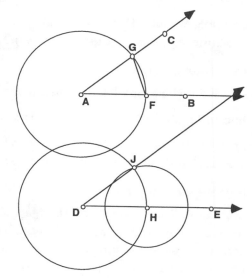

Sketch

Step 1:   Construct rays $\overrightarrow{AB}$ and $\overrightarrow{AC}$. (This is your given angle.)

Step 2:   Construct $\overrightarrow{DE}$, one side of new angle.

Step 3:   Construct circle AF and $\overline{AF}$, with F on $\overrightarrow{AB}$.

Step 4:   Construct $\overline{FG}$, where G is the point of intersection of the circle and $\overrightarrow{AC}$.

Step 5:   Construct a circle with center D and radius AF.

Step 6:   Construct H, the point of intersection of this circle with $\overrightarrow{DE}$.

Step 7:   Construct a circle with center H and radius FG.

Step 8:   Construct $\overrightarrow{DJ}$, where J is the point of intersection of these two circles.

Step 9:   If you wish, hide the circles, segments, and points H, F, and G.

Investigate

Move points A, B, C, D, or E. Do the angles remain congruent? Confirm that they're congruent by measuring them. When you try to drag J, why doesn't $\angle JDH$ change?

Present Your Findings

Discuss your construction with your partner or group. To present your findings you could create a commented script that duplicates an angle, explaining why it works.

Explore More

1. Construct two unconnected segments and an angle. Now construct a triangle by duplicating the angle and the two sides on the sides of the angle. Is there more than one way to do it? Are all the triangles you can construct this way congruent?

2. The construction described in this activity duplicates angles only in a counter-clockwise direction. (If you move your original angle past 180°, your duplicate will still have equal measure, but will have a different orientation.) Come up with a construction for duplicating an angle in the clockwise direction.

Construction: Duplicating an Angle

Student Audience: Middle School/High School

Prerequisites: None

Sketchpad Proficiency: Beginner

Class Time: 20 minutes

Example Scripts: **Duplicate Angle (CW)** and **Duplicate Angle (CCW)** (Mac) or **1lineang\dupangcw.gss** and **1lineang\dupangcc.gss** (Windows)

Construction Tips

This would be a very handy construction for students to record as a utility script for future investigations.

Encourage students to figure out the rest of the construction after step 4 for themselves.

Step 5: Select D and $\overline{AF}$ and choose Circle By Center+Radius in the Construct menu. Make sure students select $\overline{AF}$ instead of $\overrightarrow{AB}$. Repeated clicks will alternately select different objects that overlap one another.

Investigate/Conjecture

Moving A, B, or C will change both angles. Moving D or E will change the direction of $\overrightarrow{DE}$, and hence, the orientation of $\angle JDE$, but not the measure of the angle. Point J is determined by the construction, so moving it can't change the measure or orientation of the angle. Angles A and D must be congruent because they're corresponding parts of congruent triangles determined in the construction by SSS.

Explore More

1. Students can continue this investigation to discover that two sides and the angle between them uniquely determine a triangle (SAS).

2. To duplicate an angle in the clockwise direction, simply construct $\overrightarrow{DJ}$ to the other point of intersection of the circles—the point clockwise from $\overrightarrow{DE}$. Students recording scripts to duplicate angles may want their scripts to construct a double duplicate: adjacent angles each congruent to the given angle, one constructed clockwise and the other counter-clockwise from a given ray. Students using this as a utility script could simply hide the unwanted ray.

©1996 by Key Curriculum Press   Exploring Geometry

Investigation: Building an Electronic Protractor

When you use Sketchpad, you don't need a protractor to measure angles because Sketchpad will measure them electronically. It's interesting, though, that you can actually construct a protractor for measuring angles using Sketchpad's Transform menu. Creating an electronic protractor and measuring angles with it will give you a better understanding of what a protractor is and how it's used.

Sketch

Step 1: Construct a horizontal segment $\overline{AB}$, then edit the label of B to read 0.

Step 2: Select A and choose Mark Center in the Transform menu

Step 3: Select the segment and point 0 and rotate them 10°.

Step 4: Select the point 0 and the rotated point and choose Define Transform in the Transform menu. Give this custom transformation a name if you like.

Step 5: Apply this custom transformation to the first rotated segment and point to construct a segment and point at 20°. Continue applying the transformation until you've rotated 180° total. (How many 10° rotations is this?)

Step 6: Edit every other point label with degree measures in 20° increments. Also edit the point label at 90° because that's such a special angle. Hide all the other points (they're just in the way).

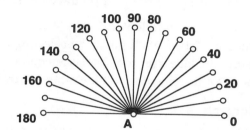

Investigate

Now use your protractor to measure some angles. Create angles with the segment or Ray tool. Use thick lines for these angles so you can distinguish them from the lines on your protractor. To measure an angle, drag $\overline{A0}$ so that A is positioned on the vertex of the angle, then move point 0 so that it lies on one side of the angle. Estimate angle measures to the nearest degree. Make sure to measure **obtuse angles** (angles with measure greater than 90°) and **acute angles** (with measures less than 90°). Check your estimates by using the Measure menu to measure the angles.

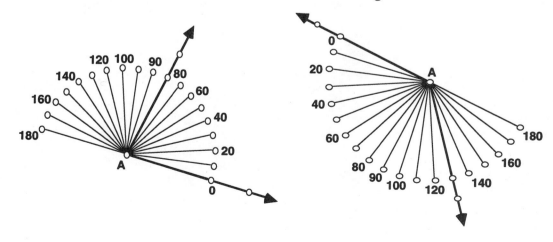

Investigation: Building an Electronic Protractor

Student Audience: Middle School/High School

Prerequisites: Students should know what a protractor is and how to use it. Students should know, or be introduced to, the terms **acute** and **obtuse**.

Sketchpad Proficiency: Experienced User

Class Time: 20-40 minutes

Example Sketch: Electronic Protractor (Mac) or **1lineang\protrac.gsp** (Windows)

Construction Tips

Consider doing this activity without the activity sheet. That is, let students figure out for themselves how to construct an electronic protractor. Or make a copy of the activity sheet and white out all the construction steps except the first two and let students take if from there, working with the diagram. Set Preferences to not autoshow labels for points. Otherwise point labels like 0′′′′′′′′ start to clutter the sketch.

Step 1: Double-click on a label with the text tool to edit it. Change B to zero (not the letter O).

Step 4: Students could do repeated rotations instead of defining a custom transformation. But this is a shortcut, as you can now complete your protractor in seconds using ⌘1 (Mac) or Ctrl+1 (Windows).

Step 6: Your labels will start to look like 0′′′′′′′′ after a few rotations. If your point labels are showing, you may want to hide the labels of all points by selecting all points (choose the Point tool and Select All Points) and hiding the labels (in the Display menu or using the appropriate keyboard shortcut). Then edit labels of points at 20° increments and hide other points (except A and 90).

Investigate/Conjecture

Students should drag the segment $\overline{A0}$ to move the protractor. Moving point A or 0 will change the size of the protractor—not a fatal problem, but potentially confusing. This protractor has numbers going only one way, which forces students to use it on one side of the angle, but it has the advantage that students won't mistake an angle measure's supplement for the angle measure.

Investigation: Angles Formed by Intersecting Lines

When two lines intersect, they form four angles whose vertices are the point of intersection. In this activity you'll investigate relationships between pairs of these angles.

Sketch

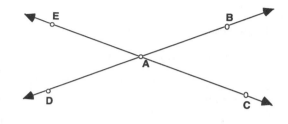

Step 1: Construct $\overleftrightarrow{AB}$ and $\overleftrightarrow{AC}$.

Step 2: Construct points D and E so that A is between D and B and also between E and C.

Step 3: Measure the four angles: $\angle BAC$, $\angle CAD$, $\angle DAE$, and $\angle EAB$.

Investigate

Drag points B and C. What do you notice about the relationships among the angles? How would you describe the angles that are equal? These are called **vertical angles**. What relationship do you see between a pair of unequal angles? Use Calculate in the Measure menu to test your conjectures. These angles that share one side and whose other sides form a line are called a **linear pair**. Can a linear pair ever be equal? Under what circumstances?

Conjecture: Write your conjectures below.

_____

_____

_____

_____

_____

_____

Present Your Findings

Discuss your results with your partner or group. To present your findings you could print a sketch with measures and captions to illustrate your conjecture. Show several examples of the lines forming different angles.

Explore More

Two intersecting lines form four angles. Using your conjectures, if you knew the measure of one of the angles, you could find the measures of the other three. What if three lines intersect in a single point to form six angles? How many angle measures would you have to know in order to find the rest? Experiment with Sketchpad, and pose yourself some problems.

Investigation: Angles Formed by Intersecting Lines

Student Audience: Middle School/High School

Prerequisites: None. This investigation introduces some very basic properties and explains the terms **vertical angle** and **linear pair**.

Sketchpad Proficiency: Beginner

Class Time: 10-20 minutes

Construction Tips

Steps 1 and *2:* It's best if students construct these lines as instructed so that they share a control point *A*. This method ensures that the point of intersection *A* will remain fixed when students move point *B* or *C*.

Step 3: To measure an angle, select three points in order: point, vertex, point.

Investigate/Conjecture

Students should make the following conjectures:

Vertical angles are equal.

Angles forming a linear pair are supplementary.

A linear pair are equal if and only if the angles are right angles.

Explore More

This is a very short investigation, leaving time to explore with Sketchpad. When three lines intersect, you can find all six angles if you know the measures of any two non-vertical angles.

Investigation: Properties of Parallel Lines

In this investigation you'll discover relationships among the angles formed when parallel lines are intersected by a third line called a **transversal**.

Sketch

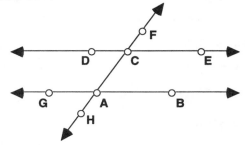

Step 1: Construct $\overleftrightarrow{AB}$ and point C, not on $\overleftrightarrow{AB}$.

Step 2: Construct a line parallel to $\overleftrightarrow{AB}$, through C.

Step 3: Construct $\overrightarrow{CA}$ and points D, E, F, G, and H as shown.

Step 4: Measure the eight angles in your figure.

Investigate

Drag point A or B and watch which angles stay equal. (Be careful not to change the point order on your lines—that will change the angles Sketchpad measures!) Make a table in your sketch to keep track of these angles' measures as the transversal is changed. In the chart below, one example of each type of angle pair is given. Fill in the chart with other angle pairs of that type, then state what relationship, if any, you observe between the angles in a pair. Note: there are more than two pairs of one of these types. Can you identify which type has more than two pairs?

Angle Type	Pair 1	Pair 2	Relationship?
Corresponding	∠FCE and ∠CAB		
Alternate Interior	∠ECA and ∠CAG		
Alternate Exterior	∠FCE and ∠HAG		
Consecutive Interior	∠ECA and ∠BAC		
Consecutive Exterior	∠FCD and ∠HAG		

Conjecture: Write your conjectures below.

_____

_____

_____

_____

Present Your Findings

Discuss your results with your partner or group. To present your findings you could print a captioned sketch showing parallel lines and the measures of the angles.

Explore More

What about the converses of the above conjectures? Start out with two lines that are not quite parallel. Intersect them with a transversal and measure corresponding angles. Now move a line until the angles are equal. Measure the slopes of the lines. If their slopes are equal, then they're parallel. Write your findings and conjectures on the back of this sheet.

Investigation: Properties of Parallel Lines

Student Audience: Middle School/High School

Prerequisites: This activity introduces the terms **transversal, corresponding angles, alternate interior, alternate exterior, consecutive interior,** and **consecutive exterior**.

Sketchpad Proficiency: Beginner

Example Sketch: **Parallel Lines and Transversal** (Mac) or **1lineang\parlines.gsp** (Windows)

Class Time: 20-40 minutes

Construction Tips

This is a straightforward construction that should present few difficulties for students.

Step 3: Make sure students locate the points as shown so that their figures correspond to the chart.

Investigate/Conjecture

This investigation serves both to guide students to discover angle relationships and to guide them in identifying angles of different types. Students should fill in the chart as shown:

Angle Type	Pair 1	Pair 2	Relationship?
Corresponding	∠FCE and ∠CAB	∠DCA and ∠GAH*	Equal
Alternate Interior	∠ECA and ∠CAG	∠DCA and ∠CAB	Equal
Alternate Exterior	∠FCE and ∠HAG	∠DCF and ∠HAB	Equal
Consecutive Interior	∠ECA and ∠BAC	∠DCA and ∠GAC	Supplementary
Consecutive Exterior	∠FCD and ∠HAG	∠FCE and ∠HAB	Supplementary

*Other pairs of corresponding angles include ∠FCD and ∠CAB and also ∠ECA and ∠GAH.

Students should make the following conjectures:

If parallel lines are cut by a transversal, then corresponding angles are equal.

If parallel lines are cut by a transversal, then alternate interior angles are equal.

If parallel lines are cut by a transversal, then alternate exterior angles are equal.

If parallel lines are cut by a transversal, then consecutive interior angles are supplementary.

If parallel lines are cut by a transversal, then consecutive exterior angles are equal.

Explore More

If students construct lines and manipulate them so that corresponding angles are equal, the lines will be parallel. You may need to tell students that you can test whether lines are parallel by measuring to see if they have equal slopes. The converses of all the other conjectures are true as well.

Investigation: Perpendicular Bisectors

In this activity, you'll use only Sketchpad's freehand tools to construct and investigate properties of perpendicular bisectors.

Sketch

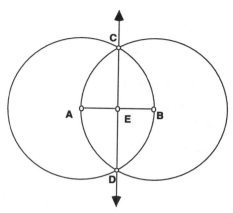

Step 1: Construct $\overline{AB}$.

Step 2: Construct circles AB and BA.

Step 3: Construct $\overleftrightarrow{CD}$, where C and D are the points of intersection of the circles.

Step 4: Construct E, the point of intersection of $\overleftrightarrow{AB}$ and $\overleftrightarrow{CD}$.

Step 5: Hide the circles.

Investigate

Line CD is the perpendicular bisector of $\overline{AB}$. Move points A and B. What's special about point E? Can you come up with a shortcut for constructing a perpendicular bisector using the Construct menu? Construct a point F on $\overleftrightarrow{CD}$. Measure the distances FA and FB. Move point F up and down the line. What can you say about any point on a segment's perpendicular bisector?

Conjecture: Write your conjectures below.

_____

_____

_____

_____

_____

Present Your Findings

Discuss your findings with your partner or group. To present your findings you could:

1. Create a script for constructing a perpendicular bisector with comments explaining why your construction works.

2. Print a captioned sketch with measures illustrating your conjectures.

Explore More

1. Construct the perpendicular bisectors of the three sides of a triangle. Investigate their point(s) of intersection. Can you construct a circle that circumscribes the triangle?

2. Construct $\overline{AC}$ and $\overline{AF}$. Mark your perpendicular bisector as mirror and reflect A, $\overline{AC}$ and $\overline{AF}$ across it. Where is A' (the reflection of A) located? How do the triangles formed by this reflection help explain why C and F are equidistant from A and B?

Investigation: Perpendicular Bisectors

Student Audience: Middle School/High School

Prerequisites: Students should know, or be introduced to, the terms **perpendicular** and **bisector**.

Sketchpad Proficiency: Beginner

Class Time: 15 minutes

Construction Tips

Step 2: Make sure students use points *B* and *A* for circle *BA* instead of merely constructing a circle with center *B* that happens to pass through *A* but is defined by a third point.

Example Script: **Perpendicular Bisector** (Mac) or **1\lineang\perpbis.gss** (Windows)

Investigate/Conjecture

Students should confirm visually that point *E* is the midpoint of $\overline{AB}$. Thus, a perpendicular bisector could be constructed using the construct menu: select the segment, construct its midpoint, construct a line through the midpoint, perpendicular to the segment.

Students should come up with this conjecture:

Every point on the perpendicular bisector of a segment is equidistant from the segment's endpoints.

Explore more

1. Students will discover that the perpendicular bisectors of the sides of a triangle intersect in a single point. This point is called the circumcenter and is the subject of another activity: Circumscribing a Triangle.

2. Point *A'* is located at point *B*. Reflection preserves distances, so triangles *ACA'* and *AFA'* are isosceles. *CA* = *CA'* = *CB*, and *FA* = *FA'* = *FB*.

     Exploring Geometry

Investigation: Slopes of Parallel and Perpendicular Lines

When you select a line, ray, or segment in Sketchpad, one of the things you can measure is its slope. In this investigation, you'll learn how you can use slope to tell if lines are parallel or perpendicular.

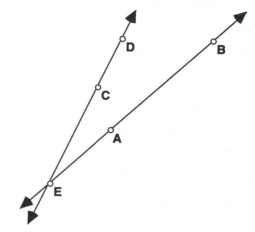

Sketch

Step 1: Construct lines $\overleftrightarrow{AB}$ and $\overleftrightarrow{CD}$ and their point of intersection, E.

Step 2: Measure $\angle CEA$.

Step 3: Measure the slopes of $\overleftrightarrow{AB}$ and $\overleftrightarrow{CD}$.

Step 4: Calculate the sum, difference, product, and ratio of the slopes of $\overleftrightarrow{AB}$ and $\overleftrightarrow{CD}$.

Investigate

Drag point D around point C to change the direction of $\overleftrightarrow{CD}$ and observe your measures and calculations. As the measure of $\angle CEA$ approaches 0, the lines approach being parallel. Display this angle to 1000ths precision and drag D to make the angle as close to zero as you can. (If you can make the lines exactly parallel, the angle will cease to exist and its measure will disappear.) What do you observe about the slopes when the lines are parallel? Drag D until $\angle CEA = 90°$. What do you observe about the slopes of perpendicular lines? What can you say about slopes of horizontal and vertical lines? Lines that rise going from left to right? Lines that fall going from left to right?

Conjecture: Write your conjectures below or on a seperate sheet of paper.

_____

_____

_____

_____

Present Your Findings

Discuss and compare your results with your partner or group. To present your findings, you could print a captioned sketch showing measures and calculations that illustrate your conjectures.

Explore More

How is the slope of a line calculated? To investigate this question, construct a triangle ACB on your line $\overleftrightarrow{AB}$. Adjust C so that $\triangle ACB$ is a right triangle with $\overline{AB}$ the hypotenuse and $\overline{AC}$ and $\overline{CB}$ horizontal and vertical legs. Measure AC and CB. Can you perform a calculation with these lengths that gives you the slope of $\overleftrightarrow{AB}$?

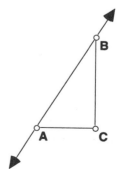

Investigation: Slopes of Parallel and Perpendicular Lines

Student Audience: High School

Prerequisites: Students should know definitions of **parallel** and **perpendicular**. Students need not know the definition of slope for this introductory investigation.

Sketchpad Proficiency: Beginner

Class Time: 15-30 minutes

Example Sketch: **Slope** (Mac) or **1lineang\slope.gsp** (Windows)

Construction Tips

There's nothing tricky about this construction. To measure slope, simple select the line and choose Slope in the Measure menu.

To measure angles to 1000ths precision, choose Preferences in the Display menu.

Investigate/Conjecture

If students can make the angle cease to exist, they should note that the slopes of the parallel lines are equal. The relationship between slopes of perpendicular lines will be less obvious. Assuming neither lines is horizontal or vertical, the only calculation that will be displaying anything interesting when the lines are perpendicular is the product. It should be very close to, if not exactly, negative one. Students who have the good fortune of being able to manipulate their lines to be exactly perpendicular are most likely to discover this relationship. The reasons for these relationships are not explored here. Instead, the intent of this investigation is to build intuition for the concepts, and provide students with an efficient way to determine if lines in Sketchpad figures are parallel or perpendicular. Students should come up with the following conjectures:

The slopes of parallel lines are equal.

The product of the slopes of perpendicular lines is -1 (assuming their slopes are defined).

The slope of a horizontal line is zero and the slope of a vertical line is undefined.

Lines that rise going from left to right have positive slopes.

Lines that fall going from left to right have negative slopes.

Explore More

Students can begin to discover how slope is defined by doing this Explore More activity. Note, however, that this method will not explain negative slopes, as lengths in Sketchpad are positive.

Investigation: Distance from a Point to a Line

Measuring the distance between two points is easy, but how do you measure the distance between a point and a line? There are lots of different distances, depending on what point you measure to on the line. What's the shortest distance? That's what you'll investigate in this activity.

Sketch

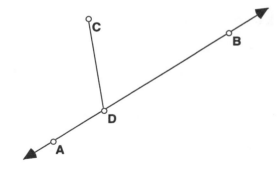

Step 1: Construct $\overleftrightarrow{AB}$.

Step 2: Construct $\overline{CD}$, where C is not on $\overleftrightarrow{AB}$ and D is on $\overleftrightarrow{AB}$.

Step 3: Measure the distance from C to $\overleftrightarrow{AB}$ and the distance from C to D.

Investigate

When you ask Sketchpad to measure the distance from a point to a line, it measures the shortest distance. How does it find the shortest distance? Drag point D until the distance CD is equal to the distance from C to $\overleftrightarrow{AB}$. What relationship do you see between $\overline{CD}$ and $\overleftrightarrow{AB}$? Construct a line through C, perpendicular to $\overleftrightarrow{AB}$. What can you say about the shortest distance from a point to a line?

Conjecture: Write your conjectures below.

_____

_____

_____

_____

_____

_____

Present Your Findings

Discuss your findings with your partner or group. To present your findings you could print a captioned sketch with measures illustrating your conjectures. Show different stages as CD approaches the shortest distance from C to $\overleftrightarrow{AB}$.

Explore More

See if you can model this problem on Sketchpad:

There's a sewage treatment plant at the point where two rivers meet. You want to build a house near the two rivers (upstream, naturally, from the sewage plant) but you want the house to be at least five miles from the sewage plant. You visit each of the rivers to go fishing about the same number of times, but, being lazy, you want to minimize the amount of walking you do. (You want the sum of the distances from your house to the two rivers to be minimal.) Where should you build your house?

Investigation: Distance from a Point to a Line

Student Audience: Middle School/High School

Prerequisites: Students should know, or be introduced to, the term **perpendicular**.

Sketchpad Proficiency: Beginner

Class Time: 10 minutes

Example Sketch: **Sewer River Problem** (Mac) or **1lineang\swrprob.gsp** (Windows)

Construction Tips

This is a very simple a construction. Just make sure students construct $\overline{CD}$ to a random point D on $\overleftrightarrow{AB}$, not A, or B.

Step 3: Select point C and $\overleftrightarrow{AB}$ to measure the distance from the point to the line.

Investigate/Conjecture

Make sure nothing else is selected when students drag point D. As CD approaches the distance from C to the line, the segment $\overline{CD}$ approaches being perpendicular to $\overleftrightarrow{AB}$. This will be confirmed when students construct the perpendicular to $\overleftrightarrow{AB}$ through C. Distance CD is minimized when D is at the intersection of $\overleftrightarrow{AB}$ and the perpendicular line.

Students should come up with the following conjecture:

The shortest distance from a point to a line is measured along a perpendicular through the given point.

Explore More

As this is such a brief investigation, many students may choose to work on the problem posed in this section. A sketch to model the problem is shown at right. The circle represents the 5-mile radius from the sewage plant at point A. Surprisingly, the optimal location for the house is on one of the banks (assuming you don't mind walking to the other river through the sewage zone).

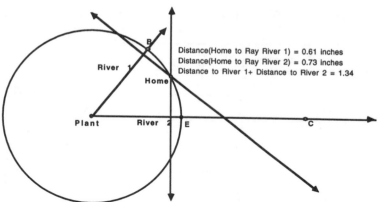

This becomes obvious when you think of the problem in terms of triangle inequality. Some students will choose not to construct the perpendicular distances but will construct segments from home to B and E, arguing that they don't want to fish in sewage zone any more than they want to live in it.

Exploring Geometry

Construction: Angle Bisectors

You can bisect an angle automatically with Sketchpad's Construct menu. But an angle bisector is not difficult to construct using only freehand tools. In this activity, you'll bisect an angle the way Euclid did it, then you'll investigate properties of angle bisectors.

Sketch

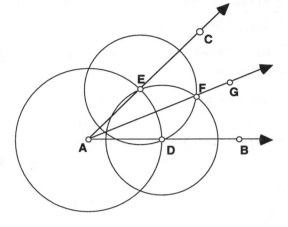

Step 1:   Construct $\overrightarrow{AB}$ and $\overrightarrow{AC}$.

Step 2:   Construct circle AD, with D on $\overrightarrow{AB}$.

Step 3:   Construct circle DE, where E is the intersection of $\overrightarrow{AC}$ and circle AD.

Step 4:   Construct circle ED.

Step 5:   Construct $\overrightarrow{AF}$, where F is the intersection of circles DE and ED that is farthest from A.

Step 6:   Hide the circles and points D, E, and F.

Step 7:   Construct a point G on the angle bisector.

Investigate

Drag point B or C. Does $\overrightarrow{AG}$ continue to bisect the angle? Measure the distances from G to $\overrightarrow{AB}$ and G to $\overrightarrow{AC}$. Move point G along the angle bisector. What do you notice about the distances to the sides of the angle?

Conjecture: Write your conjectures below.

_____

_____

_____

_____

_____

Present Your Findings

Discuss your findings with your partner or group. To present your findings you could:

1.   Create a script to construct an angle bisector and comment it to explain why it works and describe your conjectures.

2.   Print a captioned sketch with measures illustrating your conjectures.

Explore More

You'll notice that your angle bisector construction behaves strangely if you open up your angle past 180°. This behavior is different than the behavior of the angle bisector Sketchpad constructs when you choose Angle Bisector in the Construct menu. Experiment with the Construct menu Angle Bisector, then see if you can construct one that behaves that way. Hint: you'll use a midpoint.

Construction: Angle Bisectors

Student Audience: Middle School/High School

Prerequisites: Students should know, or be introduced to, the term **angle bisector**.

Sketchpad Proficiency: Beginner

Class Time: 20-30 minutes

Example Scripts: **Angle Bisectors 1 and 2** (Mac) or **1lineang\angbis1.gss** and **1lineang\angbis2.gss** (Windows)

Construction Tips

Step 3: The Circle tool will construct intersection points D and E automatically if you click and release at these intersections. Some students may have trouble releasing precisely at an intersection of a circle and ray. In that case, have them construct the intersections first, then the circle.

Step 5: If students construct $\overrightarrow{AF}$ to the closer of the circle intersections, the angle bisector will behave even more poorly, flipping to the exterior as soon as they open the angle. Make sure F lies at the intersection and that $\overrightarrow{AF}$ doesn't just happen to pass through these intersections.

Investigate/Conjecture

$\overrightarrow{AG}$ is constructed to be an angle bisector. However, because of the location of the circles that define it, at some point it may flip over to bisect the exterior region of the angle. Show all hidden to observe when and why this happens. The distances from G to either side of the angle are the same, so students should conjecture:

Every point on an angle bisector is equidistant from the two sides of the angle.

Explore More

To construct a well-behaved angle bisector, begin the construction as described in the steps. But instead of constructing $\overrightarrow{AF}$ to the intersection of circles DE and ED, construct $\overline{DE}$ and its midpoint. (Acknowledge that you could, if you wanted to, construct the midpoint using only freehand tools, then use the Construct menu instead.) Construct $\overrightarrow{AF}$ through this midpoint.

Construction: Angle Trisector

Trisecting an angle with a compass and a straightedge is a construction problem that has occupied professional and amateur mathematicians for centuries. Even though it has been proven that the construction can't be done, countless people still think they've come upon a solution. Others enjoy slightly bending the rules that govern compass-and-straightedge constructions to devise simple angle trisection methods. It is possible to trisect an angle using Sketchpad because you can rotate by marked measures and calculations.

Sketch

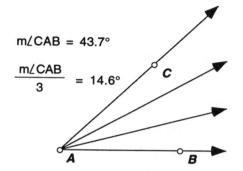

$m\angle CAB = 43.7°$

$\dfrac{m\angle CAB}{3} = 14.6°$

Step 1:   In the Display menu, choose Preferences and set Angle Unit to directed degrees.

Step 2:   Construct $\overrightarrow{AB}$ and $\overrightarrow{AC}$ as shown to form the angle you will trisect.

Step 3:   Select points B, A, and C in that order and measure the angle.

Step 4:   Calculate $m\angle BAC/3$.

Step 5:   Select this calculation and choose Mark Angle Measurement in the Transform menu.

Step 6:   Double-click point A to mark it as a center of rotation.

Step 7:   Rotate $\overrightarrow{AB}$ by the marked angle.

Step 8:   Rotate this new ray again by the marked angle.

Investigate

Drag points on the angle and observe the behavior of the trisectors. Do they stay trisectors? Your construction method was similar to what you could do with a protractor. Because you used the angle's measure to trisect it, this method doesn't qualify as a compass-and-straightedge construction. Constructions using only the freehand tools and Construct menu would be equivalent to compass-and-straightedge constructions.

Explore More

1.   Here's a compass-and-straightedge trisection method many people think should work: Draw a segment connecting the two sides of the angle. Find points at the 1/3 and 2/3 points on that segment. Draw rays through these points. Does this method seem to work? Will it hold up no matter how you drag your angle?

2.   Change your Preferences setting to degrees instead of directed degrees. How does that affect your trisectors? Why?

3.   Draw a triangle with extended sides using the line tool. Trisect the three angles. Can you find an interesting shape formed by intersecting trisectors?

Construction: Angle Trisector

Student Audience: High School

Prerequisites: Students often find it hard to believe that an angle can't be trisected with compass and straightedge. You might ask them to try it for awhile before giving them this activity.

Sketchpad Proficiency: Experienced User

Class Time: 20-30 minutes

Example Script: Angle Trisector (Mac) or **1lineang\angtri.gss** (Windows)

Construction Tips

Step 3: Selection order is important. Here points are selected in counterclockwise order because ray *AB* is going to rotated in the counterclockwise direction in Step 7.

Step 4: The calculator can be called up by double-clicking a measure or by choosing Calculate in the Measure menu.

Investigate

There's actually not much to investigate here. The activity serves best as a springboard for a discussion of what constitutes a construction. Students are fascinated by the notion that something can be proved impossible. This is a rich subject for independent student research.

Explore More

1. This is likely the first method students would try if you simply asked them to trisect an angle. It's not a bad approximation for acute angles, but it becomes obviously wrong in obtuse angles.

2. If Preferences aren't set to directed degrees, the angle trisectors will only work for one orientation of the angle. When the angle unit is set to degrees, the measured angle is always between 0 and 180°. So the ray always gets rotated in the positive, counter-clockwise direction. The rotated ray will cease being a trisector as soon as ∠*BAC* has clockwise orientation.

3. Students might discover Morley's theorem: Angle trisectors intersect to form an equilateral triangle. Morley's therom is the subject of a separate investigation in this book.

Exploring Geometry

Art: Drawing a Box with Two-Point Perspective

Perspective is a way of drawing three-dimensional objects in two dimensions: on a piece of paper or a computer screen, for example. Objects that are farther away appear smaller to us. Perspective drawing takes advantage of this principle to make flat drawings appear to have depth.

Follow these steps to draw a box with two-point perspective. Labels are shown to clarify these directions, but you probably won't want labels on your drawing.

Step 1:   Draw a long horizontal line segment, $\overline{AB}$. This will be your **horizon line**, and its endpoints will be the **vanishing points** of your perspective box.

Step 2:   Draw a short, vertical segment, $\overline{CD}$, below your horizon line. This will be the front edge of your box.

Step 3:   Construct $\overline{CA}$, $\overline{DA}$, $\overline{CB}$, and $\overline{DB}$.

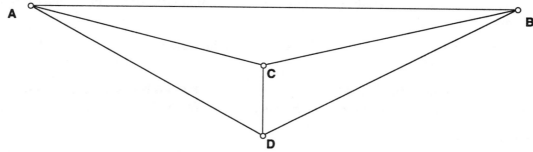

Step 4:   Construct E on $\overline{DA}$, and F on $\overline{DB}$.

Step 5:   Through points E and F, construct lines parallel to $\overline{CD}$.

Step 6:   From these lines' points of intersection with $\overline{CA}$ and $\overline{CB}$, construct $\overline{GB}$ and $\overline{HA}$.

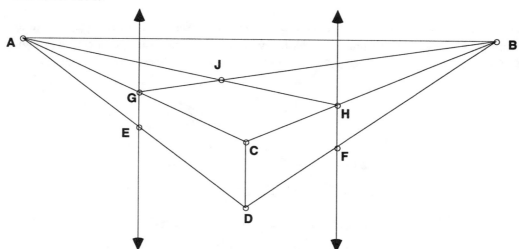

Step 7:   Construct J at the point of intersection of $\overline{GB}$ and $\overline{HA}$.

Art: Drawing a Box with Two-Point Perspective

Student Audience: Any

Prerequisites: None. Students who understand perspective will find this easy. For others, you may want to introduce the terms **horizon line** and **vanishing points** and discuss their significance. Or let students do the construction and see if they can figure it out themselves. This is a good activity for students who begin a geometry course with a unit on art and/or visualization skills.

Sketchpad Proficiency: Beginner

Class Time: 30 minutes

Example Sketches: **2-Pt. Perspective Box** and **Cabin** (Mac) or **1lineang\perspect.gsp** and **1lineang\cabin.gsp** (Windows)

Construction Tips

Follow the steps on the activity carefully and sequentially to ensure that your box obeys the rules of two-point perspective when you move it.

Steps 1-2: Hold down the Shift key while drawing the horizon line and front edge to make it easy to make horizontal and vertical segments.

Step 10: Students could stop at this step if they're content with bottomless boxes. Students should drag their front edge above the horizon line just to see that their box has no bottom.

Investigate/Conjecture

Though for space reasons this activity sheet has no Investigate section, you can ask students to write descriptions of what happens as they move the horizon line or vanishing points. How can they look at the bottom of the box? What's the position of the viewer when the horizon line is above the box? What affect does moving the vanishing points farther apart have on the view of the box?

Explore More

Students can create all kinds of more complicated drawings of houses, office buildings, or whole city blocks using two-point perspective. You can have students try boxes with one-point perspective (viewing a front face instead of a front edge). See the example sketch **Cabin** (Mac) or **1lineang\cabin.gsp** (Windows).

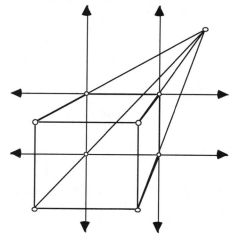

A box with one-point perspective

Art: Drawing a Box with Two-Point Perspective (continued)

Step 8: Construct $\overline{GJ}$, $\overline{JH}$, $\overline{HF}$, $\overline{FD}$, $\overline{DE}$, $\overline{EG}$, $\overline{GC}$, and $\overline{CH}$. (Your segments need not be bold. They're just shown bold here to indicate they are edges of your box.)

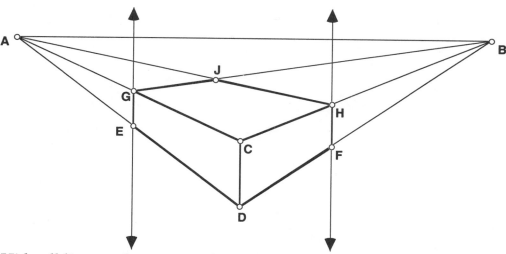

Step 9: Hide all lines and segments that are not part of your box, except for your horizon segment.

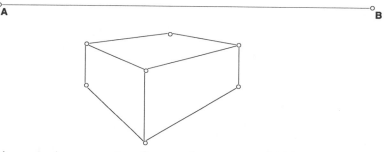

Step 10: Try moving various parts of your box, your horizon segment, and vanishing points. If you move the front edge of your box above the horizon segment, you'll discover that you haven't created the bottom of your box. Continue with the following steps to construct the missing faces and bottom.

Step 11: Construct $\overline{EB}$ and $\overline{FA}$. From their intersection, construct $\overline{KJ}$.

Step 12: Construct $\overline{EK}$ and $\overline{FK}$.

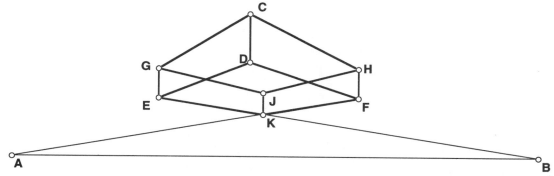

Step 13: Hide unwanted points and segments. (*A*, *B*, *C*, *D*, *E*, and *F* will be the only draggable points.)

Chapter 2

Transformations, Symmetry, and Tessellations

Investigation: Introduction to Transformations

A **transformation** is a way of moving or changing an object. There are four types of transformations that preserve the size and shape of an object. These four, **reflections**, **rotations**, **translations**, and **glide reflections**, are called **isometries**. In this activity, you'll begin to experiment with the first three of these transformations.

Sketch

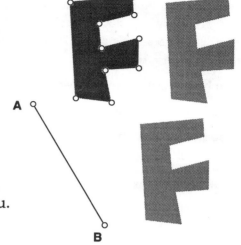

Step 1: Holding down the Shift key, use the Point tool to create the vertices of a letter F. Construct the polygon interior.

Step 2: Select the interior and choose Translate in the Transform menu. Choose any distance and angle that will keep the image on the screen. Give the translated image a different shade or color.

Step 3: Construct $\overline{AB}$, then select, in order, A and B. Choose Mark Vector in the Transform menu.

Step 4: Select the original pre-image (F) and choose Translate again. This time choose By Marked Vector.

Investigate: Move the pre-image (the original F) and watch the effect on its translated images. How are the images and pre-image related? Move B and watch the image that was translated by the vector AB. What is the effect of a translation?

Sketch

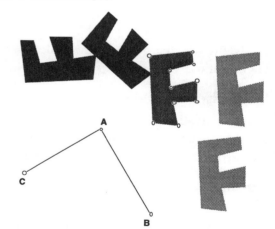

Step 5: Continuing in the same sketch, select point A and choose Mark Center in the Transform menu.

Step 6: Select the original interior and choose Rotate in the Transform menu. Choose any angle (45° is fine).

Step 7: Give your new image a different shade.

Step 8: Construct $\overline{AC}$. Select C, A, and B, in that order, and choose Mark Angle in the Transform menu.

Step 9: Select the original pre-image and choose Rotate again. This time choose By Marked Angle.

Investigate: Move the pre-image again and watch the effect on its rotated images. Move the center and observe the effect. Besides rotating by specifying a number degrees or an angle, you can rotate objects continuously as well. Press the Selection Arrow tool and drag right to choose the Rotation tool. Now select and drag the original F. How does this rotation affect the images? Can you keep track of which images were the translations and which were the rotations? (The standard Selection Arrow tool is actually a Translation tool. Rather than rotating the selection about a center, it translates the selection the distance and direction in which you drag the mouse.)

Investigation: Introduction to Transformations

Note: This investigation was designed for use with Sketchpad Version 2 for Macintosh (release date: spring 1992) or Sketchpad for Windows. If you're using Sketchpad Version 1 for Macintosh, contact Key Curriculum Press for upgrade information.

Student Audience: High School

Prerequisites: None. The terms **isometry**, **translation**, **rotation**, and **reflection** are introduced, but students are expected only to develop an informal understanding of these terms. You may want to tell students that a **vector** is a directed distance. Or you may want to let them get a sense of what a vector is by what it does when used for a translation.

Sketchpad Proficiency: Experienced User

Class Time: 40 minutes

Presentation Sketches: **Action Translate**, **Action Rotate**, and **Action Reflect** (Mac), or **present\acttrans.gsp**, **present\actrotat.gsp**, and **present\actreflc.gsp** (Windows)

Construction Tips: Turn Autoshow Labels off in Preferences for this investigation.

Step 1: It's not essential that students construct a letter F. That shape is just suggested because it has no symmetry, so it's easy to keep track of what happens to it as it's transformed. You can tell students to try to make an F but to go ahead and do the investigation with whatever shape they end up with.

Step 2: The default for the Translate dialog is Polar, in which users choose an angle and distance to translate. In Cartesian mode, users choose a horizontal and vertical distance to translate.

Step 3: Students will have to relabel these endpoints if they wish their sketch to match the diagrams shown in the activity.

Step 6: The default value for the Rotate dialog is 45°.

Step 8: By selecting points in the indicated order, the second point selected (*A*) will be the vertex of the angle marked.

Investigate/Conjecture

The investigation in this activity consists of open-ended experimentation, not intended to lead to specific insights. Instead, students begin to develop an intuitive sense of what these transformations do. Students will also get practice using Sketchpad's Transform menu.

Explore More

Students should discover that they can rotate back to their pre-image by rotating an image by the opposite (negative) number of degrees they rotated in the first place. A reflected image can be reflected back on the pre-image by reflecting it again across the same line.

The example sketch **Half Head** (Mac) or **2transfm\halfhead.gsp** (Windows) consists of segments comprising half of a whimsical head. By reflecting these segments, students can create the entire head. Moving parts on one side of the reflection axis moves the corresponding parts on the other side. Moving lips, ears, nostrils, and eyebrows yield the most amusing results.

Investigation: Introduction to Transformations (continued)

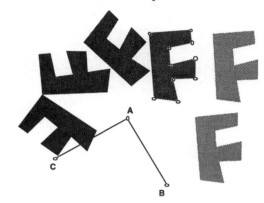

Sketch

Step 10: Continuing in the same sketch, select $\overline{AB}$ and choose Mark Mirror in the Transform menu.

Step 11: Select the original interior and choose Reflect in the Transform menu.

Step 12: Give your new image a different shade from the others.

Investigate: Move the pre-image again and watch the effect on its reflected image. Move $\overline{AB}$ and observe the effect. (Can you still recognize how all the different images were constructed? Make sure you use different shades to differentiate objects created by different transformations.) Now, in the space below, describe in your own words what a translation, rotation, and reflection does.

_____

_____

_____

_____

_____

_____

_____

_____

_____

_____

_____

_____

Present Your Findings

Discuss your findings with your partner or group. To present your findings, you could print a captioned sketch showing three objects: translate one, rotate the second, and reflect the third. Explain in your captions the effect of each transformation.

Explore More

Experiment with translating and rotating by specifying different distances or angles. Try negative numbers. Rotate or reflect objects more than one time, or across more than one line. When you rotate, how can you get back to the figure that you started with? How about reflecting? Play with the example sketch **Half Head** (Mac) or **2transfm\halfhead.gsp** (Windows).

Investigation: Properties of Reflection

When you look at yourself in the mirror, how far away do you appear to be from your image in the mirror? A reflection in geometry is called that because it has many of the same properties as reflections you see in mirrors. In this activity you'll discover some of those important properties by investigating the reflections of points across a line.

Sketch

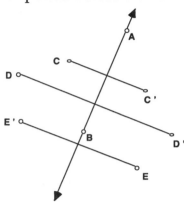

Step 1: Construct $\overleftrightarrow{AB}$.

Step 2: Construct points C, D, and E, with E on the opposite side of the line as C and D.

Step 3: Mark $\overleftrightarrow{AB}$ as mirror in the Transform menu and reflect points C, D, and E to create points C', D', and E'.

Step 4: Construct $\overline{CC'}$, $\overline{DD'}$, and $\overline{EE'}$.

Investigate

Move your points around. Do you see a relationship between the reflection axis $\overleftrightarrow{AB}$ and the segment that connects a point and its reflection? Construct the points of intersection of these segments and the reflection axis. Measure some distances. If Sketchpad didn't do reflections automatically, how could you find the reflection of a point across a line? Now reflect points C', D', and E' across $\overleftrightarrow{AB}$. What happens? What are the reflection images of points C', D', and E'?

Conjecture: Write your conjectures below.

_____

_____

_____

_____

Present Your Findings

Compare and discuss your results with your partner or group. To present your findings you could print a captioned sketch with measures that illustrate your conjectures.

Explore More

1. Pretend Sketchpad didn't have a Transform menu and come up with a construction for the reflection of a point across a line. Record and comment a script for this construction.

2. Reflect two points across a line and construct the quadrilateral with the four points (the two points and their images) as vertices. What kind of quadrilateral is this? How would you have to locate the two points to create a rectangle? A square? Can you create a parallelogram that is not a rectangle? If not, why not?

3. Look in a mirror. Measure the distance from your nose to the mirror with a ruler or tape measure. How can you use the reflection of the ruler to tell if you're measuring the shortest distance from your nose to the mirror? How far is your nose from its reflection?

Investigation: Properties of Reflection

Student Audience: High School

Prerequisites: None

Sketchpad Proficiency: Beginner

Class Time: 15-30 minutes. More if you give students time to Explore More.

Construction Tips

Students should encounter few difficulties with this construction.

Example Script and Presentation Sketch: **Point Reflector** and **Action Reflect** (Mac) or **2transfm\ptreflct.gss** and **present\actreflc.gsp** (Windows)

Investigate/Conjecture

A reflection axis is the perpendicular bisector of the segment connecting any point and its reflected image. If Sketchpad didn't construct reflections automatically, a point's reflection could be constructed by constructing a line through the point, perpendicular to the reflection axis, and constructing a point the same distance away on the other
side of the axis. The reflection of a reflected point across the same line is just the original point.

Explore More

Have all students do one or more of these Explore More activities.

1. Construct line $\overleftrightarrow{AB}$ and point C. Construct a line through C perpendicular to $\overleftrightarrow{AB}$. Construct circle DC, where D is the intersection of the lines. Construct E at the other intersection of the circle and the perpendicular line. E is the reflection of C. This construction is far less flexible than a Transform menu construction because the circle intersection won't move freely. Also, it fails to hold up when C is moved to the other side of the line, and the script of this construction will only work for points on one side of a line.

2. A quadrilateral so constructed is an isosceles trapezoid, unless the segment connecting the two points is parallel to the reflection axis, in which case the quadrilateral will be a rectangle. This is a good opportunity to begin a discussion of symmetry.

3. If you hold a ruler from your nose up to a mirror, you can tell if you're measuring the perpendicular distance because the ruler and its reflection will lie on a straight line. The distance from your nose to its reflection is twice the distance from your nose to the mirror. (Your nose's reflection is the same distance away on the other side of the mirror. This will dispel any notion students may have that a reflection is somehow on the surface of a two-dimensional mirror.)

Investigation: More Properties of Reflections

Your reflection in a mirror looks just like you, except it's backwards. Reflections in geometry have that same property. In this activity, you'll investigate the properties of reflections that make a reflection the "mirror image" of its pre-image.

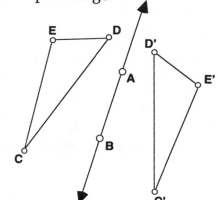

Sketch

Step 1: Construct $\overleftrightarrow{AB}$.

Step 2: Construct $\triangle CDE$.

Step 3: Mark $\overleftrightarrow{AB}$ as mirror in the Transform menu.

Step 4: Select all parts of $\triangle CDE$ and reflect them across $\overleftrightarrow{AB}$.

Investigate

Measure the lengths of one or more segments in your triangle and the corresponding reflected segments. What can you say about length under a reflection? Measure an angle in your triangle and the corresponding angle in the image. What can you say about angle measure under a reflection?

Move parts of your original triangle or its image (or $\overleftrightarrow{AB}$). How are the triangles related? Imagine you printed your triangles on a piece of paper that was red on one side and white on the other. Could you cut out your triangles and place one on top of the other to show they were congruent? Would both triangles have the same color facing up or would one be red and the other white? Your answer is tied to the two triangles' **orientation**. If you went around your triangle's vertices *C*, *D*, and *E* in counter-clockwise order, in what order would you go to travel from *C'* to *D'* to *E'*? What can you say about the orientation of a figure and its reflected image?

Conjecture: Write your conjectures below.

_____

_____

_____

_____

Present Your Findings

Compare and discuss your results with your partner or group. To present your findings you could print a captioned sketch showing a reflected figure and measures that illustrate your conjectures.

Explore More

1. Construct a ray to mark as a reflection mirror. Construct another ray so that when you reflect it across the first, the reflection axis serves as an angle bisector.

2. Use a reflection to construct an isosceles triangle.

Investigation: More Properties of Reflections

Student Audience: High School

Prerequisites: None

Sketchpad Proficiency: Beginner

Class Time: 20-30 minutes

Example Sketch and Presentation Sketch: **More Reflection** and **Action Reflect** (Mac) or **2transfm\reflmore.gsp** and **present\actreflc.gsp** (Windows)

Construction Tips

Step 4: Students could simply Select All (choose the Selection Arrow tool and choose Select All in the Edit menu or use a keyboard shortcut) to select $\triangle CDE$. Reflecting $\overleftrightarrow{AB}$ about itself will do nothing.

Investigate/Conjecture

Students will discover that all the lengths and angle measures in the image triangle are equal to the corresponding lengths and angle measures in the pre-image. Thus, the triangles are congruent. That means that if you cut it out of paper, one triangle could be placed on top of the other and would fit over it perfectly. However, if the paper had different colored sides, the triangles would have different colors facing up. Because of the reflection, the orientation of the triangles is changed. If $\triangle CDE$ has a counter-clockwise orientation, as shown in the diagram, then $\triangle C'D'E'$ has clockwise orientation. Formally, conjectures may be stated as follows:

Reflection preserves length (distance).

Reflection preserves angle measure.

Depending on your approach, you may want to include:

Reflection preserves congruence.

These conjectures apply to other isometries (rotation, translation, and glide-reflection) as well. Many books, however, use isometries to define congruence. So stating that reflection preserves congruence would be somewhat obvious, if not circular.

A conjecture that applies only to reflection and glide-reflection is:

Reflection reverses orientation.

Explore More

As this is a short activity, encourage all students do one or both of these Explore More activities.

1. The second ray should have the same starting endpoint as the first (the one used as the reflection axis). The unusual thing about the angle formed this way is that it's controlled by its bisector, so in a sense this construction doubles an angle rather than bisects one. Angles can also be tripled this way, yielding an angle that in effect is trisected.

2. Reflect a point across a line and connect it with its image. This forms the base of the isosceles triangle. Construct the legs to any point on the reflection axis.

©1996 by Key Curriculum Press Exploring Geometry

Investigation: Reflections in the Coordinate Plane

In this activity, you'll investigate what happens to the coordinates of points when they're reflected across the x- and/or y-axes in the coordinate plane.

Sketch

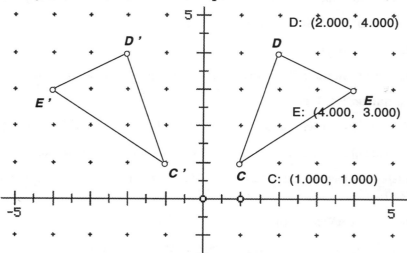

Step 1: In a new sketch, choose Show Grid in the Graph menu.

Step 2: Draw a triangle *CDE* with vertices on the grid.

Step 3: Measure the coordinates of each vertex.

Step 4: Mark the y-axis (the vertical axis) as mirror and reflect the triangle.

Step 5: Measure the coordinates of the image.

Investigate

Do you see a relationship between the coordinates of the vertices of your original triangle and the coordinates of the reflected image's vertices? Drag vertices to different points on the grid. Does the relationship hold? Now mark the x-axis (the horizontal axis) as mirror and reflect your original triangle. Before you measure coordinates, can you guess what they'll be? Measure to confirm.

Conjecture

Write your conjectures in the space below:

_____

_____

_____

Present Your Findings

Discuss your results with your partner or group. To present your findings you could print a captioned sketch or demonstrate over a network.

Explore More

1. Experiment with a reflection across the y-axis followed by a reflection across the x-axis. What can you say about the coordinates of this product of two reflections? How is this image related to the original triangle?

2. Draw a line on the grid that passes through the origin and makes a 45° angle with the x-axis (in other words, the line y = x). Reflect your triangle across this line. What do you notice about the coordinates of the vertices of this image?

Investigation: Reflections in the Coordinate Plane

Student Audience: Middle School/High School

Prerequisites: Students should know the terms **reflection**, **image**, and **coordinate**.

Sketchpad Proficiency: Beginner

Class Time: 30 minutes

Example Sketch: Coordinate Reflection (Mac) or **2transfm\coordref.gsp** (Windows)

Construction Tips

Step 2: To start with at least, Snap To Grid should be checked in the Graph menu.

Step 3: Select the points and choose Coordinate in the Measure menu.

Step 4: Select the axis and choose Mark Mirror in the Transform menu. Then select the triangle and choose Reflect.

Investigate/Conjecture

Encourage students to drag vertices of their triangle outside of the first quadrant. The relationship between corresponding coordinates under these reflections should be fairly obvious. Students may have trouble, though, expressing this relationship generally. You want conjectures like:

If a point (x, y) is reflected across the y-axis, the coordinates of its image are (–x, y).

If a point (x, y) is reflected across the x-axis, the coordinates of its image are (x, –y).

Be sure students discover the errors in such statements as "the *x*-coordinate of the image is the same as the original except that it's negative."

Explore More

Encourage students to try these. They won't take much more time or effort.

1. Reflecting across both axes changes the sign of both coordinates, as students might expect. They may be more surprised, however, to notice that this product of reflections is the same as a rotation about the origin of 180°.

2. Reflecting across the line *y* = *x* reverses the *x*- and *y*-coordinates of a point. In other words, the image of a point (*x*, *y*) reflected across the line *y* = *x* would have coordinates (*y*, *x*).

Investigation: Poolroom Math

When you hit a pool ball that bounces off a bumper and into a pocket, that ball travels the shortest possible distance to the bumper and then to the pocket (assuming no "english" on the ball and assuming it goes in.) Light bouncing off a mirror likewise travels the shortest possible distance. When you look at your toes in the mirror, light from your toes travels the shortest possible distance from your toes to the mirror to your eyes. Where is the point located on a mirror where a light ray reflects to minimize these distances? That's the question you'll investigate in this activity.

Sketch

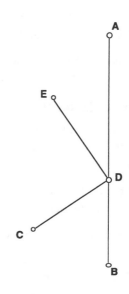

Step 1:   Construct vertical segment $\overline{AB}$.

Step 2:   Construct $\overline{CD}$ and $\overline{DE}$, where D is on $\overline{AB}$.

Step 3:   Measure CD and DE and calculate their sum. Make sure this sum is displayed to 1000th's precision.

Investigate

Move point D up and down the segment until $CD + DE$ is minimized. Can you see any relationship between $\angle ADE$ and $\angle BDC$? Measure these angles. Move C and E to different locations and minimize $CD + DE$ again. Does the angle relationship still hold?

Conjecture: Write your conjectures below.

_____

_____

_____

Investigate Further

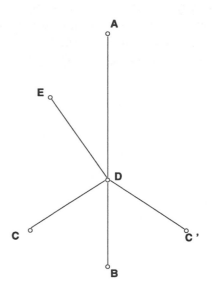

Some additional sketching will give you some ideas for why your conjecture is true. Mark $\overline{AB}$ as mirror in the Transform menu. Reflect C and segment $\overline{CD}$ across $\overline{AB}$. How are lengths CD and $C'D$ related? Move point D so that $CD + DE$ is minimized. What can you say about C', D and E? What about angles CDB, $C'DB$, and ADE? On a separate piece of paper, write an explanation for why your conjecture is true.

Hide $\overline{CD}$, $\overline{C'D}$, $\overline{DE}$, and D. Can you now construct a point F on $\overline{AB}$ such that $CF + FE$ is minimal?

Explore More

What's the shortest mirror you'd need on a wall in order to see your full reflection from your toes to the top of your head?

Investigation: Poolroom Math

Student Audience: High School

Prerequisites: Students are introduced to what a **reflection** is.

Sketchpad Proficiency: Beginner

Example Sketch: **Poolroom Math** (Mac) or **2transfm\poolroom.gsp** (Windows)

Class Time: 15-30 minutes

Construction Tips

Step 1: Hold down the Shift key while constructing straight objects to constrain them to 15° intervals. This makes it easy to construct a vertical segment.

Step 3: Set measure precision to 1000ths in Preferences, under the Display menu. This precision is necessary to find the precise point on $\overline{AB}$ that minimizes the sum of the distances.

Investigate/Conjecture

The sum $CD + DE$ will be minimized when $\angle ADE = \angle BDC$. To help students word their conjectures, you might want to introduce the terms **angle of incidence** and **angle of reflection**. Using that vocabulary, students should conjecture:

The sum of the distances from a point, to a line, and to another point is minimized when the angle of incidence is equal to the angle of reflection.

Students may also word their conjectures in terms of rays of light or the paths of pool balls.

Investigating further, students can discover how to construct this minimal path. When C is reflected across AB, $CD = C'D$. The distance from C' to D to E is minimized when the three points are collinear. In this case, $\angle CDB$ and $\angle C'DB$ are equal and $\angle C'DB$ and $\angle ADE$ are vertical angles and therefore equal. Hence, $\angle CBD = \angle ADE$.

Point F can be located by constructing $\overline{C'E}$. Point F is the intersection of $\overline{C'E}$ and $\overline{AB}$.

Explore More

A "full-length" mirror need only be half your height. You see the reflection of your toes by looking through a point in a mirror that's halfway between your eyes and your toes. Likewise you see the reflection of the top of your head through a point that's halfway between your eyes and the top of your head. This can be illustrated by your sketch. You can move point B up until it's halfway (vertically) between C and E before point F will cease to exist.

Problem: Feed and Water or Water and Feed?

A rider is traveling from point D to point E between a river and a pasture. Before she gets to E, she wants to stop at the pasture to feed her horse and at the river to water him. What path should she take? Use Sketchpad to model the problem.

Sketch

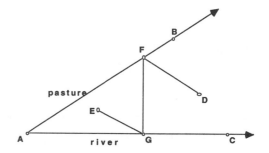

Step 1: Construct $\overrightarrow{AB}$ and $\overrightarrow{AC}$. Label these rays "pasture" and "river."

Step 2: Construct points D and E between the rays.

Step 3: Construct $\overline{DF}$, where F is on $\overrightarrow{AB}$, $\overline{FG}$, where G is on $\overrightarrow{AC}$, and $\overline{GE}$ to represent the path taken from D to pasture to river to E.

Investigate

Measure DF, FG, and GE. Calculate their sum and display its precision to the 1000ths place. Move F and G to minimize this sum.

Now construct segments to represent going to the river first, then the pasture. Measure these distances, calculate their sum, and minimize this sum. Does it make any difference whether the rider feeds then waters her horse or waters then feeds? In the space below, sketch your solutions to the problem (or print your sketch). Describe the conditions necessary for the path to be minimized.

_____

_____

_____

_____

_____

Explore More

Some additional sketching will show how your solution can be constructed. Start with a new sketch and construct the rays and points D and E between them. Reflect point D across the pasture. Reflect point E across the river. The distance $D'E'$ is the is the same as the shortest distance from D to E via the pasture and river. (Why?) Construct $\overline{D'E'}$ and use it to construct the shortest path from D to E via the pasture and the river. Hide D', E', and $\overline{D'E'}$. You should be able to move D and E and have the path change automatically to minimize the distance.

Problem: Feed and Water or Water and Feed

Student Audience: High School/College/Teacher Education

Prerequisites: Students will be most successful with this problem if they've done the investigation Poolroom Math.

Sketchpad Proficiency: Beginner

Class Time: 30-40 minutes

Example Sketches: **Feed and Water** and **Poolroom Math** or **2transfm\feedwtr.gsp** and **2transfm\poolroom.gsp** (Windows)

Construction Tips

Step 1: Click on the rays with the Text tool to display their labels. (They should be *j* and *k*.) Double-click on the labels to edit them.

Investigate/Conjecture

Students should move *F* until the sum is minimized, then move *G* to see if they can make the sum smaller still. They should then go back to *F* and "tweak" it and *G* as much as necessary until they're confident they have close to a minimal path. The sum *DF* + *FG* + *GE* will be minimized when ∠*BFD* = ∠*AFG* and ∠*FGC* = ∠*EGA*. Repeating the experiment by going to the river first, students will discover that it does make a difference. Whether it's better to go to the river or the pasture first depends on the location of the points *D* and *E*. Obviously, if they're both on the angle bisector, it doesn't matter which of the pasture or river the rider visits first. Interestingly, if *A*, *E*, and *D* are collinear, the distances are equal, regardless of how close the line through these points is to the river or pasture. Students can investigate this when they Explore More.

Explore More

Both trips—pasture to river and river to pasture—are illustrated in the example sketch Feed and Water. A special case can help you visualize which should be visited first. Suppose home (*E*) was on the river. The rider should visit the pasture first because when she then visits the river, she'll be home. In general, if you construct $\overrightarrow{DE}$ in this sketch, you can determine which to visit first. If $\overrightarrow{DE}$ intersects the river, the rider should visit the pasture first.

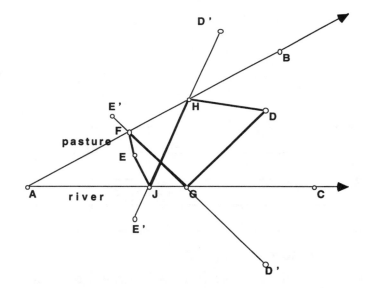

©1996 by Key Curriculum Press   Exploring Geometry

Investigation: Reflections Across Intersecting Lines

In this investigation you'll see what happens when you reflect a figure across two intersecting lines.

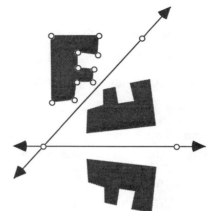

Sketch

Step 1: Construct any irregular figure. (A polygon interior will be easiest to select.)

Step 2: Construct two intersecting lines from the same starting point.

Step 3: Mark the closest line as mirror, then reflect your figure.

Step 4: Mark the other line as mirror and reflect the image from the first reflection.

Investigate

Move the lines or the figures to see how their positions are related. What do you notice about the position of the second image and the original figure? To investigate this, select the point of intersection between the lines and choose Mark Center in the Transform menu. Select the three points that define the angle between the intersecting lines and choose Mark Angle. Use the Transform menu to rotate your original figure by the marked angle. How do the rotated image and the double-reflected image compare? Check your guess: Measure the angle between the lines. Select your original figure and use the Transform menu to rotate it by the number of degrees that you think will make it coincide with the second reflection. If you miss, undo and try rotating by a different angle. (Remember, clockwise angles are negative.)

Conjecture: Write your conjectures below.

_____

_____

_____

_____

Present Your Findings

Discuss your results with your partner or group. To present your findings you could print a captioned sketch showing a figure reflected across intersecting lines and measurements that illustrate your conjecture.

Explore More

1. Rotate a figure by some arbitrary angle. Hide the center and see if you can locate two intersecting lines such that reflections across them yield the rotation.

2. Repeat the investigation, this time reflecting across the lines in the opposite order.

3. Investigate reflecting figures across parallel lines.

Investigation: Reflections Across Intersecting Lines

Note: This investigation was designed for use with Sketchpad Version 2 for Macintosh (release date: spring 1992) or Sketchpad for Windows. If you're using Sketchpad Version 1 for Macintosh, contact Key Curriculum Press for upgrade information.

Student Audience: High School/Advanced High School/College/Teacher Education

Prerequisites: Students should know the terms **reflection**, **image**, **pre-image**, and **rotation**.

Sketchpad Proficiency: Experienced User

Class Time: 30-40 minutes

Example Sketch and Presentation Sketch: **Reflection–Intersecting** and **Action Reflect/Int** (Mac) or **2transfm\reflint.gsp** and **present\actint.gsp** (Windows)

Construction Tips

Step 1: The orientation of the letter F in the example is easy to follow. Using the Point tool, hold down the Shift key and create the vertices in order. Choose Polygon Interior in the Construct menu. If students' letter F's don't come our right, tell them not to worry about it and continue the investigation with whatever figure they ended up with.

Investigate/Conjecture

It may not be obvious at first that the product of the two reflections is a rotation. That's why it's suggested that students construct an image rotated by the angle between the lines. If the points are selected in the right order, this image will come between the pre-image and double reflection, making it clear that the double reflection is a rotation through twice the angle between the lines. If selection order is reversed, the rotated image will not be as clearly related to the double reflection. Students may still figure it out, but if they have trouble, suggest they try the rotation going the other way.

Students should make this conjecture:

Two reflections across intersecting lines is equivalent to a rotation through twice the angle between the lines.

Explore More

1. Construct a segment connecting a point with its corresponding point on the image. Construct the perpendicular bisector of this segment. This is one reflection axis. Reflect the pre-image across this line. Now construct a segment connecting another point on this image to its corresponding point on the rotated image. Construct its perpendicular bisector. This is the second reflection axis.

2. Reflecting across the lines in the opposite order will rotate the figure in the other direction.

3. This is developed more fully in an activity in this book: Reflections Across Parallel Lines.

Investigation: Reflections Across Parallel Lines

In this investigation you'll see what happens when you reflect a figure across two parallel lines.

Sketch

Step 1: Construct any irregular figure.
(A polygon interior will be easiest
to select.)

Step 2: Construct two parallel lines: (Construct a
line, a point not on the line, and a parallel
line through the point.)

Step 3: Mark the closest line as mirror, then reflect
your figure and at least one of its vertices.

Step 4: Mark the other line as mirror and reflect the image from the first reflection.

Investigate

What do you notice about the position of the second image relative to the original figure? Move the lines or the figures to see if this is always true. How does the distance from the original figure to the second image compare to the distance between the two lines? You can test this with some some further investigation:

- Construct a segment, select its endpoints, and choose Mark Vector in the Transform menu.
- Select your original figure. Translate it by the marked vector.
- Drag the endpoints of the segment so that the translated image coincides with the double reflected image.
- Measure the length of the vector-defining segment.
- If necessary, use Calculate to compare the distance between the lines to the distance translated (the length of the vector).

Conjecture: Write your conjectures below.

_____

_____

_____

Present Your Findings

Discuss your results with your partner or group. To present your findings you could print a captioned sketch showing a figure reflected across parallel lines and showing measurements that illustrate your conjecture.

Explore More

1. Translate a figure by some arbitrary vector or distance and angle. See if you can locate parallel lines such that two reflections will yield the translation.

2. Repeat the investigation, but this time reflect across the farthest line first.

3. Investigate reflecting figures across intersecting lines.

Investigation: Reflections Across Parallel Lines

Note: This investigation was designed for use with Sketchpad Version 2 for Macintosh (release date: spring 1992) or Sketchpad for Windows. If you're using Sketchpad Version 1 for Macintosh, contact Key Curriculum Press for upgrade information.

Student Audience: High School/College/Teacher Education

Prerequisites: Students should know the terms **reflection**, **image**, **pre-image**, and **translation**.

Sketchpad Proficiency: Experienced User

Class Time: 30-40 minutes

Example Sketch and Presentation Sketch: **Reflection–Parallel** and **Action Reflect/Para** (Mac) or **2transfm\reflpara.gsp** and **present\actpara.gsp** (Windows)

Construction Tips

Step 1: Make sure this polygon has no symmetry. This little "flag" is an example of a shape whose position is easy to keep track of under transformations.

Step 3: The images may overlap. This is not a problem, but may obscure relationships. Students should move the figures and reflection axes anyway to see different configurations.

Investigate/Conjecture

Students may notice that the pre-image and the second reflected image are facing in the same direction. So the second image is a translation of the pre-image. The continued investigation reinforces and confirms this. The vector defines the distance between points on the pre-image and corresponding points on the translated image. This distance is twice the distance between the lines. Students may need to calculate the ratio to see this relationship. Students should state the following conjecture:

Two reflections across parallel lines is equivalent to a translation in the direction perpendicular to the lines by a distance twice the distance between the lines.

Explore More

1. Construct a segment connecting corresponding points on the pre-image and the translated image. Construct a perpendicular to this segment through one of these points. This is one reflection axis. Construct the perpendicular bisector of the segment. This is the other reflection axis.

    If your translated image is defined by a translation vector, simply construct perpendiculars through one of the endpoints of the the vector and the midpoint of the segment connecting the vector's endpoints.

2. When the reflection order is reversed, the translation goes in the opposite direction.

3. This is developed more fully as an activity in this book: Reflections Across Intersecting Lines.

Exploring Geometry

Investigation: Glide Reflections

This activity investigates an isometry called a **glide reflection**. While glide reflection is not a transformation found in the Transform menu, you'll define it as a custom transformation, and in the process, learn what a glide reflection is and what it does.

Sketch

Step 1: Construct a polygon interior whose orientation will be easy to keep track of.

Step 2: Construct a line $\overleftrightarrow{EF}$ and a point G on the line so that E and G are about an inch apart.

Step 3: Select E and G and choose Mark Vector in the Transform menu.

Step 4: Mark $\overleftrightarrow{EF}$ as mirror in the Transform menu.

Step 5: Reflect your figure about $\overleftrightarrow{EF}$.

Step 6: Translate this image by the marked vector EG. This second image is a glide reflection of your original figure. Hide the intermediate image (the first reflection).

Step 7: Select the glide reflected image and the original image and choose Define Transform. Define the transform as "Glide Reflection."

Step 8: Use Glide Reflection to construct several more images as shown.

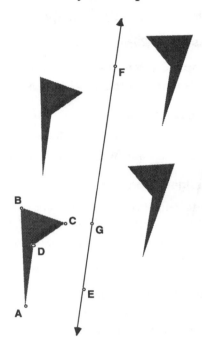

Investigate/Conjecture

Manipulate your original figure and watch the effect on the images. A glide reflection is the product of two transformations. What are they?

_____

A translation is also the product of two transformations. What are they?

_____

So a glide reflection can be thought of as a product of what three transformations?

_____

Present Your Findings

Discuss your results with your partner or group. To present your findings you could print a captioned sketch showing a figure glide-reflected several times.

Explore More

1. Glide reflect a figure without using Translate in the Transform menu.

2. Experiment with reflections across three random lines. Does this produce a glide reflection?

3. What's the product of a rotation and a reflection? What's the product of a rotation and a translation?

Investigation: Glide Reflections

Note: This investigation was designed for use with Sketchpad Version 2 for Macintosh (release date: spring 1992) or Sketchpad for Windows. If you're using Sketchpad Version 1 for Macintosh, contact Key Curriculum Press for upgrade information.

Student Audience: High School/College/Teacher Education

Prerequisites: Students should know the terms **reflection**, **image**, **pre-image**, and **translation**.

Sketchpad Proficiency: Experienced User

Class Time: 20-40 minutes

Example Sketch and Presentation Sketch: **Glide Reflect** and **Threeflect** (Mac) or **2transfm\glreflct.gsp** and **present\3flect.gsp** (Windows)

Construction Tips

The construction steps are described pretty explicitly in the activity, the assumption being that students will be unfamiliar with some of these commands.

Investigate/Conjecture

A glide reflection is the product of a reflection and a translation. In this activity, the translation was in the direction of the reflection axis. This need not be the case, though if it's not, the reflection axis and the glide reflection symmetry axis will not be the same.

A translation is the product of two reflections across parallel lines.

So a glide reflection can be thought of as the product of three reflections. Students will be inclined to expect that two of the reflection axes need to be parallel to one another and perpendicular to the third, and many books describe glide reflection this way, but in fact, the reflection axes can be any three lines. Students may discover this if they try the Explore More suggestion.

Explore More

1. Students could construct a line for the reflection then two lines perpendicular to it for the translation.

2. If students try reflecting about three random lines, they'll discover that this is a glide reflection as well (though it may not be obvious). They can confirm this by selecting the image and pre-image and defining the three reflections as a custom transformation. When they apply this repeatedly, they'll see the glide reflection pattern.

3. A rotation followed by a reflection is a glide reflection (or, in the special case where the center of rotation is on the reflection line, a simple reflection). Remember, the rotation is the product of two reflections. A rotation followed by a translation is a rotation by a different angle with a different center.

Exploration: Symmetry in Regular Polygons

A figure has **reflection symmetry** if you can reflect it across a line (called an **axis of reflection** or **axis of symmetry**) and get the same figure; that is, the image and pre-image coincide. It has **rotation symmetry** if you can rotate some number of degrees about some point and get the same shape in the same position. In this exploration you'll look for reflection and rotation symmetries of regular polygons.

Sketch

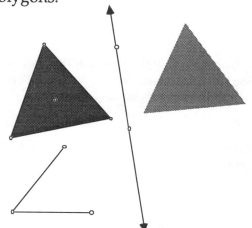

Step 1: Construct any regular polygon and its interior: equilateral triangle, square, pentagon, hexagon, or other. (Construct it from scratch, or use a script.)

Step 2: If the polygon's center doesn't already exist, construct it.

Step 3: Construct a line and reflect your figure's interior across the line. Give the image a light shade.

Investigate

Move the line until the image of your polygon coincides with the pre-image. When the image of a reflection is exactly the same as a pre-image, the reflection line is an axis of symmetry. Try the line in another position. How many reflection axes does your polygon have?

To look for rotation symmetries, select the center of the polygon and choose Mark Center in the Transform menu, then construct an angle, select the points that define it, and choose Mark Angle in the Transform menu. Measure the angle. Rotate the figure by this angle, then manipulate the angle so that the rotated image fits exactly over the pre-image. What angle measure(s) cause(s) the figures to coincide? Repeat the exploration with other regular polygons.

Describe the reflection and rotation symmetries of the regular polygons. Be precise describing the lines that act as axes of symmetry, and state how many there are. List the angles that give the polygon rotation symmetry. Use your findings to make a conjecture about the reflection and rotation symmetries of a regular *n*-gon. Use a separate sheet of paper, if necessary.

Equilateral Triangle: _____

Square: _____

Pentagon: _____

Hexagon: _____

N-gon: _____

Explore More

1. Explore ways to construct these shapes using reflections and rotations, taking advantage of their symmetries.

2. Explore symmetries in other figures: rhombuses, rectangles, isosceles trapezoids, and kites, for example.

Exploration: Symmetry in Regular Polygons

Student Audience: High School

Prerequisites: Introduce reflection and rotation symmetry with examples in nature: butterflies, starfish, flowers, snowflakes, etc. Students should know the terms **regular polygon, perpendicular bisector, reflection, rotation, symmetry,** and **axis of reflection** or **symmetry.**

Sketchpad Proficiency: Experienced User

Class Time: 30-50 minutes

Example Sketch and Presentation Sketches: **Symmetry, Action Rot-Symmetry,** and **Action Refl-Symmetry** (Mac) or **2transfm\symmetry, present\actrosym.gsp,** and **present\actresym.gsp** (Windows). Scripts for regular polygons can be found in the **Regular Polygons** folder (Mac) or **regpoly** directory (Windows).

Construction Tips: This exploration can go fairly quickly if students know how to open and play scripts. Sample scripts for many regular polygons come with Sketchpad. Some of these have centers already.

Step 2: Necessary only if center isn't a script given. See what methods students come up with for constructing centers. In even-sided polygons they can construct two segments connecting pairs of opposite vertices. In odd-sided polygons they'll need to connect vertices with midpoints of opposite sides.

Step 3: Make sure students don't use any points on their figures to construct the line. The line should be free to move independently of the figure.

Investigate/Conjecture

Students should discover axes of symmetry by positioning the line so that the image lands perfectly on top of the pre-image. For the equilateral triangle shown here they should find three such locations for the line. Likewise, in the case of the equilateral triangle students will find three positions for the angle that cause the image and pre-image to coincide. Unless they've chosen directed degrees for angle measure under Preferences, however, two of the angles will measure 120°. (Directed degrees will display the angles as 120° and ¯120°.) You may also have to point out that they should count the 360° rotation.

Some possible conjectures for *n*-gons include:

Regular polygons with an even number of sides have axes of symmetry through opposite vertices and through the midpoints of opposite sides.

Regular polygons with an odd number of sides have axes of symmetry through each vertex and the midpoint of the opposite side.

A regular n-gon has n *axes of symmetry.*

A regular n-gon has rotation symmetries of multiples of 360/n.

Explore More

Students can experiment more with the Transform menu to explore symmetry in shapes besides regular polygons. Have students use rotations and reflections to construct symmetrical figures. They can print these out with explanations of the symmetries.

Investigation: Tessellating with Regular Polygons

In this investigation you'll try tessellating, or tiling the plane, with different regular polygons. To do this investigation you'll need scripts for creating equilateral triangles, squares, regular pentagons, and regular hexagons. These scripts must create the figures given two vertices on one side of the polygons. They're available as example scripts, or you may want to create them yourself.

Sketch

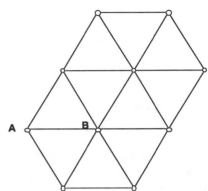

Step 1: Construct two points and play a script to construct an equilateral triangle.

Step 2: Select two other points on the triangle and play the script again. If nothing appears to happen, try again, selecting the points in different order.

Step 3: Keep playing the script until triangles completely surround at least two points.

Investigate

So far, you've demonstrated that equilateral triangles can tessellate, that is, you can tile the plane with them without gaps or overlapping. Why do equilateral triangles work? Repeat the investigation with squares, pentagons, and hexagons. Which will tessellate and which won't? Why? Will a regular heptagon tessellate? In the space below, write a paragraph explaining what's required for a regular polygon to tessellate.

_____

_____

_____

_____

_____

Conjecture: Write your conjectures below.

_____

_____

Present Your Findings: Compare and discuss your results with your partner or group. To present your findings you could:

1. Print sketches that show different regular polygons tessellating to fill your paper.

2. Create and add comments to scripts that tessellate to fill your sketch window.

Explore More

1. Instead of tessellating by playing scripts, use reflections and/or rotations.

2. Try some semi-regular tessellations—tessellations that use two different shapes: squares and equilateral triangles, for example.

3. Try tessellating with semi-regular shapes: rhombuses and equilateral or equiangular polygons, for example.

Investigation: Tessellating with Regular Polygons

Student Audience: Middle School/High School

Prerequisites: Introduce the concept of **tessellation** with a familiar example like a tiled floor.

Sketchpad Proficiency: Experienced User

Class Time: 30-40 minutes

Example Scripts: You may want students to use scripts found in the **Regular Polygons** folder (Mac) or **regpoly** directory (Windows).

Construction Tips

Step 2: Students are most likely to encounter the problem of selecting givens and playing a script so that it constructs a figure on top of an existing figure. The selection order required for playing scripts seems random at first, but students will notice patterns with practice.

Step 3: Surrounding a single point with copies of a figure doesn't guarantee the figure will tessellate. Make sure students construct enough copies of the polygon to establish that it will continue to tessellate indefinitely.

Investigate/Conjecture

Students will discover that equilateral triangles, squares, and hexagons all tessellate. Pentagons won't because the measure of each angle in a pentagon (108) doesn't divide 360 evenly. By the same reasoning, students should conclude that a heptagon will not tessellate either. Students should conjecture:

Regular polygons will tessellate if and only if the measure of each angle divides 360 evenly.

Three angles in a regular hexagon meet at each vertex in a tessellation. Three angles in a heptagon would exceed 360°. It's impossible for fewer than three angles to surround a vertex so no regular polygons beyond the hexagon will tessellate. Question students to guide them to the more precise conjecture:

Equilateral triangles, squares, and regular hexagons are the only regular polygons that will tessellate.

Explore More

Tessellating by rotations will reinforce the relationship between angle measure and tessellation.

       Exploring Geometry

Art: A Tumbling Block Design

A tumbling block design is commonly found in Amish quilt patterns. Its an example of op art because of the interesting optical effect suggested by its name. A tumbling block design can be created very efficiently with Sketchpad using **translations**.

Sketch

First, construct a regular hexagon:

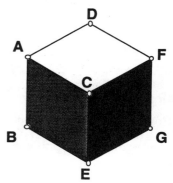

Step 1: Use your own method or a script like **6/Hexagon (By Edge)** (Mac) or **regpoly\6byedge.gss** (Windows) to construct a regular hexagon.

Step 2: If it doesn't already exist, construct the center of the hexagon.

Step 3: Construct segments and polygon interiors, and shade the hexagon as shown at right.

In the next few steps, you'll translate this figure to create a row of these blocks.

Step 4: Select points *A* and *F*, in that order, and choose Mark Vector in the Transform menu.

Step 5: Select All, then deselect the points. Translate by vector *AF*.

Step 6: Translate again two more times so that you have a row of four blocks.

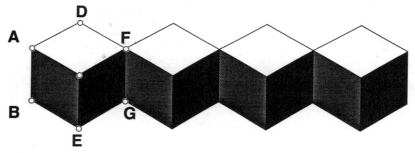

Step 7: Mark *AE* as vector.

Step 8: Select All (including the points) and translate the row of blocks by vector *AE*.

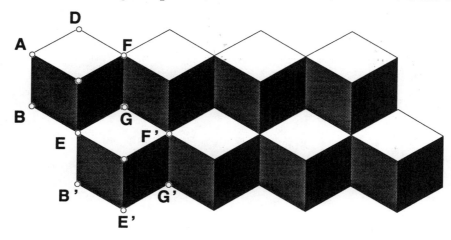

Art: A Tumbling Block Design

Student Audience: Any

Prerequisites: Students should know what a **regular hexagon** is and should know or be introduced to the term **translation**.

Sketchpad Proficiency: Experienced to Power User. Students need to know how to construct a regular hexagon or know how to use a script to construct one. It's helpful for students to be handy with some advanced selection techniques.

Class Time: 30-50 minutes

Example Sketch and Script: Tumbling Blocks (Mac Sketch) and **6/Hexagon (By Edge)** (Mac Script) or **2transfm\tumblk.gsp** and **regpoly\6byedge.gss** (Windows)

Construction Tips

Step 2: Construct the intersection of any two diagonals.

Step 3: The segments and polygon interiors constructed in this step divide the hexagon into three congruent rhombuses.

Step 4: Student labels are unlikely to match the figure. Students need to select appropriate points to translate the figure horizontally by the width of the block.

Step 5: Select All is in the Edit menu when the Selection Arrow tool is chosen in the Toolbox. While everything is selected, hold down Shift and click on each point to deselect it. Translate the remaining selected objects. Make sure to choose By Marked Vector in the Translate dialog.

Step 6: The translated figure from the previous step will be selected, ready to translate again.

Step 11: Choose the Point tool and choose Select All Points in the Edit menu. While all the points are selected, hold down Shift, choose the Selection Arrow tool, and click on *A* and *B* to deselect them. Hide the remaining selected points.

Describe Your Design

Students should note that the tumbling blocks design is comprised of regular hexagons divided into rhombuses. Point out to students that this is an example of a tessellation, or tiling the plane without gaps or overlap.

The blocks tend to pop in and out. One moment you see blocks coming out of the page, another moment it may appear is if you're looking up from beneath and new blocks appear, with the old blocks turning inside out.

Art: A Tumbling Block Design (continued)

Step 9: Mark *DB'* as vector.

Step 10: Select All and translate the two rows of blocks by vector *DB'* to create four rows total.

Step 11: Hide all the points except *A* and *B*.

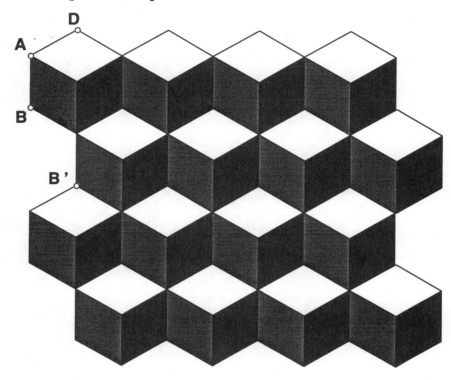

Describe Your Design

In the space below, describe the shapes that make up your design. Also describe the optical effect of this design.

_____

_____

_____

_____

_____

_____

_____

_____

Investigation: Tessellating with Triangles

In this investigation, you'll learn a method for tessellating with any triangle and discover why this is possible.

Sketch

Step 1:   Construct triangle *ABC* and its interior.

Step 2:   Mark *AC* as vector and translate the triangle interior by the marked vector.

Step 3:   Repeat to construct a row of four triangles.

Step 4:   Mark *AB* as vector.

Step 5:   Translate the row of triangle interiors by the marked vector. Repeat to construct three or more rows.

Investigate

Move the vertices of your original triangle. What can you say about the white triangles formed by the space between your triangle interiors? Since you can manipulate your original triangle into any size or shape, what does this demonstrate about tessellating with triangles? You can prove this by looking at any vertex of the tessellation that's completely surrounded by triangles. What's the sum of the angles surrounding this point? What do you know about the angles in triangles that guarantees this sum?

Conjecture: Write your conjectures below.

_____

_____

Present Your Findings

Discuss your results. To present your findings, you could print a captioned sketch of tessellating triangles along with your conjectures and explanation of why you think they're true.

Explore More

Try this investigation with any quadrilateral.

Investigation: Tessellating with Triangles

Student Audience: Middle School/High School/College/Teacher Education

Prerequisites: Introduce the concept of **tessellation** with a familiar example like a tiled floor. It could be useful if students had experience tessellating with regular polygons.

Sketchpad Proficiency: Experienced User

Class Time: 20 minutes

Example Script: **Triangle Tiles** (Mac) or **2transfm\tritiles.gsp** (Windows)

Construction Tips

Step 3: Mark Vector and Translate are found in the Transform menu. Choose By Marked Vector in the Translate dialog.

Investigate/Conjecture

Students create a tessellation of alternating shaded triangles and white space triangles. The white space triangles are congruent to the shaded ones by SSS. The tessellation holds as the original triangle is manipulated, demonstrating that any triangle will tessellate. Ask students why they think this should be so. They should notice that surrounding each vertex are two of each angle from the triangles. Since the three angles in the triangles add up to 180°, and there are two of each, that guarantees that each vertex of the tessellation is surrounded by angles whose sum is 360°.

Explore More

This investigation will also work for any quadrilateral. With quadrilaterals you need to translate by the vectors defined by the diagonals. Quadrilaterals tessellate because the four angles of the quadrilateral meet at each vertex of the tessellation and the sum of these angles is 360°.

(Not on activity sheet) Ask students if their tessellations suggest ways to explain why the sum of the angles in a triangle is 180°, or how it demonstrates relationships among angles formed by parallel lines and a transversal.

Art: A Translation Tessellation

Many regular shapes can tessellate or tile the plane so that it is completely covered without any gaps or overlap. The square may be the most common example of a shape used to tile a floor or a shower. You could tile a floor with rectangles, too. In this activity, you'll learn how to construct a seemingly irregularly-shaped tile based on a rectangle. Then you'll use translations to tessellate with it.

Sketch

Construct a Rectangle.

Step 1: Construct $\overline{AB}$.

Step 2: Construct lines perpendicular to $\overline{AB}$ through A and B.

Step 3: Construct C on one of the lines and a line through C, parallel to $\overline{AB}$.

Step 4: Construct D, the fourth vertex of the rectangle.

Step 5: Hide the three lines, and replace them with segments: $\overline{AC}, \overline{CD},$ and $\overline{DB}$.

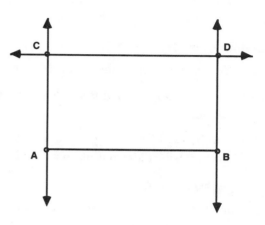

Use translations to create irregularly-shaped edges.

Step 6: Construct three or four random, connected segments from A to C.

Step 7: You want to translate this irregular edge to the opposite side of the rectangle. To do this, first select points A and B, in order, and choose Mark Vector in the Transform menu.

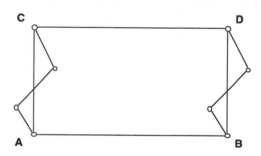

Step 8: Select the segments and their connecting points of the irregular edge from A to C and translate by marked vector AB.

Step 9: Construct an irregular edge from C to D, mark points C and A as vector in the Transform menu, and translate the segments and points of this irregular edge. Vector CA will translate these objects from the top to the bottom of your rectangle. You now have the shell of your tile that will tessellate.

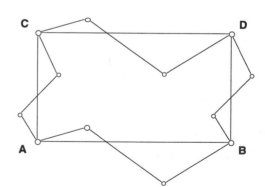

Construction: A Translation Tessellation

Student Audience: Middle School/High School/College/Teacher Education

Prerequisites: Introduce the concept of **tessellation** with a familiar example like a tiled floor. It could be useful if students had experience tessellating with regular polygons.

Sketchpad Proficiency: Experienced User

Class Time: 30 minutes

Example Sketches: **Translation Tessellation** and **Twisted Δ's** (Mac) or **2transfm\trantess.gsp** and **2transfrm\twisttri.gsp** (Windows)

Construction Tips

Step 1-5: Any parallelogram would do, but a rectangle is easy to keep track of.

Step 6: More segments give more flexibility in altering the finished design, but are harder to select and manipulate.

Step 13: When you're done, you can't make out the tessellation because all the tiles are identical and just run together. Select alternating interiors by clicking in them while holding down Shift.

Explore More

(Not on student activity sheet). Students can try other tessellations based on other regular polygons. The sketch **Twisted Δ's** (Mac) or **2transfm\twisttri.gsp** (Windows) is a tessellation based on equilateral triangles using 120° rotations on two sides and a 180° rotation about the midpoint on the third side.

Step 10: Select the vertices of your tile in order and construct the polygon interior.

Step 11: Translate this interior by your marked vector *CA*. Repeat to create a column of three or four tiles.

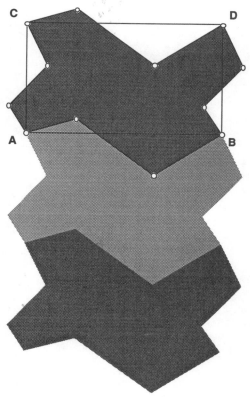

Step 12: Mark points *A* and *B* as vector, select the polygon interiors in your column of tiles, and Translate them by vector *AB*. Repeat to create three or four columns.

Step 13: Select alternate tiles in some kind of checkerboard pattern so that you can change their shades and see your tessellation.

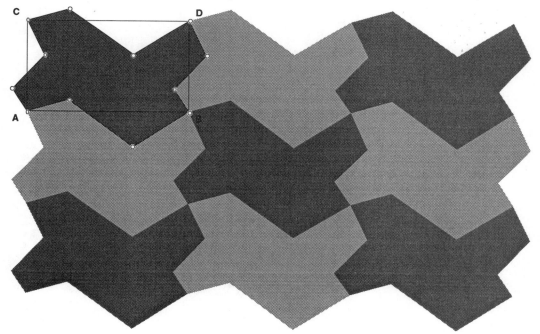

Adjust vertices of your original tile until you get a shape you like or that is recognizable as some interesting form.

Chapter 3
Triangles

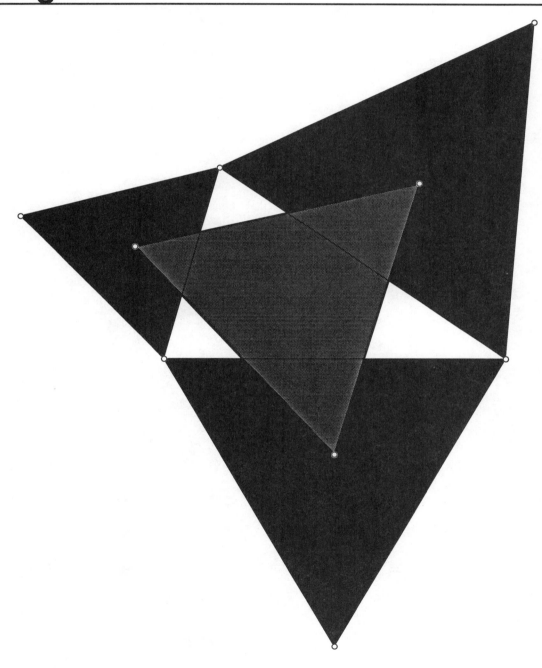

Investigation: Angle Bisectors in a Triangle

In this investigation you'll discover some properties of angle bisectors in a triangle. You might want to record a script of your construction so you can demonstrate your investigation.

Sketch

Step 1: Construct triangle *ABC*.

Step 2: Construct the bisectors of ∠*A* and ∠*B* and their point of intersection, *D*.

Step 3: Construct the bisector of ∠*C*.

Step 4: Measure the distances from *D* to each of the three sides.

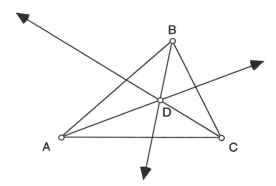

Investigate

When you constructed the third angle bisector did it pass through the point of intersection of the other two angle bisectors? Drag any vertex or side of your triangle. Do the three bisectors always intersect in a single point? The point of concurrency of the three angle bisectors is called the **incenter**.

How are the distances from *D* to each side of the triangle related? Measure these distances and manipulate your triangle. Does this give you an idea for how to construct a circle inscribed in your triangle?

Conjecture: Write your conjectures below.

_____

_____

_____

Present Your Findings

Discuss your results with your partner or group. To present your findings you could:

1. Create a script and comment it to explain the steps of your construction and your conjectures.

2. Add captions to your sketch, print it out, and write an explanation of your investigation and conjectures.

Explore More

1. Does your circle stay inscribed when you alter your triangle? Can you construct a circle that will always stay inscribed? Record a script to inscribe a circle in a triangle. Write a description of what you did on the back of this sheet.

2. Can you inscribe a circle in any quadrilateral, or only some? What about other polygons?

Investigation: Angle Bisectors in a Triangle

Student Audience: Middle School/High School

Prerequisites: Students should know the term **angle bisector**. It would be helpful for students to know how to classify triangles.

Sketchpad Proficiency: Beginner

Class Time: 15-30 minutes

Example Script: Inscribed Circle (Mac) or **3triangl\inscirc.gss** (Windows)

Construction Tips

Steps 2-3: Select three points (point, vertex, point) to enable the Angle Bisector command in the Construct menu. Construct two bisectors, then the intersection. A point of intersection of two lines can be constructed by clicking on the intersection with the Selection Arrow or Point tool. If you construct the three angle bisectors before you construct the point of intersection, you'll need to select two and use the Construct menu: Point At Intersection.

Investigate/Conjecture

As students manipulate their triangles, they should notice that the three angle bisectors always intersect in a single point. (We say that the three angle bisectors are **concurrent**.) That may not strike them as unusual unless they've thought about the chances of three random lines intersecting in a single point. An exercise investigating points of intersection of two, three, and more lines might be a good pre-activity to this one. To measure distances from the incenter to the three sides students can select the point and the segment and choose Distance from the Measure menu. You may choose to have students construct a perpendicular to a side and measure the distance to the point of intersection of this perpendicular and the side. This will supply the point needed to construct the inscribed circle. Encourage all students to try the Explore More suggestion. Some conjectures students might make include:

The angle bisectors in any triangle intersect in a single point (are concurrent).

The incenter is equidistant from the three sides of a triangle.

Introduce the terms **incenter** and **concurrent** after students have made the first conjecture. Make sure that students understand that a Sketchpad triangle can represent *all* triangles because of its potential for being manipulated.

Explore More

1. At first, students are likely to try to "eyeball" it—construct a circle that appears tangent to the three sides, but which is defined by an arbitrary point. Such a circle will not stay inscribed as students manipulate their triangles. To construct a true incircle, construct a line through the incenter, perpendicular to any side. Construct the circle to the point of intersection of this line and side.

2. Students will find they can construct a circle tangent to three sides of a quadrilateral using for a center the point of intersection of two angle bisectors. A fourth side, however, may or may not be tangent to this circle. A good investigation might be to have students start with a circle and construct a quadrilateral around it (construct four tangents). See if they can discover any special properties of such a quadrilateral.

Demonstration: Excircles of a Triangle

In this demonstration you'll define an **excircle** and investigate its properties.

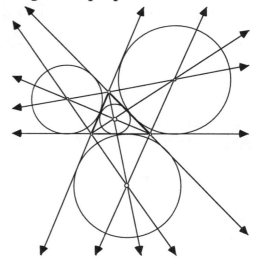

Sketch

Step 1: Open the sketch: **(In)excircles in a Δ** (Mac) or **3triangl\excircl.gsp** (Windows). You'll see a small triangle with a small circle inside it (the incircle) and three larger circles outside of it (excircles), with centers connected to form a larger triangle.

Step 2: Drag any of the vertices of the small triangle.

Investigate

The sides of the small triangle are extended to form exterior angles. The exterior angles and the angles of the triangle are bisected. As you drag a vertex of the triangle, the circles change, but maintain certain relationships with the triangle. See how many of these relationships you can discover.

Conjecture: Write as many conjectures as you can about relationships in this sketch.

_____

_____

_____

_____

_____

_____

_____

_____

_____

Define: Define **Excircle**.

_____

_____

Explore More

See if you can recreate this sketch from scratch. For hints, try showing all hiddens, or open the sketch to "include work" and use undo and redo to recreate its construction.

Demonstration: Excircles of a Triangle

Student Audience: High School/College

Prerequisites: Students should know the terms **exterior angles** and **angle bisector**.

Sketchpad Proficiency: Beginner

Class Time: 15-30 minutes

Sketch Needed: **(In)excircles in a** Δ (Mac) or **3triangl\excircl.gsp** (Windows)

Construction Tips

Students don't need to construct anything in this activity. Instead, they manipulate a pre-made sketch.

Investigate/Conjecture

Some conjectures students might make include:

The three angle bisectors in a triangle intersect in a single point.

An angle bisector in a triangle passes through the intersection of the angle bisectors of the angles exterior to the other two angles.

The intersection of the angle bisectors in a triangle (the incenter) is the center of a circle inscribed in the triangle.

The intersection of the angle bisectors of two exterior angles is the center of a circle tangent to a side of the triangle and the lines extending the other two sides.

The angle bisectors of the exterior angles of a triangle intersect to form another triangle that has the same angle bisectors as the original triangle.

An Excircle is a circle tangent to a side of a triangle and the lines extending the other two sides.

See H. S. M. Coxeter, *Geometry Revisited* for more on excircles.

Investigation: Circumscribing a Triangle

In this investigation you'll discover properties of perpendicular bisectors in a triangle. You'll also learn how to construct a circle that passes through each vertex of a triangle. You might want to record a script of your construction so that you can demonstrate your investigation.

Sketch

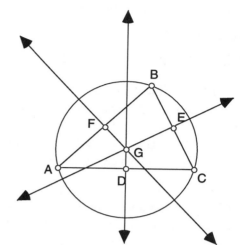

Step 1: Construct triangle *ABC*.

Step 2: Construct the midpoints, *F*, *E*, and *D*, of sides $\overline{AB}$, $\overline{BC}$, and $\overline{CA}$.

Step 3: Construct lines perpendicular to $\overline{AB}$ through *F* and perpendicular to $\overline{BC}$ through *E*. Construct the point of intersection, *G*, of these lines.

Step 4: Construct a line perpendicular to $\overline{CA}$ through *D*.

Step 5: Construct a circle with center *G* and radius endpoint *A*.

Investigate

When you constructed the third perpendicular bisector did it pass through the point of intersection of the other two perpendicular bisectors? Drag any vertex or side of your triangle. Do the three bisectors always intersect in a single point? Does the circle *GA* always pass through vertices *B* and *C*? What does this tell you about the distances from *G* to *A*, *B*, and *C*? Notice that as you move a vertex, *G* may fall inside, on, or outside the triangle. Measure ∠*ABC* and drag *B* to investigate these three cases.

The point of concurrency of the three perpendicular bisectors is called the **circumcenter**.

Conjecture: Write your conjectures below. (Use the back of this sheet if necessary.)

_____

_____

_____

_____

Present Your Findings

Discuss your results with your partner or group. To present your findings you could:

1. Add comments to your script then play or step through it to explain to someone how you arrived at your conjectures.

2. Add captions to your sketch, print it out, and write an explanation of your investigation and conjectures.

Explore More

See if you can circumscribe other shapes besides triangles. Describe what you try and include any additional conjectures you come up with on the back of this sheet.

Investigation: Circumscribing a Triangle

Student Audience: Middle School/High School

Prerequisites: Students should know the term **perpendicular bisector**. It would be helpful for students to know how to classify triangles.

Sketchpad Proficiency: Beginner

Class Time: 15-30 minutes

Example Script: **Circumscribed Triangle** (Mac) or **3triangl\circumsc.gsp** (Windows)

Construction Tips: *Steps 2-3:* You can select all three segments and construct the midpoints simultaneously using the Construct menu. Perpendiculars need to be constructed one at a time: select a side and its midpoint and choose Perpendicular Line from the Construct menu. Construct two perpendiculars, then the intersection. A point of intersection of two lines can be constructed by clicking on the intersection with the Selection Arrow or Point tool. If you construct the three perpendicular bisectors before you construct the point of intersection, you'll need to select two and use the Construct menu: Point At Intersection.

Step 5: Students may mistakenly construct an arbitrary circle that goes through the vertices without actually using one of the vertices as the radius defining point. If they do this, the circle won't circumscribe the triangle when it's distorted.

Investigate/Conjecture: As students manipulate their triangles, they should come up with some of the following conjectures:

The perpendicular bisectors in any triangle intersect in a single point (are concurrent).

The circumcenter is equidistant from the three vertices of a triangle.

The circumcenter in a triangle is the center of the circumscribing circle.

The circumcenter lies inside an acute triangle, on the hypotenuse of a right triangle, and outside an obtuse triangle.

Any triangle inscribed in a semicircle is a right triangle.

The hypotenuse of a right triangle is a diameter of the circumscribing circle.

The three pairs of angles formed by the perpendicular bisectors are equal to the angles in the triangle.

Introduce the terms **circumcenter** and **concurrent** after students have made the first conjecture. Make sure that students understand that a Sketchpad triangle can represent *all* triangles because of its potential for being manipulated.

Explore More: Students can try to circumscribe other shapes using this method. If they try to circumscribe quadrilaterals, for example, they'll discover that some can and some can't be circumscribed. A good investigation would be to start with a circle and inscribe a quadrilateral in it. Look for special properties of the quadrilateral (opposite angles are supplementary). Quadrilaterals that can be circumscribed are called **cyclic**.

The second conjecture can be easily proved using the fact that all points on a perpendicular bisector are equidistant from the endpoints of the bisected segment.

The last three conjectures above can be explored in more depth (and may be discovered) when students are studying circles and relationships between chords and arc measures.

Exploring Geometry

Problem: A Tricky Telescope

Seasoned sailor Sergio Dramamini always had trouble sailing in a straight line. Consequently, he had a special telescope made with mirrors so that he could see both the point towards which he was traveling and the point from which he left. As long as he could keep both points in view he knew he was on a straight line. One day, a so-called friend pulled the cruel trick of altering the mirrors so that instead of seeing what was directly in front of him, he was actually seeing what was directly to his right. (He could still see what was directly behind him.) So when he sighted the island towards which he wanted to sail, he was actually facing at a right angle to the direction he should have been going, and he didn't notice that he had to constantly change his path to keep both the dock and the island in view. What path did Sergio sail?

Sketch

Step 1: Construct points *A* and *B*. Edit their labels to "Dock" and "Island."

Step 2: Construct $\overrightarrow{AC}$.

Step 3: Construct a line through *B* (Island) perpendicular to $\overrightarrow{AC}$.

Step 4: Construct *D*, the intersection of $\overrightarrow{AC}$ and the line. Edit this label to "Sergio." Select the point and choose Trace Locus in the Display menu.

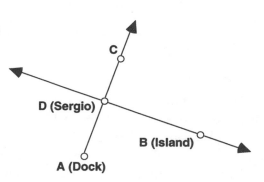

Investigate

This construction locates Sergio given the direction he's facing at some point in his trip. Wherever Sergio is (point *D*) the direction he's facing ($\overrightarrow{AC}$) is perpendicular to the direction of the island (point *B*). Move point *C* clockwise to change the direction Sergio is facing. This will force him to sail to keep the island and dock in view. What kind of path does Sergio sail? Now see if you can apply your solution to this problem to a conjecture. (What kind of triangle is *ADB* and what is it inscribed in?)

Conjecture: Write your conjectures below.

_____

_____

_____

_____

Present Your Findings

Compare and discuss your findings with your partner or group. To present your findings you could:

1. Print a captioned sketch showing several circumscribed right triangles.

2. Record and add comments to a script to construct and circumscribe a right triangle.

Explore More

What kind of path would Sergio sail if his telescope reflected at something other than a 90° angle?

Problem: A Tricky Telescope

Student Audience: High School

Prerequisites: Students should know the terms **perpendicular, inscribe,** and **circumscribe**.

Sketchpad Proficiency: Beginner

Class Time: 15-30 minutes

Example Sketches: **Tricky Telescope** and **Tricky Telescope 2** (Mac) and **3triangl\tricktel.gsp** and **3triangl\trick2.gsp** (Windows)

Construction Tips

Step 1: Double-click on a label with the Text tool to edit it. Words in parentheses in the diagram show how the point labels should be edited.

Step 4: When Trace Locus is checked for a selected object, that object will leave behind a trace of where it's been as it's dragged.

Investigate/Conjecture

Students need to understand that to make Sergio sail, they must move point *C*, not the point labeled Sergio. That's because Sergio's location is defined by the construction, and he's not free to move anywhere he likes. If students attempt to drag Sergio, they'll drag the whole construction. In this construction, Sergio's position is determined by the direction he's facing ($\overrightarrow{AC}$). Dragging point *C* causes Sergio to move along a semi-circle. Students should make the following conjecture:

Any right triangle can be inscribed in a semicircle, where the hypotenuse is the diameter.

Explore More

If Sergio's telescope reflected at a different angle, the path he sailed would be a different fraction of a circle. For example, if the angle were 120°, Sergio's path would trace one-third of a circle. Students are more likely to discover this relationship if they've already studied circles, arcs, and inscribed angles. To try different angles, construct *A*, *B*, and $\overrightarrow{AC}$. Construct a line through *B*, parallel to $\overrightarrow{AC}$. Select *B* and choose Mark Center in the Transform menu. Rotate the line through *B* by the desired angle. (For example, if you rotate the line by 120°, the rotated line and $\overrightarrow{AC}$ will for a 120° angle). Hide the parallel line through *B* and trace the intersection of the rotated line and $\overrightarrow{AC}$. See example sketch **Tricky Telescope 2** (Mac) or **3triangl\trick2.gsp** (Windows).

Investigation: Altitudes in a Triangle

In this investigation you'll discover some properties of altitudes in a triangle. An **altitude** is a segment running from a vertex of a triangle to the opposite side, perpendicular to that side.

Sketch

Step 1: Construct acute triangle *ABC*.

Step 2: Construct a line perpendicular to $\overline{AC}$ through point *B*.

Step 3: Construct segment $\overline{BD}$ along the perpendicular line to intersect $\overline{AC}$, then hide the line.

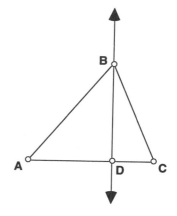

Investigate

Drag point *B* so that ∠*A* or ∠*C* becomes obtuse. What happens to $\overline{BD}$? Devise a method for constructing $\overline{BD}$ so that it always appears, even when it falls outside the triangle. Record a script for this construction, and use your script to construct the altitudes from points *A* and *C*.

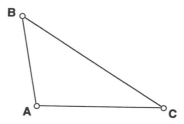

Conjecture: Write your conjectures below.

_____

_____

_____

_____

Present Your Findings

Compare and discuss your results with your partner or group. To present your findings you could:

1. Add comments to your script so that you can use it to present your findings to your classmates, then play or step through your script and explain to someone how you arrived at your conjectures.

2. Add captions to your sketch, print it out, and write an explanation of your investigation and conjectures.

Explore More

1. Do you know a formula for the area of a triangle? Build three different expressions using different altitudes and bases that give the area of the triangle.

2. Are altitudes in a triangle concurrent? (You may need to extend them so they intersect.) Experiment with altitudes and write any further conjectures or findings on the back of this sheet.

Investigation: Altitudes in a Triangle

Student Audience: High School

Prerequisites: Students should know the term **perpendicular** and **acute**. The activity introduces the term **altitude**.

Sketchpad Proficiency: Beginner

Example Sketch/Script: **Altitudes in a Δ** (Mac sketch) and **Altitude** (Mac script) or **3triangl\altintri.gsp** and **3triangle\altitude.gss** (Windows)

Class Time: 20-40 minutes

Construction Tips

Steps 2-3: The line is not an altitude. Students need to construct a segment along this line. They can use the Segment tool and simply click at B, drag along the line, and release at the intersection of the line and $\overline{AC}$. They can then hide the line. Some students may prefer to construct the intersection first, hide the line, then construct the segment.

Investigate/Conjecture

The construction described in the Sketch steps deliberately fails to construct an altitude that can be generalized for all triangles. Students are forced to think about what must be true of the altitude from B when $\angle A$ or $\angle C$ is obtuse. They will see the altitude approaches the side of the triangle as $\angle A$ approaches 90°, and should conjecture that the altitude will fall outside the triangle when $\angle A$ becomes greater than 90°. It's left to them to figure out how to construct this altitude that falls outside the triangle. To do this, extend $\overline{AC}$ by constructing a line $\overleftrightarrow{AC}$. Construct a line through B perpendicular to this line and the point of intersection of the perpendicular and line $\overleftrightarrow{AC}$ (instead of segment $\overline{AC}$). Hide $\overleftrightarrow{AC}$ if you wish, and hide the perpendicular line. Students may make the following conjectures:

In an obtuse triangle, two altitudes fall outside of the triangle.

To construct an altitude from an acute angle in an obtuse triangle, the opposite side must be extended.

Explore More

1.   Students who know the formula for the area of a triangle can use the Calculate command on the three sides and altitudes to build three expressions that give the area of the triangle. Confirm these calculations by constructing the Polygon Interior of the triangle and measuring the area.

2.   The lines formed by extending the altitudes in a triangle are concurrent: that is, they intersect in a single point. This point is called the **orthocenter**. The orthocenter falls inside an acute triangle and outside an obtuse triangle.

Investigation: The Centroid of a Triangle

In this investigation you'll discover properties of the medians in a triangle. Record a script of your construction so that when you finish you can demonstrate what you did.

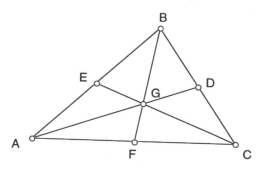

Sketch

Step 1: Construct triangle *ABC*.

Step 2: Construct midpoints on each side.

Step 3: Construct two medians, $\overline{AD}$ and $\overline{BF}$, and their point of intersection *G*.

Step 4: Construct the third median.

Step 5: Measure the distances from *B* to *G* and from *F* to *G*.

Investigate

When you constructed the third median did it pass through the point of intersection of the other two medians? Drag any vertex or side of your triangle. Do the three medians always intersect in a single point? Perform some calculations on *BG* and *GF* and see if you can build an expression that remains constant as you manipulate the triangle. Build similar expressions for *CG* and *GE* and for *AG* and *GD*.

The point of concurrency of the three medians is called the **centroid**.

Conjecture: Write your conjectures below.

_____

_____

_____

_____

_____

Present Your Findings

Discuss your results with your partner or group. To present your findings you could:

1. Add comments to your script so that you can use it to present your findings to your classmates. Then play or step through your script and explain to someone how you arrived at your conjectures.

2. In your sketch, change the label of *G* to Centroid. Add captions to your sketch, print it out, and write an explanation of your investigation and conjectures.

Explore More

1. Construct interiors of the small triangles like *AFG*, and investigate relationships among areas.

2. Investigate special cases (equilateral, isosceles triangles, etc.). Do medians have any special properties in these special cases? Write your conjectures on the back of this sheet.

Investigation: The Centroid of a Triangle

Student Audience: Middle School/High School

Prerequisites: Students should know the terms **midpoint** and **median**. It would be helpful for students to know how to classify triangles.

Sketchpad Proficiency: Beginner

Class Time: 20 minutes

Example Script: **Centroid** (Mac) or **3triangl\centroid.gss** (Windows)

Construction Tips

Step 2: You can select all three segments and construct the midpoints simultaneously.

Steps 3-4: A point of intersection of two lines can be constructed by clicking on the intersection with the Selection Arrow or Point tool. If you construct the three medians before you construct the point of intersection, you'll need to select two and use the Construct menu: Point At Intersection.

Step 5: Measuring point-to-point distances is easier than constructing overlapping segments and measuring lengths.

Investigate/Conjecture: As students manipulate their triangles, they should notice that the three medians always intersect in a single point. (We say that the three medians are **concurrent**.) That may not strike them as unusual unless they've thought about the chances of three random lines intersecting in a single point. An exercise investigating points of intersection of two, three, and more lines might be a good pre-activity to this one. Two conjectures students might make are:

The three medians in any triangle intersect in a single point (are concurrent).

The centroid in a triangle divides each median into two parts, the ratio of whose lengths is 2/1.

Introduce the terms **centroid** and **concurrent** after students have made the first conjecture. Students can make the second conjecture by observing that the ratio of these measure remains constant, even as the triangle and the length measures change. You may need to emphasize the importance of an unchanging Sketchpad value to students. A value that remains constant as a figure is changed is a good clue that a conjecture can be made.

Explore More

1. The six small triangles have equal areas. Ask students to explain why this is so for a pair that lie on the same side. Or, for a challenge, ask them to prove it for all six triangles. You can also ask students to make conjectures about the medium sized triangles (the pairs formed by each median).

2. A median from the vertex angle of an isosceles triangle (or any median in an equilateral triangle) is also an angle bisector, altitude, and perpendicular bisector.

3. (Not on student activity sheet) Have students construct the intersection of the angle bisectors (the incenter), the altitudes (the orthocenter), the perpendicular bisectors (the circumcenter), and the medians (the centroid). This will be easy if students have saved scripts for these constructions. As students find each point, they should give it a meaningful label and hide the lines that define it so that the figure doesn't get too cluttered. Students can discover that three of these points are collinear in any triangle. The line is called the Euler line, and the incenter isn't on it, except in isosceles triangles. The four points are coincident in an equilateral triangle.

4. (Not on student activity sheet) The centroid is the "center of gravity" of a triangle. Students can print their triangles, place them over oaktag (manila folder) or cardboard, and use thumbtacks to make holes that mark the vertices of the triangle and the centroid on the cardboard. Then they can cut out the cardboard triangle and balance it on an eraser point held at the centroid.

©1996 by Key Curriculum Press

Modeling a Problem: The Surfer and the Spotter

Two shipwreck survivors manage to swim to a desert island. As it happens, the island is in the shape of a perfect equilateral triangle. The survivors turn out to have very different dispositions. Sarah soon discovers that the surfing is outstanding on all three of the island's coasts. She crafts a surfboard from a fallen tree and surfs every day. As there is plenty of food on the island, she's content to surf the rest of her days. Spencer, on the other hand, is more a social animal and sorely misses civilization. Every day he goes to a different corner of the island and searches the waters for passing ships. Each castaway wants to locate a home in the place that best suits their respective needs. (They have no interest in living in the same place, though if it turns out the be advantageous, neither is against the idea either.) Sarah wants to find the spot closest to her three beaches. (She visits them with equal frequency.) Spencer wants his house to be situated so that he can beat the shortest possible paths to the three corners of the islands. In other words, the sum of the distances to the sides of the triangle must be minimized for Sarah; the sum of the distances to the vertices must be minimized for Spencer. Where should they locate their huts?

Sketch

Step 1:   Construct an equilateral triangle *ABC*.

Step 2:   Construct $\overline{DA}$, $\overline{DB}$, and $\overline{DC}$, where *D* is any point inside the triangle.

Step 3:   If you wish, relabel *D* as Spencer.

Step 4:   Construct *E* anywhere inside the triangle.

Step 5:   Construct a perpendicular to $\overline{AB}$ through *E*. Repeat to construct perpendiculars to $\overline{BC}$ and $\overline{AC}$ through *E*.

Step 6:   Construct $\overline{EF}$, $\overline{EG}$, and $\overline{EH}$, where *F*, *G*, and *H* are the points where the perpendiculars intersect the sides of the triangle.

Step 7:   Hide the perpendicular lines. Relabel *E* as Sarah, if you wish.

Step 8:   Measure *DA*, *DB*, and *DC*. (Edit these measures to read *DA* =, etc.)

Step 9:   Calculate *DA* + *DB* + *DC*.

Step 10:   Measure *EF*, *EG*, and *EH*. (Edit these measures.)

Step 11:   Calculate *EF* + *EG* + *EH*.

Investigate: Move points *D* and *E* (Spencer and Sarah) around inside your triangle. See if you can find the best locations for each castaway. What are these locations? Describe your findings below. Explain why these are the best locations.

_____

_____

_____

_____

(This problem is adapted from *Geometry*, by Harold Jacobs. © 1974 by W. H. Freeman and Company. Used with permission.)

Problem: The Surfer and the Spotter

Student Audience: High School

Prerequisites: Students should know the term **equilateral triangle** and should know how to construct one with Sketchpad (or at least how to use a script to construct one).

Sketchpad Proficiency: Experienced User

Class Time: 20-30 minutes

Example Sketch: **Surfer & Spotter** (Mac) or **3triangl\surfspot.gsp** (Windows)

Construction Tips

Step 1: The script **3/Triangle (By Edge)** (Mac) or **regpoly\3byedge.gss** (Windows) can be used to construct the equilateral triangle.

Steps 6-7: Students may prefer to construct the intersections, hide the lines, then construct the segments. The lines are not hidden in the diagram.

Step 8: Double-click on a measure with the Text tool to edit it.

Investigate/Conjecture

Spencer needs to be located at the center of the equilateral triangle to minimize his distances. It turns out that Sarah can be located anywhere. The sum of her distances remains constant as you move her point around the inside of the triangle. Students may notice that in both cases, the "paths" (to the island corners or beaches) form equal angles (120°). For Spencer, this only happens at the center. For Sarah, this is true for any location. Students may also note that Sarah's sum is equal to the length of one altitude in the triangle.

Explore More (not on student activity sheet)

1. Students could try this problem with non-equilateral triangles. In a non-equilateral triangle, Sarah must be located at the vertex from which the shortest altitude can be drawn. Spencer must again be located so that his paths to the island corners form 120° angles.

2. Students can also try this problem for non-triangular islands. On a quadrilateral island, for example, Spencer's optimal location is easy to find. Sarah's presents some special challenges, as it may not always be possible for her path to the beach to be perpendicular to it.

Investigation: Midsegments of a Triangle

A **midsegment** in a triangle connects the midpoints of two sides. In this investigation you'll discover some relationships between midsegments and the sides of a triangle.

Sketch

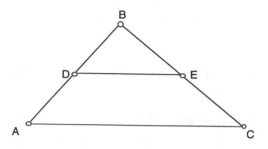

Step 1:   Construct $\triangle ABC$.

Step 2:   Construct points D and E, the midpoints of $\overline{AB}$ and $\overline{BC}$.

Step 3:   Construct $\overline{DE}$, the midsegment of $\triangle ABC$.

Investigate

Measure DE and AC. Calculate AC/DE. Drag various parts of the triangle and watch the relationship between the lengths of the midsegment $\overline{DE}$ and the base $\overline{AC}$. Also note their directions. Is there anything special about the direction of $\overline{DE}$ compared to $\overline{AC}$? How can you confirm this? Does this relationship hold for all triangles?

Conjecture: Write your conjectures below.

_____

_____

Present Your Findings

Discuss your results with your partner or group. To present your findings you could print a captioned sketch showing a triangle with one or more midsegments and measures that illustrate your conjectures.

Explore More

1. Mark B as center and dilate points A and C by a scale factor of 1/3 (or some other scale factor). Construct $\overline{A'C'}$. How do the length and direction of $\overline{A'C'}$ compare with those of $\overline{AC}$?

2. Construct the triangle's interior, measure its area, and see if you can come up with an area formula for a triangle that uses the length of a midsegment. Construct lines through D and E, perpendicular to $\overline{DE}$. Construct a line through B parallel to $\overline{AC}$. These lines, along with $\overline{AC}$, form a rectangle. How does the area of this rectangle compare to the area of the triangle? Why?

3. Construct a triangle with all three midsegments. This divides the triangle into four smaller triangles. Investigate properties of these triangles.

4. Record a script for constructing a triangle and the midpoints of its sides. Before you stop recording, select the midpoints and click Loop to record a recursive step, then stop recording. Experiment playing this script to different levels of recursion. make conjectures about the smaller successive midpoint triangles.

5. Repeat this investigation for the midsegment of a trapezoid.

Investigation: Midsegments in a Triangle

Student Audience: Middle School/High School

Prerequisites: This activity introduces the term **midsegment**.

Sketchpad Proficiency: Beginner

Class Time: 15-45 minutes, depending on how much time you give students to explore

Example Sketch and Script: **Midsegment in Δ** and **Midpoint Δ's** (Mac) or **3triangl\midsgmnt.gsp** and **3triangl\mdpttris.gss** (Windows)

Construction Tips

This is a simple construction with which students should have little trouble.

Investigate/Conjecture

There are various ways students can see if these segments are parallel. They could measure slopes. If students construct a line parallel to $\overline{AC}$ through D, the line will contain $\overline{DE}$. Or students could extend both segments with lines and see if Sketchpad will construct their point of intersection (it won't). Students should conjecture:

A midsegment in a triangle, connecting midpoints of two sides, is parallel to the third side and half its length.

Explore More

1. $\overline{A'C'}$ will have length 1/3 AC and will be parallel to $\overline{AC}$.

2. A formula for the area of a triangle could be $A = mh$, where m is the length of the midsegment and h is the height (measured to the base parallel to the midsegment). This is equivalent to $A = (1/2bh)$, since $m = (1/2b)$. This can be illustrated further by constructing the rectangle shown. The rectangle $FGHJ$ can be seen to have area equal to $\triangle ABC$ because the small triangles FAD and CJE are congruent to $\triangle GBD$ and $\triangle BHE$ respectively. They could be cut off and stuck in the corners of the rectangle.

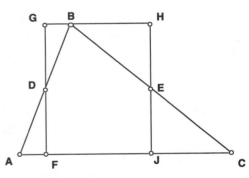

3. The four small triangles are congruent to one another and similar to the original triangle.

4. These smaller and smaller "in-triangles" converge to the centroid of the triangle (the intersection of the medians).

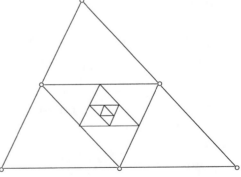

5. Midsegments of a trapezoid are the subject of a separate investigation, or they can be explored as an extension to this investigation.

     Exploring Geometry

Investigation: Triangle Sum

This is a two-part investigation. First, you'll investigate and make a conjecture about the sum of the measures of the angles in a triangle, then you'll continue sketching to demonstrate why your conjecture is true.

Sketch

Step 1:   Construct △ABC.

Step 2:   Measure its three angles. Calculate the sum of the angle measures.

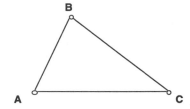

Investigate

As you manipulate your triangle, what happens to the sum of the angle measures? What can you say about the sum of the measures of the angles in any triangle?

Conjecture: Write your conjectures below.

_____

_____

Investigate Further

Construct the polygon interior of △ABC. Mark *AC* as vector and translate the triangle and its interior by vector *AC*. What would fill the space between your two triangles? Construct the midpoint of $\overline{BC}$, mark it as center, and rotate the interior of △ABC 180° about this point. What can you say about the three angles that now meet at a single point (point *C* of the original triangle)? How does this confirm the Triangle Sum Conjecture?

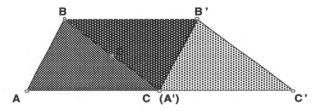

_____

_____

_____

Present Your Findings

Discuss your results with your partner or group. To present your findings print a sketch with measures and captions to illustrate your conjecture. Show several examples of triangles and their angle sums.

Explore More

1. Investigate angle sums in other polygons.

2. See if you can think of other ways to use Sketchpad to demonstrate the Triangle Sum Conjecture.

Investigation: Triangle Sum

Student Audience: Middle School/High School

Prerequisites: None

Sketchpad Proficiency: Beginner/Experienced User (depending on how much you ask students to do)

Class Time: 20-30 minutes

Example Sketch: **Triangle Sum** (Mac) or **3triangle\trisum.gsp** (Windows)

Construction Tips

Step 2: To measure an angle, select three points in order: point, vertex, point. To calculate with these measures, select them and choose Calculate from the Measure menu. The measures appear on a pop-up menu in the middle of the calculator.

Investigate/Conjecture

The sum of the angles remains constant as the triangle is manipulated. Students should conjecture:

The sum of the measures of the angles in any triangle is 180°.

Depending on students' Sketchpad experience, you may want to investigate further to see why the above conjecture is true. Mark Vector and Translate are found in the Transform menu. (Select *A* and *C*, in order, to mark *AC* as vector.) Since the three angles of the triangle meet at a single point to form a straight line, their sum must be 180°.

Explore More

1. This is worthy of a complete investigation. Have students construct any polygon and divide it into triangles by constructing diagonals from one vertex. They should discover that they can create $n - 2$ triangles in an n-gon. Thus, it follows that the sum of the angles in an n-gon is $(n - 2)180$. Have students reason this out before they measure angles in their polygon to confirm it.

2. There are a variety of ways to illustrate the Triangle Sum Conjecture using Sketchpad. One way is to extend the sides with lines, mark one of the vertices as center in the Transform menu, and use the Dilate tool to scale the triangle down to a single point. When the triangle is so shrunken, you're left with a single point surrounded by six angles. What are the six angles? They're the three angles of the triangle and their three vertical angles. The sum of these angles (360°) is twice the sum of the angles in the triangle.

    Another method is shown here. Construct $\triangle ABC$, midpoints *D* and *E*, and midsegment $\overline{DE}$. Mark $\overline{DE}$ mirror in the Transform menu, and reflect *B* across it. Triangles ADB' and $B'EC$ are isosceles, with equal base angles.

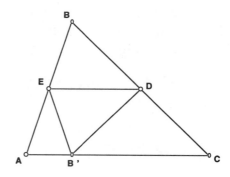

©1996 by Key Curriculum Press   Exploring Geometry

Investigation: Exterior Angles in a Triangle

An **exterior angle** of a triangle is formed when one of the sides is extended. An exterior angle lies outside the triangle. In this investigation, you'll discover a relationship between an exterior angle and the sum of the measures of two remote interior angles.

Sketch

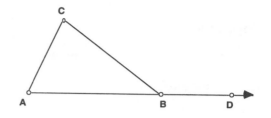

Step 1:   Construct ray $\overrightarrow{AB}$.

Step 2:   Construct $\overline{AC}$ and $\overline{CB}$ to create $\triangle ABC$.

Step 3:   Construct D on $\overrightarrow{AB}$, outside of the triangle.

Step 3:   Measure exterior angle CBD.

Step 4:   Measure the remote interior angles $\angle ACB$ and $\angle CAB$.

Investigate

Do you see a relationship between the remote interior angles and the exterior angle? Manipulate your triangle. Make the exterior angle a "nice" measure, like 100°. Does that help reveal the relationship? Use Calculate to confirm your conjecture.

Conjecture: Write your conjectures below.

_____

_____

Present Your Findings

Discuss your results with your partner or group. To present your findings you could print a captioned sketch showing a triangle and an exterior angle with measures to illustrate your conjecture.

Explore More

Can you explain why your conjecture is true? It has to do with the Triangle Sum Conjecture. Construct polygon interior ABC. Copy it, and paste two free copies. Arrange them (use the freehand Rotate tool as necessary) so that angles A and C fit into $\angle CBD$. Write an explanation of your conjecture on the back of this paper or on a separate sheet of paper.

Investigation: Exterior Angles in a Triangle

Student Audience: Middle School/High School

Prerequisites: Students are introduced in this activity to the terms **exterior angle** and **remote interior angle**. While remote interior angle is not defined, it should be clear from the context.

Sketchpad Proficiency: Beginner

Class Time: 10-20 minutes

Example Sketch: Exterior Angles in Δ (Mac) or **3triangl\extangtri.gsp** (Windows)

Construction Tips

This is a very simple construction. Novice Sketchpad users may need to be reminded that to measure an angle they need to select three points in order: point, vertex, point.

Investigate/Conjecture

Students should make the following conjecture:

The measure of an exterior angle in a triangle is equal to the sum of the measures of the remote interior angles.

Explore More

This is a very short investigation, and all students should do this Explore More. Give students time in cooperative groups to discuss why remote interior angles would add up to an exterior angle. They should come up with paragraph proofs along these lines:

An exterior angle forms a linear pair with one angle in a triangle (angles 2 and 1). Therefore, the sum of the exterior angle and this angle is 180°. The sum of the three angles in the triangle is also 180°. Hence, the measure of the exterior angle must be equal to the sum of the measures of the remote interior angles.

$m\angle 1 + m\angle 2 = 180$

$m\angle 1 + m\angle 3 + m\angle 4 = 180$

Hence, $m\angle 2 = m\angle 3 + m\angle 4$

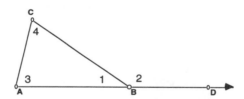

 Exploring Geometry

Investigation: Triangle Inequalities

In this investigation you'll discover relationships among the measures of the sides and angles in a triangle.

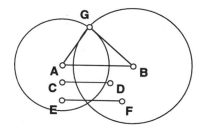

Sketch

Step 1: Construct $\overline{AB}$, then $\overline{CD}$ and $\overline{EF}$, slightly shorter than, and directly under $\overline{AB}$.

Step 2: Construct a circle with center A and radius CD and a circle with center B and radius EF.

Step 3: Construct $\overline{AG}$ and $\overline{BG}$, where G is one point of intersection of the circles. (If the circles don't intersect, shorten $\overline{AB}$ a little.)

Investigate/Conjecture

Measure AB, CD (or AG), and EF (or BG). Drag point B to make AB longer. What happens to the triangle? At what point does AB become "too long"? Calculate $CD + EF$ and compare this to AB. Write a conjecture below:

_____

_____

Now measure the three angles in the triangle. Manipulate your triangle so you can fill in the chart below.

Triangle 1   Triangle 2   Triangle 3

$\overline{AB}$ longest side	Largest Angle?_____	$\overline{AG}$ longest side	Largest Angle?_____	$\overline{BG}$ longest side	Largest Angle?_____
$\overline{AG}$ shortest side	Smallest Angle?_____	$\overline{BG}$ shortest side	Smallest Angle?_____	$\overline{AB}$ shortest side	Smallest Angle?_____

Write a conjecture below.

_____

_____

Present Your Findings

Discuss your findings with your partner or group. To present your findings you could:

1. Print a captioned sketch showing several different triangles, illustrating what happens as the length of the longest side approaches the sum of the lengths of the other two sides and showing the relationships among unequal sides and angles.

2. Create and print a sketch showing three connected segments that can't form a triangle.

3. Demonstrate with real objects (pencils, rulers, meter sticks) why some lengths can form a triangle while others can't.

Explore More

Investigate inequalities in the medians or altitudes of a triangle. Write your findings or conjectures on the back of this sheet.

Investigation: Triangle Inequality

Student Audience: Middle School/High School

Prerequisites: None.

Sketchpad Proficiency: Beginner

Class Time: 20-30 minutes

Example Sketch: Δ Inequality (Mac) or **3triangl\triineq.gsp** (Windows)

Construction Tips

Step 2: Select point A and segment $\overline{CD}$. Choose Circle By Center+Radius in the Construct menu. Repeat for B and $\overline{EF}$.

Investigate/Conjecture

As $\overline{AB}$ is stretched, the triangle begins to collapse, as AG and BG are being held constant. As AB approaches the sum of AG and BG, the triangle approaches a line segment. Students should conclude from this that in any triangle, the length of a side must be less than the sum of the lengths of the other two sides. The rest of the investigation has to do with angle measures. Students should fill in the chart as shown:

Triangle 1		Triangle 2		Triangle 3	
$\overline{AB}$ longest side	Largest Angle? $\angle G$	$\overline{AG}$ longest side	Largest Angle? $\angle B$	$\overline{BG}$ longest side	Largest Angle? $\angle A$
$\overline{AG}$ shortest side	Smallest Angle? $\angle B$	$\overline{BG}$ shortest side	Smallest Angle? $\angle A$	$\overline{AB}$ shortest side	Smallest Angle? $\angle G$

Students should make the following conjectures:

The length of one side of a triangle must be greater than the sum of the lengths of the other two sides.

The largest angle in a triangle is opposite the longest side and the smallest angle is opposite the shortest side.

Explore More

The longest median and altitude in a triangle are drawn to the shortest side. The shortest median and altitude are drawn to the longest side.

Investigation: Properties of Isosceles Triangles

In this activity you'll learn how to construct an **isosceles triangle** (a triangle with at least two sides the same length). Then you'll discover properties of isosceles triangles.

Sketch

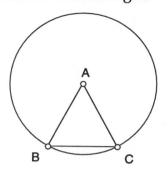

Step 1:   Construct a circle *AB*.

Step 2:   Construct $\overline{AB}$.

Step 3:   Construct $\overline{AC}$ with point *C* on the circle.

Step 4:   Construct $\overline{BC}$ and hide the circle.

Investigate and Conjecture

Drag different parts of your triangle to see how they affect your figure. Do you see why different points act in different ways? How do you know your triangle is isosceles, without measuring the sides? Measure angles $\angle ABC$ and $\angle ACB$. (These are called the **base angles** of the isosceles triangle.) Write a conjecture about the base angles below

_____

_____

_____

Sketch

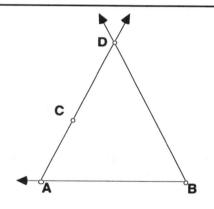

Step 5:   In a new sketch, construct $\overline{AB}$, ray $\overrightarrow{AC}$ and ray $\overrightarrow{BA}$.

Step 6:   Select *C*, *A*, and *B* and choose Mark Angle in the Transform menu.

Step 7:   Mark *B* as center in the Transform menu and rotate $\overrightarrow{BA}$ by the marked angle.

Step 8:   Construct the point of intersection, *D*, of this ray and $\overrightarrow{AC}$.

Your construction guarantees that the base angles of $\triangle ABD$ are equal. Measure *AD* and *BD*. What else can you say about $\triangle ABD$? Write your findings as a conjecture. This should be the converse of the conjecture above.

_____

_____

_____

Present Your Findings

Discuss your results with your partner or group. To present your findings you could:

1. Print a captioned sketch showing several different isosceles triangles and the measures of the angles. Write about your findings.

2. Record and comment a script to construct an isosceles triangle, then demonstrate your construction and findings to a classmate.

Investigation: Properties of Isosceles Triangles

Student Audience: Middle School/High School

Prerequisites: This activity introduces the terms **isosceles**, and **base angles**.

Sketchpad Proficiency: Beginner (first part) to Experienced User (second part)

Example Script and Sketch: **Isosceles Δ 1** (Mac script) and **Equal Base Angles** (Mac sketch) or **3triangl\isotris\isotri1.gss** and **3triangl\equiang.gsp** (Windows)

Class Time: 15-30 minutes

Construction Tips

This is a straightforward construction that should present few difficulties for students.

Step 2: Make sure students use the same points for their segment (*A* and *B*) that they used to create the circle.

Step 6: This marks ∠*CAB* as an angle for rotation. This is a clockwise angle.

Step 7: Ray *AB* is rotated by an angle equal in measure to ∠*CAB* in the clockwise direction.

Investigate/Conjecture

By dragging points *A* or *B* in the first construction, students can change everything about the triangle (except the fact that it's isosceles). Point *C* is constrained to a circle so that $\overline{AB}$ is the same length as $\overline{AC}$. Students should make the following conjecture:

The base angles of an isosceles triangle are equal.

To investigate the converse of this conjecture, students are asked to construct a triangle so that two angles are equal. This triangle can be manipulated by dragging points *A*, *B*, or *C*. Though *C* is not a vertex of the triangle, it controls the base angles. When students measure the sides, they can conjecture:

If two angles of a triangle are equal, then the triangle is isosceles.

Explore More

A separate activity—Exploration: Constructing an Isosceles Triangle—suggests extensions to this investigation.

1. Another easy way to construct an isosceles triangle is to construct a line $\overleftrightarrow{AB}$ and a point *C* not on the line. Reflect *C* across the line and construct Δ*ACC′*. The disadvantage of this construction is that the triangle is controlled by a fourth point: point *B*. Another method: Construct a segment and its perpendicular bisector. Construct a point on the bisector and connect it to the segment endpoints.

2. Isosceles triangles are defined as having *at least* two equal sides, so an equilateral triangle is also isosceles. All three of its angles could be considered base angles and are all equal.

3. The median, altitude, and angle bisector constructed from the vertex angle of an isosceles triangle are all the same segment. This segment also lies on the perpendicular bisector of the base.

Exploration: Constructing Isosceles Triangles

How many ways can you come up with to construct
an isosceles triangle? Make sure you use the
Transform menu as well as the Construct menu
and Toolbox. Write brief descriptions of your
construction methods, along with the properties of
isosceles triangles that make that method work.

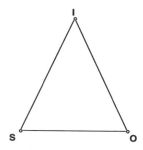

Method 1: _____

_____

_____

_____

Properties: _____

_____

Method 2: _____

_____

_____

_____

Properties: _____

_____

Method 3: _____

_____

_____

_____

Properties: _____

_____

Investigate and conjecture

What happens if you manipulate an isosceles triangle so that all three sides are equal; is
it still isosceles? What are its properties? Investigate medians, altitudes, angle bisectors,
and perpendicular bisectors in an isosceles triangle. Write any findings or conjectures
below.

_____

_____

_____

_____

_____

Exploration: Constructing Isosceles Triangles

Student Audience: Middle School/High School

Prerequisites: Students need to know what an **isosceles triangle** is, and should know some of its properties. In the activity Investigation: Properties of Isosceles Triangles, students learn the first and fifth methods described below.

Sketchpad Proficiency: Experienced User

Example Scripts and Sketch: Isosceles Δ 1–4 (Mac scripts) and **Equal Base Angles** (Mac sketch) or **3triangl\isotris\isotri1.gss**, etc., and **3triangl\isotris\equiang.gsp** (Windows)

Class Time: 50 minutes

Construction Tips

Depending on how much time you give students and their Sketchpad proficiency, students should come up with one or more of the following methods:

1. Construct a circle AB and radii $\overline{AB}$ and $\overline{AC}$. Construct $\overline{BC}$. Property: An isosceles triangle has two equal sides.

2. Construct a line $\overleftrightarrow{AB}$ and a point C off the line. Reflect C across the line. Triangle ACC' is isosceles. Property: An isosceles triangle has reflection symmetry.

3. Construct a segment $\overline{AB}$ and its midpoint C. Construct a perpendicular through C. Construct D on the perpendicular. Triangle ABD is isosceles. Property: The perpendicular bisector of the base of an isosceles triangle passes through the vertex of the vertex angle.

4. Construct rays $\overrightarrow{AB}$ and $\overrightarrow{AC}$. Construct the angle bisector of angle BAC. Construct D on the angle bisector and a line through D perpendicular to the angle bisector. construct the points of intersection E and F of this line with rays $\overrightarrow{AB}$ and $\overrightarrow{AC}$. Triangle AEF is isosceles. Property: The angle bisector of the vertex angle of an isosceles triangle is perpendicular to the base.

5. Construct a segment $\overline{AB}$, ray $\overrightarrow{BA}$, and ray $\overrightarrow{AC}$. Select C, A, and B, and choose Mark Angle in the Transform menu. Select B and choose Mark Center in the Transform menu. Rotate $\overrightarrow{AC}$ By Marked Angle. Construct the point of intersection, D, of this ray and $\overrightarrow{AC}$. Triangle ABD is isosceles. Property: The base angles of an isosceles triangle are equal.

Example scripts correspond to the first four methods above. The example sketch **Equal Base Angles** (Mac) or **3triangl\isotris\equiang.gsp** (Windows) corresponds to the fifth method.

Investigate/Conjecture

Isosceles triangles are defined as having *at least* two equal sides, so an equilateral triangle is also isosceles. All three of its angles could be considered base angles and are all equal. The median, altitude, and angle bisector constructed from the vertex angle of an isosceles triangle are all the same segment. This segment also lies on the perpendicular bisector of the base.

©1996 by Key Curriculum Press

Investigation: Napoleon's Theorem

French emperor Napoleon Bonaparte fancied himself as something of an amateur geometer and liked to hang out with mathematicians. The theorem you'll investigate in this activity is attributed to him.

Sketch

Create a script to construct an equilateral triangle and its centroid:

Step 1: Open a new script and click Record.

Step 2: Construct equilateral triangle *ABC*. (Use a script or construct from scratch.)

Step 3: Construct the midpoints of $\overline{AC}$ and $\overline{BC}$ and two medians.

Step 4: Construct the centroid, the point of intersection of the two medians.

Step 5: Hide the medians and midpoints. Stop your script.

Start with a blank sketch and play your script on a triangle:

Step 6: Construct any triangle *ABC*.

Step 7: Play your equilateral triangle script on the endpoints of each of the three sides. If an equilateral triangle falls inside your triangle, undo and try again, selecting the two given points in reverse order.

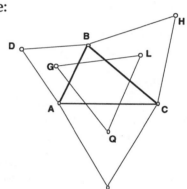

Step 8: Connect the centroids of the equilateral triangles. Δ*GLQ* is called the outer Napoleon triangle of Δ*ABC*.

Investigate: Drag vertices and sides of your triangle *ABC*. What can you say about the triangle connecting the centroids of the equilateral triangles?

Conjecture: Write what you think Napoleon's Theorem might be below.

_____

_____

Present Your Findings: To present your findings, you could print a captioned sketch with an explanation and statement of Napoleon's Theorem.

Explore More

1. Construct segments connecting each vertex of your original triangle with the most remote vertex of the equilateral triangle on the opposite side. What can you say about these three segments?

2. Construct the inner Napoleon triangle by reflecting each centroid across its corresponding edge in the original triangle. Measure the areas of the original triangle and the outer and inner Napolean triangles. How do these areas compare?

3. Do some research on Napoleon's interest in mathematics.

Investigation: Napoleon's Theorem

Student Audience: High School/Advanced High School/College/Teacher Education

Prerequisites: Students should know the terms **equilateral triangle**, **midpoint**, **median**, and **centroid**.

Sketchpad Proficiency: Experienced User

Class Time: 15 minutes

Example Sketch: **Napolean's Theorem** (Mac) or **3triangl\napolthm.gsp** (Windows)

Construction Tips

This is an easy construction, rated for the experienced user only because it suggests using a script. This investigation is a good way to introduce using scripts to speed up a construction.

Step 6: The sides of the triangle are shown with thick lines in the example. This will help make the triangle stand out.

Step 7: If you prefer not to use a script, the equilateral triangle/centroid construction can simply be repeated on each of the three sides of the triangle.

Investigate/Conjecture

The following conjecture (Napoleon's Theorem) should be obvious when the triangle is manipulated:

Segments joining the centroids of equilateral triangles constructed on the sides of any triangle, themselves form an equilateral triangle.

Explore More

1. Segments joining the original triangle's vertices with the remote vertices of the equilateral triangles on the opposite sides will be equal in length and will intersect in a single point. This was discovered by geometric artist M. C. Escher.

2. The difference between the areas of the outer and inner Napoleon triangles is the area of the original triangle. If students don't notice this, have them try to make the inner triangle shrink to nothing. (This happens when the outer Napoleon triangle and the original triangle are identical.) Then have students try to make the areas of the outer and inner Napoleon triangles equal. (This happens when the original triangle is collapsed to a segment with no area.)

3. *An Introduction to the History of Mathematics*, by Howard Eves, makes some interesting references to Napoleon and his interest in math and mathematicians. H. S. M. Coxeter, in *Geometry Revisited*, recounts that Laplace once told Napoleon, "General, the last thing we need from you is a geometry lesson."

4. (Not on student activity sheet) Rotate the original triangle 120° and 240° about each of the centers of the equilateral triangles. Construct equilateral triangles on the sides of the rotaed images. Can you continue this indefinitely, filling the plane? Explain why. Explain how this tessellation proves Napoleon's Theorem.

Investigation: Morley's Theorem

You may know that it's impossible to trisect an angle with compass and straightedge. Sketchpad, however, makes it easy to trisect an angle. In this investigation, you'll trisect the three angles in a triangle and discover a surprising fact about the intersections of these angle trisections.

Construct

Step 1: Use the ray tool to construct triangle *ABC*, drawing your rays in counter-clockwise order as shown.

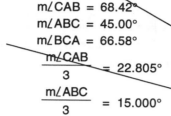

$m\angle CAB = 68.42°$
$m\angle ABC = 45.00°$
$m\angle BCA = 66.58°$
$\dfrac{m\angle CAB}{3} = 22.805°$
$\dfrac{m\angle ABC}{3} = 15.000°$
$\dfrac{m\angle BCA}{3} = 22.195°$

Step 2: Measure each angle of the triangle.

Step 3: Use Sketchpad's calculator to calculate 1/3 of each angle.

Step 4: Select point *A* and choose Mark Center in the Transform menu.

Step 5: Select the measurement $\dfrac{m\angle CAB}{3}$ and choose Mark Angle Measurement in the Transform menu.

Step 6: Rotate ray *AB* by the marked angle. Rotate it again to trisect $\angle CAB$.

Step 7: Repeat steps 4 through 6 on points *B* and *C* to trisect angles *ABC* and *BCA*.

Investigate

Morley's theorem states that certain intersections of these angle trisectors form an equilateral triangle. Can you find it? Experiment. Once you think you have it, drag your triangle around to confirm this inner triangle is equilateral. State Morley's theorem in the space below:

_____

_____

Present Your findings

Discuss your results with your partner or your group. To present your findings, you could print a captioned sketch stating and demonstrating Morley's theorem, or create a presentation sketch using hide and show action buttons that demonstrate your construction and conclusion.

Explore More

1. See if you can find other relationships or special triangles in your figure.

2. Construct rays from the vertices of your original triangle through the opposite vertices of the equilateral triangle. What do you notice?

3. Construct a triangle using lines instead of rays. Trisect one set of exterior angles. Can you find an equilateral triangle among the intersections of these trisectors?

Investigation: Morley's Theorem

Student Audience: High School/Advanced High School/College/Teacher Education

Prerequisites: Students need to be able to identify an equilateral triangle.

Sketchpad Proficiency: Power User

Class Time: 30 minutes

Example Sketch: Morley's Theorem (Mac) or **3triangl\morley.gsp** (Windows)

Construction Tips

This construction employs rotation by a marked angle measure calculation. Experience using the calculator and the Transform menu would be helpful. Students should have an easier time with this construction if they've already done the activity Trisecting an Angle.

Step 1: It's important to construct the triangle using rays going counter-clockwise so that these rays can be used in positive (counter-clockwise) rotations.

Investigate/Conjecture

The figure at right shows the angle trisectors that intersect to form an equilateral triangle. They are one set of alternating vertices of a hexagon formed by the trisectors. The other set of vertices in this hexagon, interestingly, don't form an equilateral triangle. It's difficult to state Morley's theorem succinctly because it's difficult to identify the correct intersecting trisectors. One way of stating it would be:

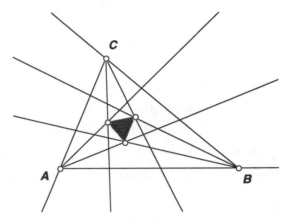

The intersections of the adjacent angle trisectors in any triangle are the vertices of an equilateral triangle.

Explore More

1. The three triangles surrounding the equilateral triangle are all isosceles. There are numerous angle relationships that students may discover. These no doubt play a role in the proof. You might ask students to try to prove the theorem, but the proof is beyond the scope of this book (i.e. it's beyond the author at the moment, working under a deadline!).

2. Rays from the original triangle's vertices through the opposite vertices of the equilateral triangle are concurrent. Students might expect them to be angle bisectors, but they're not.

3. Trisectors of one set of exterior angles intersect to form a hexagon. One set of alternating vertices of this hexagon are the vertices of the original triangle. The other set form an equilateral triangle.

See *Geometry Revisited*, by Coxeter and Greitzer, for more on Morley's theorem.

Demonstration: Triangle Congruence—SSS?

In this demonstration you'll work with a sample sketch to see how many different triangles can be created given the lengths of the three sides.

Sketch

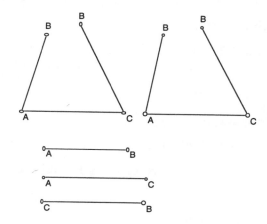

Step 1: Open the sketch: **SSS** (Mac) or **3triangl\congrnce\sss.gsp** (Windows). You'll see two broken triangles and three separate segments.

Step 2: Drag different parts in the broken triangles. Note that you can't change the lengths of the sides of these "triangles."

Step 3: Drag the two points labeled *B* in the broken triangles so that they coincide, forming triangles.

Step 4: See if you can construct two different shaped triangles in this way.

Step 5: Change the lengths of one or more of the "given" sides (the free segments below the triangles) and try the experiment again.

Investigate

Could you form triangles with different sizes or shapes given the three sides? If you were given two triangles with three pairs of congruent sides, would that be enough information to determine that the triangles were congruent?

Conjecture: Write your conjectures below.

_____

_____

_____

_____

Explore More

1. Change the three given segments so that you can no longer connect the points *B* to create a triangle. Under what conditions will the points *B* not reach each other?

2. Open a new sketch and see if you can create this demonstration yourself. For a hint, show all the hiddens in the demonstration sample sketch. The command Circle By Center+Radius was used to construct congruent segments.

Demonstration: Triangle Congruence—SSS?

Student Audience: High School

Prerequisites: Students should know the term **congruent**.

Sketchpad Proficiency: Beginner

Class Time: 10-20 minutes. You may want to do this activity in the same class period as other triangle congruence investigations: SAS, SSA, ASA, AAA.

Sketch Needed: SSS (Mac) or **3triangl\congrnce\sss.gsp** (Windows)

Construction Tips

Students don't need to construct anything in this activity; instead they manipulate a pre-made sketch.

Students can tell when points B overlap because the labels overlap perfectly too (assuming students haven't messed with them).

Investigate/Conjecture

Students will find that whatever they try, the two triangles with the given sides will be congruent. They can confirm this by constructing the interior of one, cutting, pasting, and dragging the free copy into the other triangle. It should fit perfectly if they haven't rotated either triangle. Students should conjecture:

If two triangles have three pairs of congruent sides, then the triangles are congruent (SSS).

Explore More

1. This demonstrates triangle inequality in the same way as the investigation of that name.

Demonstration: Triangle Congruence—AAA?

In this demonstration you'll work with a sample sketch to see how many different triangles you can create given the three angles.

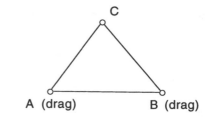

Sketch

Step 1: Open the sketch: **AAA** (Mac) or **3triangl\congrnce\aaa.gsp** (Windows). You'll see a triangle and three separate angles.

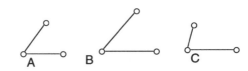

Step 2: Drag one of the points on the sides of the separate angles, ∠A or ∠B. Notice that ∠C changes as you do this. You can't directly change its measure because it was constructed so that the measures of the three given angles add up to 180°.

Step 3: Drag point *A* or point *B* in the triangle. Again, you can't drag point *C* in the triangle, because ∠C is determined by ∠A and ∠B.

Investigate

Using three given angles, is it possible to make two triangles that are not congruent? If you were given two triangles with three pairs of congruent angles, would that be enough information to guarantee that the triangles were congruent?

Conjecture: Write a conjecture.

_____

_____

_____

_____

Explore More

1. Mark some point as center and dilate △ABC using the Transform menu. Your two triangles are not congruent. Have their angles changed?

2. Change the given angles ∠A or ∠B so that ∠C disappears. What happened to ∠C? When is it impossible for two particular angles to be in the same triangle?

Demonstration: Triangle Congruence—AAA?

Student Audience: High School

Prerequisites: Students should know the term **congruent**.

Sketchpad Proficiency: Beginner

Class Time: 10-20 minutes. You may want to do this activity in the same class period as other triangle congruence investigations: SSS, SAS, SSA, ASA.

Sketch Needed: **AAA** (Mac) or **3triangl\congrnce\aaa.gsp** (Windows)

Construction Tips

Students don't need to construct anything in this activity; instead they manipulate a pre-made sketch.

Point C in the triangle cannot be dragged freely.

Investigate/Conjecture

Students should observe that even though the three angles in the triangle are determined by the givens, the triangle can be enlarged or shrunk to any size. They should make the conjecture:

If the three angles in one triangle are congruent to the three angles in another triangle, the triangles are the same shape, but not necessarily the same size.

This wording assumes students are not yet familiar with the concept of similarity.

Explore More

1. The angles in the dilated triangle are congruent to corresponding angles in the original. Clearly the triangles are not congruent. They are similar.

2. As angles A or B are dragged so that their sum approaches 180°, the measure of $\angle C$ approaches 0. When the sum of angles A and B exceeds 180°, $\angle C$ ceases to exist.

Demonstration: Triangle Congruence—SAS?

In this demonstration you'll work with a sample sketch to see if you can make two non-congruent triangles given two sides and the angle between them.

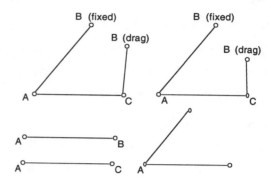

Sketch

Step 1: Open the sketch: **SAS** (Mac) or **3triangl\congrnce\sas.gsp** (Windows). You'll see two broken triangles and two separate segments and an angle.

Step 2: Drag different parts of the broken triangles. You'll find that some lengths and angles can't be changed because they're constrained by the "givens."

Step 3: Drag endpoint *B* (drag) of $\overline{BC}$ in one broken triangle so that the points *B* overlap, forming a triangle.

Step 4: With the second broken triangle, see if you can form a triangle with a different size and/or shape.

Step 5: Change the given sides and/or angle and try the experiment again.

Investigate

Could you form non-congruent triangles given two sides and the angle between them? If you were given two triangles with two pairs of corresponding sides and the angles between them congruent, would that be enough information to determine that the triangles were congruent?

Conjecture: Write a conjecture below.

_____

_____

_____

_____

Explore More

See if you can create this demo sketch yourself. Use the script **Duplicate Angle CW** (Mac) or **1lineang\dupangcw.gss** (Windows) or your own utility script to duplicate angles and use the Construct menu command Circle By Center+Radius to duplicate segments.

Demonstration: Triangle Congruence—SAS?

Student Audience: High School

Prerequisites: Students should know the term **congruent**.

Sketchpad Proficiency: Beginner

Class Time: 10-20 minutes. You may want to do this activity in the same class period as other triangle congruence investigations: SSS, AAA, SSA, ASA.

Sketch Needed: **SAS** (Mac) or **3triangl\congrnce\sas.gsp** (Windows)

Construction Tips

Students don't need to construct anything in this activity; instead they manipulate a pre-made sketch.

Only one of the points *B* on each triangle can be dragged freely.

Investigate/Conjecture

Students will find that the only triangles they can make given two sides and the angle between them are congruent. They should make the conjecture:

If two sides and the angle between them in one triangle are congruent to two sides and the angle between them in another triangle, then the triangles are congruent.

Demonstration: Triangle Congruence—SSA?

In this demonstration you'll work with a sample sketch to see how many different triangles can be created given two sides and an angle not between them.

Sketch

Step 1: Open the sketch **SSA** (Mac) or **3triangl\congrnce\ssa.gsp** (Windows). You'll see two broken triangles and two separate segments and an angle.

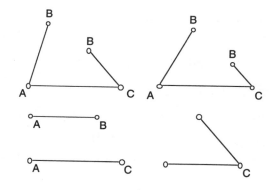

Step 2: Drag different parts of the broken triangles. You'll find that some lengths and angles can't be changed because they're "given."

Step 3: Drag the points *B* in one broken triangle so that they overlap, forming a triangle.

Step 4: See if you can connect the points *B* in the other triangle so that the two triangles are not congruent.

Step 5: Change the given sides and/or angle and try the experiment again.

Investigate

How many different triangles can you form given two sides and the angle not between them? Do two sides and an angle not between them uniquely determine a triangle? If you were given two triangles with two pairs of corresponding sides and the angles not between them congruent, would that be enough information to determine that the triangles were congruent?

Conjecture: Write your conjectures below.

_____

_____

_____

_____

_____

_____

Explore More

By changing the given sides and angle, you'll find that in some cases you can't create any triangle and with some combinations you can create only one triangle. Under what conditions can you create only one triangle given two sides and an angle not between them?

Demonstration: Triangle Congruence—SSA?

Student Audience: High School

Prerequisites: Students should know the term **congruent**.

Sketchpad Proficiency: Beginner

Class Time: 10-20 minutes. You may want to do this activity in the same class period as other triangle congruence investigations: SSS, AAA, SAS, ASA.

Sketch Needed: SSA (Mac) or **3triangl\congrnce\ssa.gsp** (Windows)

Construction Tips

Students don't need to construct anything in this activity; instead they manipulate a pre-made sketch.

Step 3: The length of segment $\overline{AB}$ in the triangle is fixed but the angle is not. Move that point B so that it lies on $\overline{CB}$ in the triangle. Now drag the endpoint B of $\overline{CB}$ (whose angle is fixed) until the B's overlap.

Investigate/Conjecture

Students will find that they can make two non-congruent triangles as shown:

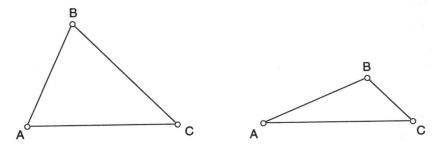

Students should make the conjecture:

If two sides and the angle not between them in one triangle are congruent to two sides and the angle not between them in another triangle, then the triangles are not necessarily congruent.

Explore More

The length of given segment $\overline{AB}$ can be adjusted so that $\overline{AB}$ just brushes $\overline{CB}$. In this case, you can make only congruent triangles, and $\angle ABC$ is a right angle.

Demonstration: Triangle Congruence—ASA?

In this demonstration you'll work with a sample sketch to see if you can create two different triangles given two angles and the side between them.

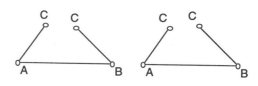

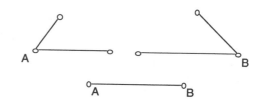

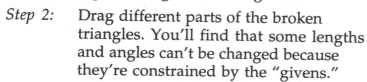

Sketch

Step 1: Open the sample sketch **ASA** (Mac) or **3triangl\congrnce\asa.gsp** (Windows). You'll see two broken triangles and two separate angles and a segment.

Step 2: Drag different parts of the broken triangles. You'll find that some lengths and angles can't be changed because they're constrained by the "givens."

Step 3: Drag the points C in one broken triangle so that they overlap, forming a triangle.

Step 4: See if you can connect points C in the other broken triangle to create a second triangle, not congruent to the first.

Step 5: Change the given sides and/or angle and try the experiment again.

Investigate

Could you form non-congruent triangles given two angles and the side between them? If you were given two triangles with two pairs of corresponding angles and the sides between them congruent, would that be enough information to determine that the triangles were congruent?

Conjecture: Write a conjecture.

_____

_____

_____

_____

Explore More

Just for kicks, see if you can make the two points C overlap by changing the givens instead of dragging the points themselves.

Demonstration: Triangle Congruence—ASA?

Student Audience: High School

Prerequisites: Students should know the term **congruent**.

Sketchpad Proficiency: Beginner

Sketch Needed: **ASA** (Mac) or **3triangl\congrnce\asa.gsp**

Class Time: 10-20 minutes. You may want to do this activity in the same class period as other triangle congruence investigations: SSS, AAA, SAS, SSA.

Construction Tips

Students don't need to construct anything in this activity; instead they manipulate a pre-made sketch.

Step 3: The lengths of segments $\overline{AC}$ and $\overline{BC}$ in the triangle are not fixed but the angles are. Move one point C so that $\overline{AC}$ is quite long. Now drag the other point C so that it lies on $\overline{AC}$. Drag the first C back so that the C's overlap.

Investigate/Conjecture

Students will find that the only triangles they can make are congruent. They should conjecture:

If two angles and the side between them in one triangle are congruent to two angles and the side between them in another triangle, then the triangles are congruent.

Explore More

There's nothing new to be learned in this explore more suggestion, but it's a fun way to manipulate the sketch. You might also ask students to try to make a sketch like this using utility scripts for duplicating angles.

Chapter 4
Quadrilaterals

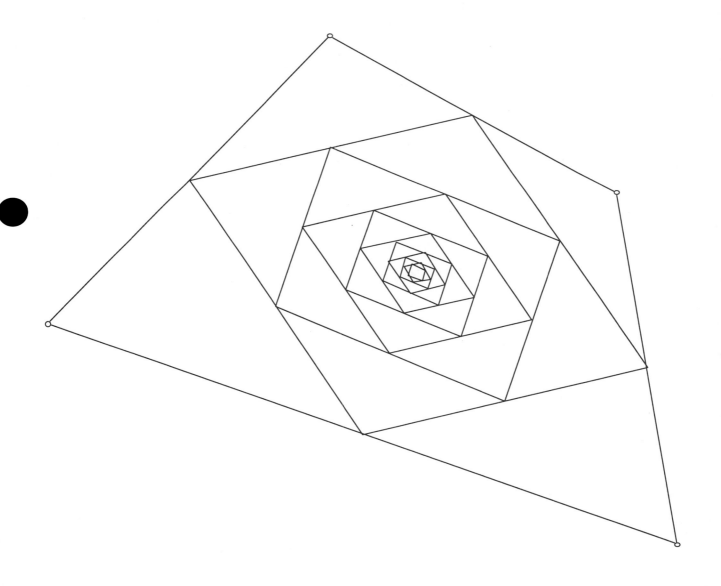

Investigation: Defining Special Quadrilaterals

Parallelograms, rectangles, rhombuses, and squares have special properties that distinguish them from other quadrilaterals. In this investigation, you'll experiment with these shapes to discover what makes them different from "ordinary" quadrilaterals and from one another.

Investigate

Open the sketch **Special Quads** (Mac) or **4quads\spquads.gsp** (Windows). Drag various parts of these quadrilaterals. Each quadrilateral has a different set of constraints in its construction that keeps it what it is. For example, no matter what part you drag, the square stays a square. What properties does a square have that makes it a square? What about the rhombus? You can drag its vertices to make different shapes but you'll still have a rhombus. What

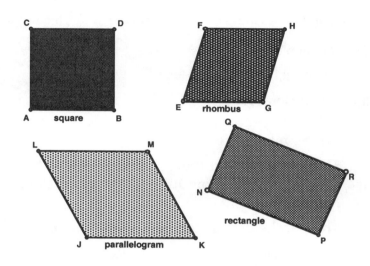

properties define the rhombus? Measure lengths, slopes, and angles to discover the properties that define these shapes.

As you manipulate these shapes, you'll also notice that some can be made into others. This may help you in your definitions. Try the following:

1. Manipulate the shapes so that all four are identical. What shape is this? Is this the only shape that all four can be? _____

2. Are there any shapes that exactly two of the four shapes can be? What are they? _____

3. Make one of the shapes a shape that none of the others can be. What is this shape?_____

Write your definitions below. Compare your definitions with your partner or group. Make your definitions as concise and accurate as possible.

Parallelogram: _____

_____

Rectangle: _____

_____

Rhombus:_____

_____

Square: _____

_____

Explore More: See if you can come up with methods for constructing special quadrilaterals.

Investigation: Defining Quadrilaterals

Student Audience: Middle School/High School

Prerequisites: Students should know that lines with equal slopes are parallel.

Sketchpad Proficiency: Beginner

Example Sketch: **Special Quads** (Mac) or **4quads\spquads.gsp** (Windows)

Class Time: 30-45 minutes, depending on how much time you give students to discuss their definitions

Construction Tips

Students use a pre-made sketch for this investigation.

Investigate/Conjecture

1. All four of the shapes can be made into a square. This is the only shape that all four can be made into.

2. The rectangle and the parallelogram can be made into a rectangle that's not a square and the rhombus and the parallelogram can be made into a rhombus that's not a square.

3. The parallelogram can be a shape that is not a rectangle, rhombus, or square.

Interestingly, there is no shape that exactly three of the four shapes can be made into.

Students using their findings from the first part of the investigation might word their definitions this way.

Parallelogram: A parallelogram is a quadrilateral with two pairs of parallel sides.

Rectangle: A rectangle is a parallelogram (quadrilateral) with a (four) right (equal) angle(s).

Rhombus: A rhombus is a quadrilateral with four equal sides.

Square: A square is a quadrilateral with equal sides and equal angles. Or, a square is rhombus and a rectangle.

Other definitions are certainly possible, but you should ask students to trim their definitions of any unnecessary facts. For example, if a parallelogram had a different name, it might be defined as "a quadrilateral with equal opposite sides." But "a quadrilateral with equal and parallel opposite sides" is not as concise as it could be.

Exploring Geometry

Exploration: Properties of Quadrilaterals

Use the Segment tool to construct any quadrilateral and its diagonals. Measure the lengths of the sides, diagonals, and angles. (Measure any other distances you think might be important.) Manipulate the quadrilateral to make it approximate a rectangle, then a parallelogram, rhombus, square, kite, and finally, a trapezoid. List any properties you discover below or on a separate piece of paper:

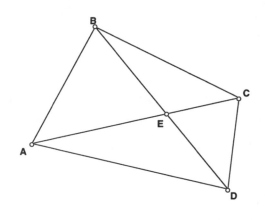

Quadrilateral: _____

_____

_____

Rectangle: _____

_____

_____

_____

start with this

Parallelogram: _____

_____

_____

_____

drag top

Rhombus: _____

_____

_____

_____

drag side
until sides
are equal

Square: _____

_____

_____

_____

drag top

Kite: _____

_____

_____

_____

drag vertex

Trapezoid: _____

_____

_____

Exploration: Properties of Quadrilaterals

Student Audience: Middle School/High School

Prerequisites: Students should know the names and definitions of quadrilaterals: **parallelogram**, **rectangle**, **rhombus**, **square**, **trapezoid**, and **kite** (a quadrilateral with two distinct pairs of adjacent, congruent sides.) Students should know some or all of the following terms: **parallel**, **supplementary**, **diagonal**, **perpendicular bisector**, **consecutive angles**, and, **opposite angles**.

Sketchpad Proficiency: Beginner

Class Time: 35-50 minutes

Construction Tips: The relatively long time suggested gives students time to write a lot. The initial construction will take seconds. Students need to understand that all they've constructed is an ordinary quadrilateral. They'll manipulate it to *appear* to be a parallelogram, but nothing in its construction guarantees that it is precisely a parallelogram. Point out that when they approximate these figures, measures will be approximate. You don't want conjectures like, "Opposite sides of a parallelogram differ in length by .02 units." Students can measures slopes, angles, and side lengths to confirm that they've manipulated the quadrilateral into the desired shape.

Rectangles are easiest to create freehand, because computer screen resolution makes it easy to tell when you have a horizontal or vertical line. Hold down the Shift key to constrain segments to 15° intervals, making it easy to construct horizontal and vertical segments. If students follow the suggested dragging sequence, they'll get relatively accurate results.

Investigate/Conjecture: Students' lists of properties will vary widely. Some you might hope to see include:

Rectangle: Has four right angles; opposite sides are equal; opposite sides are parallel; diagonals are equal; diagonals bisect each other.

Parallelogram: Opposite sides are parallel; opposite sides are equal; opposite angles are equal; consecutive angles are supplementary; diagonals bisect each other.

Rhombus: All four sides are equal; opposite sides are parallel; opposite angles are equal; consecutive angles are supplementary; diagonals are perpendicular bisectors of each other.

Square: All four sides are equal; has four right angles; opposite sides are parallel; diagonals are equal; diagonals are perpendicular bisectors of each other (all the properties of rectangles and rhombuses).

Kite: Has two distinct pairs of consecutive, equal sides; diagonals are perpendicular.

Trapezoid: Has one pair of parallel sides. If isosceles, diagonals are equal.

Explore More: A good follow-up activity is to organize these findings in a chart. Have students make a chart with rows for different quadrilaterals and columns for properties. Check off boxes to match quadrilaterals with properties. Use these findings to create a classification tree or Venn diagram to classify quadrilaterals. You might have students debate their classification schemes. For example, some students may want to consider parallelograms as special case trapezoids (defining trapezoid as having *at least* one pair of parallel sides). Students may also have different opinions as to whether rhombuses are kites.

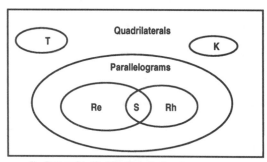

T = Trapezoid, K = Kite, Re = Rectangle,
S = Square, and Rh = Rhombus

©1996 by Key Curriculum Press   Exploring Geometry

Investigation: Properties of Parallelograms

A **parallelogram** is a quadrilateral with the opposite sides parallel. But in this investigation, you'll discover that a parallelogram has many special properties besides parallel opposite sides.

Sketch

Step 1: Construct $\overline{AB}$ and $\overline{AC}$.

Step 2: Construct a line parallel to $\overline{AB}$ through C and a line parallel to $\overline{AC}$ through B.

Step 3: Construct $\overline{CD}$ and $\overline{DB}$, where D is the point of intersection of the lines.

Step 4: Construct diagonals $\overline{AD}$ and $\overline{BC}$ and their point of intersection, E.

Step 5: Hide the lines. $ABDC$ is a parallelogram.

Investigate

Measure the four angles of parallelogram $ABDC$. Use Calculate to investigate relationships among these angles. Measure the lengths of the four sides. How are the sides related? (Make sure to manipulate your parallelogram to confirm that these relationships hold for all parallelograms.) Measure AE, ED, CE, and EB. What can you conjecture about the diagonals of a parallelogram? What kind of symmetry does a parallelogram have?

Conjecture: Write your conjectures below.

_____

_____

_____

_____

_____

_____

_____

Present Your Findings

Compare and discuss your results with your partner or group. To present your findings, you could print a captioned sketch showing measures that illustrate the properties of parallelograms you discovered in this investigation.

Explore More

1. Adjust your parallelogram so that it appears to be a rectangle. (It's not difficult to make opposite sides horizontal and vertical.) Can you make another conjecture about the diagonals of a parallelogram that is a rectangle?

2. Use the properties of parallelograms that you just discovered to invent new ways of constructing a parallelogram or rectangle. How many ways can you come up with? Here's a hint for one quick way to construct a parallelogram using its symmetry properties: Construct a triangle and the midpoint of one side. Do a rotation. (We'll leave it to you to figure out what to rotate and by how much.)

Investigation: Properties of Parallelograms

Student Audience: Middle School/High School

Prerequisites: Students should know the definition of a **parallelogram**.

Sketchpad Proficiency: Beginner

Class Time: 20-40 minutes

Example Scripts: **Parallelogram Investigation** and **Parallelograms 1-4** (Mac) or **4quads\parinv.gss** and **4quads\parlgrms\para1.gss**, etc. (Windows)

Construction Tips

Step 2: These parallel lines must be constructed one at a time.

Step 3: $\overline{CD}$ and $\overline{DB}$ lie on the lines.

Investigate/Conjecture

The relationship between opposite angles will be obvious (they're equal) but students may need to use Calculate to discover that consecutive angles are supplementary. (You may want to introduce the term **consecutive angles** to describe angles that share a side.) To investigate symmetry, they should construct the Polygon Interior and try to reflect it (that won't work) or rotate it (that will work—180° around the center) so that the image still fits in the figure. Students should make the following conjectures

Opposite sides in a parallelogram are equal.

Opposite angles in a parallelogram are equal.

Consecutive angles in a parallelogram are supplementary.

Diagonals in a parallelogram bisect each other.

Students may also come up with conjectures like:

The diagonals in a parallelogram divide the parallelogram into four pairs of congruent triangles.

A parallelogram has 180° rotation symmetry.

Explore More

1. A Sketchpad parallelogram nicely illustrates that a rectangle is also a parallelogram. The construction is based strictly on the definition of a parallelogram, yet the figure can be manipulated into a rectangle. Students should conjecture that in a rectangle, diagonals are equal. They may also make conjectures about the angles in a rectangle.

2. A parallelogram can also be constructed by constructing a triangle and the midpoint of one side. Rotate the triangle 180° about this midpoint. Another method for constructing a parallelogram uses the fact that opposite sides are equal: Construct two consecutive sides. From the endpoint of one side, construct a circle with that center and radius the other side. Do the same with the endpoint of the other side. Construct segments to where these circles intersect. Here's a method that uses the fact that diagonals of a parallelogram bisect each other: Construct a segment and its midpoint. (This will be one diagonal of the parallelogram. Construct a circle with center the midpoint and any radius. Construct a line through the center and radius-defining point. Construct a diameter of the circle. (This is the other diagonal of the parallelogram.) These methods are illustrated by the scripts Parallelograms 2-4.

3. (Not on student activity sheet) Print the text of one or more of the parallelogram scripts and give this to students. Tell them these are "mystery scripts," and their job is to figure out what they construct. Try this with or without computers.

Investigation: Properties of Rectangles

A **rectangle** is a quadrilateral with four right angles. In this investigation, you'll discover that a rectangle has many special properties besides its equal angles.

Sketch

Step 1: Construct $\overline{AB}$.

Step 2: Construct lines perpendicular to $\overline{AB}$ through A and B.

Step 3: Construct $\overline{AC}$, where C is on one of these lines.

Step 4: Construct a line through C perpendicular to $\overline{AC}$.

Step 5: Construct $\overline{CD}$ and $\overline{DB}$, where D is the intersection of the perpendicular lines through C and B.

Step 6: Hide the lines.

Step 7: Construct diagonals $\overline{AD}$ and $\overline{BC}$ and their point of intersection, E.

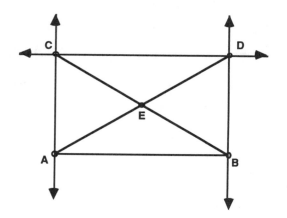

Investigate

Measure the lengths and slopes of the four sides of rectangle $ABDC$. How are the sides related? (Make sure to manipulate your rectangle to confirm that these relationships hold for all rectangles.) Measure AE, ED, CE, and EB. What can you conjecture about the diagonals of a rectangle? What kind of symmetry does a rectangle have?

Conjecture: Write your conjectures below.

_____

_____

_____

_____

_____

_____

_____

Present Your Findings

Compare and discuss your results with your partner or group. To present your findings, you could print a captioned sketch showing measures that illustrate the properties of rectangles you discovered in this investigation.

Explore More

Use the properties of rectangles that you just discovered to invent new ways of constructing a rectangle. How many ways can you come up with? Here's a hint for one way to construct a rectangle using its symmetry properties: Construct a pair of perpendicular lines. Construct a point not on either line. The rest is up to you.

Investigation: Properties of Rectangles

Student Audience: Middle School/High School

Prerequisites: Students should know the definition of a **rectangle**.

Sketchpad Proficiency: Beginner

Class Time: 20-40 minutes

Example Scripts: **Rectangles 1-6** (Mac) and **4quads\rectngls\rect1.gss**, etc. (Windows)

Construction Tips

Step 2: These perpendicular lines can be constructed simultaneously.

Step 6: Students may need to construct segments $\overline{CD}$ and $\overline{DB}$, if they didn't in step 5.

Investigate/Conjecture

If students investigate symmetry, they should construct the polygon interior. Rotate it or reflect it so that the interior image still fits in the figure. Students should make the following conjectures:

Opposite sides in a rectangle are equal.

Diagonals in a rectangle are equal and bisect each other.

Students may also come up with conjectures like:

The diagonals in a rectangle divide the rectangle into four pairs of congruent isosceles triangles.

A rectangle has 180° rotation symmetry and two lines of reflection symmetry through midpoints of opposite sides.

Explore More

1. Construct a pair of perpendicular lines and a point not on either line. Reflect the point across one line, then reflect the point and its image across the other line. These four points are vertices of a rectangle.

    Here's another easy method: Construct a segment and its midpoint. This segment will be a diagonal of the rectangle. Construct a circle with this segment as a diameter. Construct a line through the circle's center (not collinear with the segment). The intersections of this line with the circle are the endpoints of the rectangle's other (equal) diagonal.

2. (Not on student activity sheet) Print the text of one or more of the rectangle scripts and give them to students. Tell them these are "mystery scripts," and their job is to figure out what they construct. Try this with or without computers.

Investigation: Properties of Rhombuses

A **rhombus** is an equilateral quadrilateral. In this investigation, you'll discover many other properties of rhombuses.

Sketch

Step 1:   Construct circle AB and $\overline{AB}$.

Step 2:   Construct $\overline{AC}$, where C is on circle AB.

Step 3:   Construct circles BA and CA.

Step 4:   Construct $\overline{BD}$ and $\overline{CD}$, where D is a point of intersection of the two circles in step 3.

Step 5:   Construct diagonals $\overline{AD}$ and $\overline{BC}$ and their point of intersection, E.

Step 6:   Hide the circles.

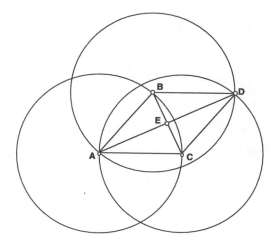

Investigate

The figure you've constructed is a rhombus because its four sides are equal. (Why?) Besides being equal, what can you say about opposite sides? Measure slopes. What kind of special quadrilateral is a rhombus? What conjectures can you make about the diagonals of a rhombus? Measure $\angle BED$. Measure the diagonals' lengths and the lengths of $\overline{BE}$ and $\overline{AE}$. Measure angles BAC, BAE, ABD, and ABE. (Make sure to manipulate your rhombus to confirm these relationships hold for all rhombuses.) What kind of symmetry does a rhombus have?

Conjecture: Write your conjectures below.

_____

_____

_____

_____

_____

_____

Present Your Findings

Compare and discuss your results with your partner or group. To present your findings, you could print a captioned sketch showing measures that illustrate the properties of rhombuses you discovered in this investigation.

Explore More

1. Adjust your rhombus so that one of its angles is 90°. What shape have you created? Is it still a rhombus? Does this give you an idea for a definition of this shape?

2. Use the properties you've just discovered to invent new ways to construct a rhombus. How many methods can you come up with?

Investigation: Properties of Rhombuses

Student Audience: Middle School/High School

Prerequisites: Students should know the definition of a **rhombus**.

Sketchpad Proficiency: Beginner

Class Time: 20-40 minutes

Example Scripts: **Rhombuses 1-8** (Mac) or **4quads\rhombses\rhombus1.gss**, etc. (Windows). Rhombus 2 is the method described in the steps of this activity.

Construction Tips

Step 3: Press and hold on point *B*, drag, and release on point *A*. Repeat for *C* and *A*.

Step 4: Make sure students use the correct point of intersection to get a rhombus.

Investigate/Conjecture

The four sides are equal because they're radii of three congruent circles (you used radii of the first circle for the second and third circles). If students investigate symmetry, they should construct the Polygon Interior. Rotate it or reflect it to see if the image still fits in the figure. Students should make the following conjectures:

Opposite sides of a rhombus are parallel. (A rhombus is a parallelogram.)

The diagonals of a rhombus are perpendicular bisectors of each other.

The diagonals of a rhombus bisect the angles.

Opposite angles of a rhombus are equal and consecutive angles are supplementary.

The diagonals of a rhombus are axes of reflection symmetry.

A rhombus has 180° rotation symmetry.

Explore More

1. A Sketchpad rhombus nicely illustrates that a square is also a rhombus. The construction is based strictly on the definition of a rhombus, yet the figure can be manipulated into a square. Students could define a square as a rhombus with a (four) right angle(s).

2. This question is the subject of a separate investigation, Using Properties of a Rhombus. See teacher comments for that investigation for alternate constructions of a rhombus. The example scripts **Rhombuses 1-8** (Mac) or **4quads\rhombses\rhombus1.gss** etc. (Windows) are based on that investigation.

3. (Not on student activity sheet) Print the text of one or more of the rhombus scripts and give this to students. Tell them these are "mystery scripts," and their job is to figure out what they construct. Try this with or without computers.

 Exploring Geometry

Investigation: Midpoints in a Quadrilateral

In this investigation, you'll discover something surprising about the quadrilateral formed by joining the midpoints of another quadrilateral.

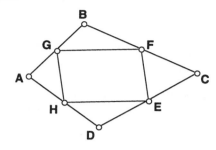

Sketch

Step 1: Construct quadrilateral *ABCD*.

Step 2: Construct the midpoints of the four sides: *E*, *F*, *G*, and *H*.

Step 3: Connect these midpoints to form quadrilateral *EFGH*.

Investigate

Drag the vertices or sides of the outer quadrilateral. Make sure to drag it into a variety of sizes and shapes, including concave quadrilaterals. What do you notice about the midpoint quadrilateral? What can you measure to confirm this conjecture?

Conjecture: Write your conjectures below.

_____

_____

_____

Present Your Findings

Compare and discuss your findings with your partner or group. To present your findings you could:

1. Create a commented script that does the construction and describes your conjectures.

2. Print a captioned sketch that shows several examples of quadrilaterals and their midpoint quadrilaterals. Show measures that support your conjectures.

Explore More

1. Draw a diagonal of your original quadrilateral. With this diagonal, can you explain why your conjecture about midpoint quadrilaterals is true?

2. What is the midpoint quadrilateral of a midpoint quadrilateral?

3. What's the midpoint quadrilateral of a trapezoid? An isosceles trapezoid? A parallelogram? A kite? A rhombus? A rectangle? A square?

4. Record a script to construct a quadrilateral and its midpoints. Before you stop recording, select the midpoints in order and click Loop to record a recursive step. Experiment with playing this script to different recursion depths.

5. Construct the polygon interiors of a quadrilateral and its midpoint quadrilateral. Measure their areas. What can you conjecture about these areas?

6. Under what conditions is a midpoint quadrilateral a rectangle? A rhombus? A square? See if you can construct the most general quadrilateral whose midpoint quadrilateral is one of these.

Investigation: Midpoints in a Quadrilateral

Student Audience: Middle School/High School

Prerequisites: To make conjectures, students should be able to identify **parallelograms**, **kites**, and other special quadrilaterals.

Sketchpad Proficiency: Beginner

Class Time: 20-40 minutes

Example Sketches: **Midpoint Quadrilaterals** and **Special Midpoint Quads** (Mac) or **4quads\mdptquad.gsp** and **4quads\mdptqua2.gsp** (Windows)

Construction Tips

This is an easy construction.

Step 2: If students select all four sides, they can construct the midpoints simultaneously. A keyboard shortcut for Point At Midpoint is ⌘M (Mac) or Ctrl+M (Windows).

Investigate/Conjecture

Students should come quickly to the following conjecture:

The quadrilateral connecting the midpoints of any quadrilateral is a parallelogram.

There's a great deal more to explore in this investigation, and students should be encouraged to try some of the Explore More questions.

Explore More

1. A diagonal divides the quadrilateral into two triangles. Two sides of the midpoint quadrilateral are midsegments in these triangles and are hence parallel to the diagonal (and, thus, each other).

2. A midpoint quadrilateral in general is a parallelogram. A midpoint quadrilateral of a midpoint quadrilateral is still just a parallelogram.

3. The conditions under which a midpoint quadrilateral is a special parallelogram are not obvious. In general, the midpoint quadrilateral of a trapezoid is a parallelogram, of an isosceles trapezoid is a rectangle, of a parallelogram is a parallelogram, of a kite is a rectangle, of a rhombus is a rectangle, of a rectangle is a rhombus, of a square is a square. See 6 below for more discussion of special midpoint quadrilaterals.

4. Successive midpoints quadrilaterals are alternately similar, that is, the third midpoint quadrilateral is a parallelogram similar to the first. The fourth is similar to the second, and so on. These parallelograms converge on the point of intersection of segments connecting midpoints of opposite sides.

5. The area of a midpoint quadrilateral is half the area of the original quadrilateral.

6. The example sketch **Special Midpoint Quads** (Mac) or **4quads\mdptqua2.gsp** (Windows) illustrates the most general quadrilaterals whose midpoint quadrilaterals are special parallelograms. This sketch is the subject of the Exploration: Special Midpoint Quadrilaterals. The midpoint quadrilateral of any quadrilateral whose diagonals are equal is a rhombus. The midpoint quadrilateral of any quadrilateral whose diagonals are perpendicular is a rectangle. The midpoint quadrilateral of any quadrilateral whose diagonals are equal and perpendicular is a square.

 Exploring Geometry

Exploration: Special Midpoint Quadrilaterals

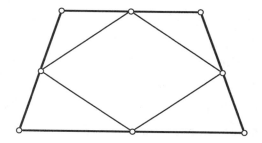

You may already know that if you connect the midpoints of any quadrilateral in consecutive order, you always form a parallelogram. Some special cases yield special parallelograms. For example, the midpoint quadrilateral of an isosceles trapezoid is a rhombus. Is the isosceles trapezoid the only quadrilateral whose midpoint quadrilateral is a rhombus? In this exploration, you'll try to discover the most general types of quadrilaterals whose midpoint quadrilaterals are special parallelograms.

Investigate

Before you open the sketch you are to explore, you might want to experiment on your own with the following constructions:

Construct the most general quadrilateral whose midpoint quadrilateral is a rhombus.

Construct the most general quadrilateral whose midpoint quadrilateral is a rectangle.

Construct the most general quadrilateral whose midpoint quadrilateral is a parallelogram.

Conjecture

After you've tried the constructions for awhile, open the sketch **Special Midpoint Quads** (Mac) or **4quads\mdptqua2.gsp** (Windows). Manipulate these quadrilaterals. What properties do they have? Write these properties below:

Midpoint Quadrilateral is a rhombus: _____

_____

Midpoint Quadrilateral is a rectangle: _____

_____

Midpoint Quadrilateral is a square: _____

_____

Try again to construct shapes with the above properties.

Present Your Findings

Compare and discuss your findings with your partner or group. To present your findings you could:

1. Create a commented script that constructs a quadrilateral with a special midpoint quadrilateral.

2. Print a captioned sketch that shows several examples of quadrilaterals and their midpoint quadrilaterals. Show measures that support your conjectures.

Explore More

Explain why the quadrilateral whose midpoint quadrilateral is a rhombus, rectangle, or square has the properties that it does.

Exploration: Special Midpoint Quadrilaterals

Student Audience: Middle School/High School

Prerequisites: Students should be familiar with properties of parallelograms, rectangles, rhombuses, and squares. They should know that a midpoint quadrilateral of any quadrilateral is a parallelogram. (They can discover this in the Investigation: Midpoints in a Quadrilateral.)

Sketchpad Proficiency: Experienced User

Class Time: 20-40 minutes (depends on how long you give students to explore before they open the sketch)

Sketch Needed: **Special Midpoint Quads** (Mac) or **4quads\mdptqua2.gsp** (Windows)

Investigate/Conjecture

Students are unlikely on first try to come up with the surprising, most general quadrilaterals that yield special midpoint quadrilaterals. They may not even identify what's special about the quadrilaterals in the sketch without a hint. If they seem stuck for too long, give them this big hint: construct the diagonals of the quadrilaterals. In time, they should come up with the following properties:

Midpoint quadrilateral is a rhombus: diagonals of the original quadrilateral are equal.

Midpoint quadrilateral is a rectangle: diagonals of the original quadrilateral are perpendicular.

Midpoint quadrilateral is a square: diagonals of the original quadrilateral are equal and perpendicular.

Even more surprisingly, these properties hold for non-convex quadrilaterals, if you consider diagonals that fall outside the figure.

Explore More

Again, drawing diagonals holds the key to why these shapes yield special midpoint quadrilaterals. For example, a side of a midpoint quadrilateral is always half the length of and parallel to a diagonal of the original quadrilateral. In the case where the diagonals are equal, the sides of the midpoint quadrilateral are equal, and so the midpoint quadrilateral is a rhombus.

Exploration: Using Properties of Rectangles

Use what you know about the properties of rectangles, or just experiment, to come up with as many different ways as you can to construct a rectangle with Sketchpad. Consider how you might use diagonals, and don't forget to use the Transform menu.

In the space below, describe each method you used, and list the property or properties you used in each method. (Continue on a separate sheet, if necessary). Record scripts for each method. Which script is the most efficient (has the fewest steps)? Why?

Compare your findings with those of other students.

Method 1: _____

_____

_____

_____

Properties: _____

_____

_____

Method 2: _____

_____

_____

Properties: _____

_____

_____

Method 3: _____

_____

_____

Properties: _____

_____

_____

Method 4: _____

_____

_____

Properties: _____

_____

Exploration: Using Properties of Rectangles

Student Audience: High School

Prerequisites: Students should know several properties of rectangles such as:

A rectangle has four equal (90°) angles.

Diagonals in a rectangle are equal and bisect each other.

A rectangle has two lines of symmetry through midpoints of opposite sides.

A rectangle has 180° rotation symmetry.

Opposite sides of a rectangle are equal and parallel.

Sketchpad Proficiency: Experienced User

Class Time: 20-40 minutes (depends entirely on how long you choose to set students loose)

Example Scripts: **Rectangles 1-6** (Mac) or **4quads\rectngls\rect1.gss**, etc. (Windows)

Construction Tips: The longer you give students, the more methods they'll come up with. Make sure students manipulate their constructions after they make them to ensure that they stay rectangles. Also, encourage them to avoid creating "special rectangles," that is, rectangles that can't be manipulated into any shape or size. Here are some methods they may discover:

1. Construct a segment. Construct perpendicular lines through the endpoints. From a point on one of the perpendiculars, construct a perpendicular line (or a line parallel to the original segment). Property: a rectangle is a quadrilateral with four right angles.

2. Construct a segment $\overline{AB}$. Construct a line through A, perpendicular to $\overline{AB}$. Construct $\overline{AC}$ on this line. Construct a circle with center C and radius AB. Construct a circle with center B and radius AC. Construct $\overline{BD}$ and $\overline{CD}$, where D is the intersection of the circles. Properties: a rectangle has at least one right angle and the opposite sides are congruent.

3. Construct a segment $\overline{AB}$ and its midpoint, C. Construct circle CA. Construct ray $\overrightarrow{DC}$, where D is on the circle. Construct E, the intersection of the ray and the circle. Construct $\overline{AD}$, $\overline{DB}$, $\overline{DE}$, and $\overline{EA}$. Properties: The diagonals of a rectangle are equal and bisect each other.

4. Construct a segment $\overline{AB}$ and its midpoint C. Construct a line through C, perpendicular to $\overline{AB}$. Construct circle CD, where D is on the perpendicular line. Construct E, the other intersection of the circle with the line. Construct lines through D and E, perpendicular to $\overline{DE}$ (or parallel to $\overline{AB}$). Construct lines through A and B perpendicular to $\overline{AB}$ (or parallel to $\overline{DE}$). Properties: The segments connecting midpoints of opposite sides of a rectangle bisect each other and are perpendicular to the sides of the rectangle. A rectangle has two perpendicular lines of symmetry.

5. Construct a segment $\overline{AB}$. Construct a line perpendicular to $\overline{AB}$, through A. Construct $\overline{AC}$ on this line. Construct $\overline{CB}$ and D, the midpoint of $\overline{CB}$. Rotate A, $\overline{AB}$, and $\overline{AC}$ 180° about D. Properties: A rectangle has at least one right angle and has 180° rotation symmetry.

6. Construct two perpendicular lines. Construct a point not on either line. Reflect it across one of the lines. Now reflect the two points across the other line. Property: A rectangle has two perpendicular lines of symmetry.

Different methods are interesting because they yield different control points for manipulating the rectangle. The most efficient script can be made for the last method, though that script has three givens. Each of these methods has a corresponding example script.

Exploration: Using Properties of Rhombuses

Use what you know about the properties of rhombuses, or just experiment, to come up with as many different ways as you can to construct a rhombus with Sketchpad. Consider how you might use diagonals.

In the space below, describe each method you use, and list the property or properties you use in that method. (Continue on a separate sheet, if necessary). Record scripts for each method. Which script is the most efficient (has the fewest steps)? Why?

Compare your findings with those of other students.

Method 1: _____

_____

_____

_____

Properties: _____

_____

_____

Method 2: _____

_____

_____

_____

Properties: _____

_____

_____

Method 3: _____

_____

_____

_____

Properties: _____

_____

_____

Method 4: _____

_____

_____

_____

Properties: _____

_____

Exploration: Using Properties of Rhombuses

Student Audience: High School

Prerequisites: Students should know several properties of rhombuses such as:

A rhombus has four equal sides.

Diagonals in a rhombus are perpendicular bisectors of each other.

A rhombus has two lines of symmetry through opposite vertices.

A rhombus has 180° rotation symmetry.

Opposite sides of a rhombus are parallel.

Sketchpad Proficiency: Experienced User

Class Time: 20-40 minutes (depends on how long you choose to set students loose)

Example Scripts: **Rhombuses 1-6** (Mac) or **4quads\rhombses\rhombus1.gss**, etc. (Windows)

Construction Tips: The longer you give students, the more methods they'll come up with. Make sure students manipulate their constructions after they make them to ensure that they stay rhombuses. Also, encourage them to avoid creating "special rhombuses," that is, rhombuses that can't be manipulated into any shape or size. Here are some methods they may discover:

1. Construct circles *AB* and *BA*. Construct a rhombus connecting the centers and the two points of intersection of the circle. (This is a special rhombus, comprised of two equilateral triangles.) Property: A rhombus has four equal sides.

2. Construct circles *AB* and *BA*. Construct circle *CA*, where *C* is a point on circle *AB*. Construct *D* at the point of intersection of circles *BA* and *CA*. *ABDC* is a rhombus. Property: A rhombus has four equal sides.

3. Construct a circle *AB* and two radii. Construct a parallel to each radius through the endpoint of the other. Properties: A rhombus has equal consecutive sides and parallel opposite sides.

4. Construct a segment $\overline{AB}$ and its midpoint *C*. Construct a line through *C*, perpendicular to $\overline{AB}$. Construct circle *CD*, where *D* is on the perpendicular line. Construct *E*, the other intersection of the circle with the line. *ADBE* is a rhombus. Property: The diagonals of a rhombus bisect each other.

5. Construct circle *AB* and $\overline{BC}$ where *C* is on the circle. Reflect *A* across $\overline{BC}$. *ABA'C* is a rhombus. Properties: A rhombus has a pair of equal consecutive sides and a line of symmetry through their unshared endpoints.

6. Construct a segment $\overline{AB}$ (to be a diagonal) and its midpoint, *C*. Construct a perpendicular through *C*. Reflect *C* across $\overline{AB}$. *ACBC'* is a rhombus. Properties: The diagonals of a rhombus are perpendicular and are axes of reflection symmetry.

7. Construct a segment $\overline{AB}$ to serve as half a diagonal. Construct a perpendicular through *B* (or *A*). Construct a point *C* on the perpendicular. Rotate *A* and *C* 180° about *B*. *ACA'C'* is a rhombus. Properties: The diagonals of a rhombus are perpendicular and their point of intersection is a center of 180° rotation symmetry.

8. Construct a circle *AB* and *C* on the circle. Bisect angle *BAC*. Construct circle *BA* and point *D*, the intersection of this circle and the bisector. *ABDC* is a rhombus. Properties: The sides of a rhombus are equal and the diagonals bisect the angles.

Each of these methods has a corresponding example script.

Investigation: Properties of Isosceles Trapezoids

A **trapezoid** is a quadrilateral with exactly one pair of parallel sides. An isosceles trapezoid is just what you'd expect: its legs (the non-parallel sides) have equal length. In this activity, you'll construct an isosceles trapezoid and investigate its properties.

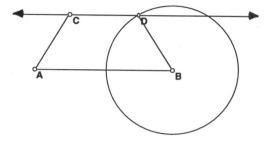

Sketch

Step 1:   Construct $\overline{AB}$ and point C, not on $\overline{AB}$.

Step 2:   Construct a line parallel to $\overline{AB}$, through C.

Step 3:   Construct $\overline{AC}$.

Step 4:   Construct a circle with center B and radius AC.

Step 5:   This circle intersects the line in two points. Construct $\overline{BD}$ and $\overline{DC}$ so that D is the point of intersection that gives a trapezoid. (What figure would you get if you used the other point of intersection?)

Step 6:   Hide the circle and line.

Step 7:   Construct $\overline{CD}$.

Investigate

Measure the four angles in your trapezoid. Drag points A, B, and C to make trapezoids of different sizes and shapes (make sure you note when your trapezoid turns into a parallelogram). What can you say about the base angles of an isosceles trapezoid? (Both of the parallel sides are considered bases, so a trapezoid has two pairs of base angles.) What about pairs that aren't at the same base? Investigate the diagonals in an isosceles trapezoid. Can you find a line of symmetry in an isosceles trapezoid? Construct this line, mark it as mirror in the Transform menu, and reflect the trapezoid to confirm that this is a line of symmetry.

Conjecture: Write your conjectures below (or on a separate sheet of paper).

_____

_____

_____

Present Your Findings: Compare and discuss your results with your partner or group. To present your findings you could print a captioned sketch showing different isosceles trapezoids and the measures of the angles. Write about your findings.

Explore More

1. The vertices in your construction can be dragged so that your figure is no longer a trapezoid. What shape can you make? Do your conjectures apply to this shape?

2. Investigate properties of non-isosceles trapezoids. Which, if any, of your conjectures still apply?

3. What happens if you drag C to D? If you drag C past D?

4. Try another construction for an isosceles trapezoid: Construct a line and two points not on the line. Reflect the two points across the line. You're on your own from there. Is there any other shape that can be formed with these four points?

Investigation: Properties of Isosceles Trapezoids

Student Audience: Middle School/High School

Prerequisites: This activity introduces the term **trapezoid**. Students should know the term **isosceles.**

Sketchpad Proficiency: Beginner

Example Sketch: **Isosceles Trapezoid** (Mac) or **4quads\isotrap.gsp** (Windows)

Class Time: 20-40 minutes. You may want to do this investigation if students have extra time after doing Properties of Isosceles Triangles.

Construction Tips

Step 5: If students choose the other intersection, they'll construct parallelograms instead of trapezoids.

Investigate/Conjecture

As its vertices are dragged, this figure can become other than an isosceles trapezoid. It's possible to manipulate it into a parallelogram or a self-intersecting polygon. Make sure students understand which properties they discover apply only to isosceles trapezoids. They should make the following conjectures:

The base angles of an isosceles trapezoid are equal.

Pairs of angles of different bases in an isosceles trapezoid are supplementary.

The diagonals of an isosceles trapezoid are equal.

An isosceles trapezoid has a line (an axis) of symmetry through the midpoints of the bases.

Explore More

1. The first conjecture doesn't apply when the isosceles trapezoid becomes a parallelogram. It does, however, apply to the case when it becomes self-intersecting. The second and third conjectures apply to parallelograms.

2. Pairs of angles of on the same side but different bases are supplementary in all trapezoids.

3. When *C* and *D* overlap, you have an isosceles triangle. When *C* moves past *D*, the trapezoid becomes self-intersecting. (The diagonals become the sides, and vice versa.)

4. The isosceles trapezoid constructed by this method can be manipulated into a rectangle.

Puzzle: Dissecting a Special Isosceles Trapezoid

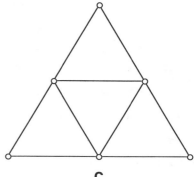

If you construct an equilateral triangle, it's easy to divide it into four congruent parts as shown. Now imagine you lop off the top triangle. That leaves you with an isosceles trapezoid. It's easy to divide such a trapezoid into three congruent parts: three equilateral triangles. Can you divide the isosceles trapezoid into *four* congruent parts?

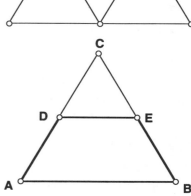

Sketch

Step 1: Construct an equilateral triangle using a script or any method you like.

Step 2: Construct D and E, the midpoints of $\overline{AC}$ and $\overline{BC}$.

Step 3: Hide $\overline{AC}$ and $\overline{BC}$.

Step 4: Construct $\overline{AD}$, $\overline{DE}$, and $\overline{BE}$.

Investigate

Now construct segments and move them as necessary to divide the trapezoid into four congruent parts. When you find a solution, sketch it in the trapezoid at right, or print your sketch.

Present Your Findings

Compare your solution with your partner or group. (Don't give your answer away, though, until your classmates have their own!) Make some measurements to make sure your parts are as close to congruent as you can make them.

Explore More

1. Can you make a construction that gives an *exact* solution to this puzzle?

2. Dissection puzzles can be found in many geometry books and other recreational mathematics books. Find some other puzzles and try them on Sketchpad.

Puzzle: Dissecting an Isosceles Trapezoid

Student Audience: Middle School/High School

Prerequisites: Students should know the terms **equilateral triangle**, **congruent**, and **isosceles trapezoid**. They should know how to construct an equilateral triangle with Sketchpad (or at least how to use a script to construct one).

Sketchpad Proficiency: Experienced User

Example Sketch: **Trapezoid Puzzle** (Mac) or **4quads\trappuzz.gsp** (Windows). Show all hiddens for solutions.

Class Time: 20-30 minutes

Construction Tips

Step 1: The script **3/Triangle (By Edge)** (Mac) or **regpoly\3byedge.gss** (Windows) can be used to construct the equilateral triangle. While an isosceles trapezoid can be constructed in a number of ways, the trapezoid needed for this problem must have 60° base angles and sides with length equal to the short base.

Investigate/Conjecture

Students are asked to construct an exact solution under Explore More. For the investigation, have them construct segments that can be moved along the sides of the trapezoid, so that they can experiment to find an answer. There are two solutions that we know of. Perhaps Sketchpad using students and teachers will find more:

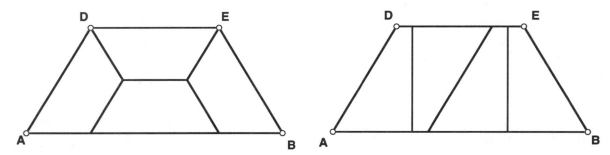

Explore More

1. There are a variety of ways to construct the solution shown at left. The key to the solution shown at right is that the shortest side of each piece is 1/8 the length of the short (top) base. Use midpoints, perpendiculars, and parallels to construct the solution.

Investigation: The Midsegment of a Trapezoid

The **midsegment** in a trapezoid connects the midpoints of the legs. In this activity, you'll investigate relationships between the midsegment and the bases of a trapezoid.

Sketch

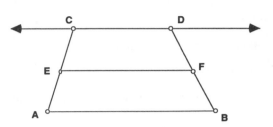

Step 1:   Construct $\overline{AB}$ and C not on $\overline{AB}$.

Step 2:   Construct a line through C, parallel to $\overline{AB}$.

Step 3:   Construct $\overline{CD}$ on this line and construct $\overline{AC}$ and $\overline{DB}$.

Step 4:   Hide the line. $ACDB$ is a trapezoid.

Step 5:   Construct E and F, the midpoints of $\overline{AC}$ and $\overline{BD}$.

Step 6:   Construct $\overline{EF}$. $\overline{EF}$ is the midsegment of the trapezoid.

Investigate

Measure CD, EF, and AB. Do you see a relationship? Drag various parts of the trapezoid and watch the the lengths of the midsegment $\overline{EF}$ and the bases $\overline{AB}$ and $\overline{CD}$. Use Calculate to check your conjecture about the relationship of these lengths. Is there anything special about the direction of $\overline{EF}$ compared to $\overline{AB}$ and $\overline{CD}$? Try measuring slopes. Or construct a line parallel to $\overline{AB}$ through E. What can you say about that line and $\overline{EF}$? Does this relationship hold for all trapezoids?

Conjecture: Write your conjectures below.

_____

_____

_____

_____

Present Your Findings

Discuss your results with your partner or group. To present your findings you could print a captioned sketch showing a trapezoid with its midsegment and measures that illustrate your conjectures.

Explore More

1. Construct the trapezoid's interior and measure its area. Can you come up with an area formula for a trapezoid that uses the length of its midsegment?

2. Is there anything special about the segment that connects midpoints of the bases of a trapezoid? Explain.

Investigation: The Midsegment of a Trapezoid

Student Audience: High School

Prerequisites: Students should know the terms **midsegment**, **trapezoid**, **base**, and **legs**. (Many books refer to the midsegment of a trapezoid as a median and refer to midsegments of a triangle as midlines. Both these terms cause confusion that can be easily avoided by using the term midsegment.)

Sketchpad Proficiency: Beginner

Class Time: 15-45 minutes (depending on how much time you give students to explore more)

Example Sketch: **Trapezoid Midsegment** (Mac) or **4quads\trapmdsg.gsp** (Windows)

Construction Tips

Step 3: If students use the Segment tool, point D will be created automatically upon releasing the mouse.

Investigate/Conjecture

Students may have to use trial and error with Calculate to build an expression that gives a value equal to EF. When they succeed, they'll discover:

A midsegment in a trapezoid, connecting midpoints of two legs, is parallel to the bases and its length is the average of the lengths of the bases.

Explore More

1. A formula for the area of a trapezoid could be $A = mh$, where m is the length of the midsegment and h is the height. The usual formula is $h(b_1 + b_2)/2$. But m is equal to $(b_1 + b_2)/2$.

2. The segment that connects the midpoints of the bases divides the trapezoid into two trapezoids that have equal area. If the legs and this segment were extended, they would intersect in a single point. The segment would lie on a median of the triangle created by extending the trapezoid's legs.

Chapter 5
Polygons

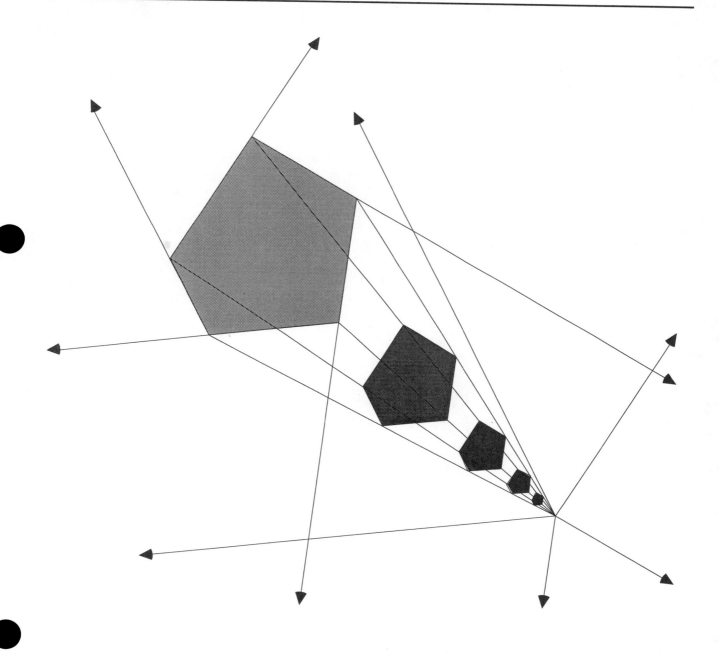

Investigation: Exterior Angles in a Polygon

An exterior angle of a polygon is formed when one of the sides is extended. Exterior angles lie outside the polygon. In this investigation, you'll discover the sum of the measures of the exterior angles in a polygon, starting with a pentagon.

Sketch

Step 1: Construct rays $\overrightarrow{AB}$, $\overrightarrow{BC}$, $\overrightarrow{CD}$, $\overrightarrow{DE}$, and $\overrightarrow{EA}$.

Step 2: Adjust the points, if necessary, so that pentagon $ABCDE$ is convex.

Step 3: On the rays, outside of the pentagon, construct points F on $\overrightarrow{AB}$, G on $\overrightarrow{BC}$, H on $\overrightarrow{CD}$, J on $\overrightarrow{DE}$, and K on $\overrightarrow{EA}$.

Step 4: Measure the exterior angles: $\angle KAB$, $\angle FBC$, $\angle GCD$, $\angle HDE$, and $\angle JEA$. Calculate the sum of these angle measures.

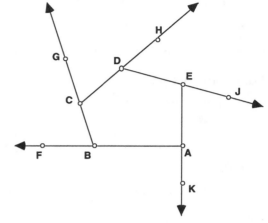

Investigate

Move parts of the pentagon to see if the sum changes. (Make sure your pentagon remains convex.) Is the sum of these exterior angles the same for any pentagon? (Note: This construction creates only one set of exterior angles. Another set would be constructed if you went the opposite direction with your rays.) Try similar constructions using rays to make triangles, quadrilaterals, hexagons, or other polygons with a set of exterior angles. What's the sum of the measures of one set of exterior angles in these polygons?

Conjecture: Write a conjecture below.

_____

_____

Present Your Findings

Discuss your results with your partner or group. To present your findings you could:

1. Print a captioned sketch showing a polygon and the measures of its exterior angles to illustrate your conjecture.

2. Try the Explore More suggestion below and show it to a classmate. Explain what's going on.

Explore More

In your sketch of a polygon with exterior angles, mark any point as center in the Transform menu. Select All, then use the Dilate tool to drag the selection toward the center point. As the polygon gets smaller and smaller, what happens to the exterior angles? What can you say about the angles as the polygon approaches a single point? How does this illustrate your exterior angle conjecture? Write a paragraph to describe your observations.

Investigation: Exterior Angles in a Polygon

Student Audience: Middle School/High School

Prerequisites: Students should know (or be introduced to) the terms **exterior angle** and **convex polygon**.

Sketchpad Proficiency: Beginner

Class Time: 15-30 minutes

Example Sketch: **Dilate Polygon** (Mac) or **5polygns\dilate.gsp** (Windows)

Construction Tips

Step 1: Make sure to construct the endpoint of each new ray from the control point of the previously constructed ray.

Step 3: Click on these rays with the point tool so that points *F*, *G*, *H*, *J*, and *K* are positioned outside the pentagon.

Step 4: Remember, selection order (point, vertex, point) is important when measuring angles.

Investigate/Conjecture

Make sure students try this investigation with other polygons in addition to the pentagon shown in the example. They could actually manipulate their pentagon into a quadrilateral or triangle, making one or more angle measures disappear. The Explore More suggestion is simple and worth doing here. It's a good place to introduce the Dilate tool. Students should make the following conjecture:

The sum of the measures of one set of exterior angles in a convex polygon is 360°.

Interestingly, this conjecture applies to concave polygons too if you consider the "exterior" angles that fall inside the polygon to be negative. Students may discover this as they manipulate their polygons.

Ask students if their conjecture would apply to the other set of exterior angles, just to confirm that they understand what exterior angles are.

Explore More

Encourage all students to try this. It's easy to do and it's a dazzling demonstration that the sum of these angles is 360°. As you dilate the figure toward any point, the polygon will shrink towards that point, leaving you with only the angles going all the way around a common vertex.

Of course you'll want to discuss the fact that when you dilate a polygon, the measures of the angles remain constant. You can measure the exterior angles before you dilate and students will see that the angle measures don't change.

You can have students print out their polygons with the exterior angles and actually cut out the exterior angles. Then have them rearrange the angles around a single point.

Investigation: Inscribed Stars

In this investigation you'll discover a relationship among the angles of a five-pointed star inscribed in a circle.

Sketch

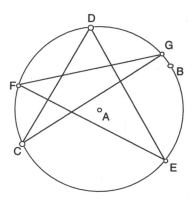

Step 1:   Construct circle *AB*.

Step 2:   Start anywhere on the circle and construct segments to make a five-pointed star. In this example, the segments were connected in order: $\overline{CD}, \overline{DE}, \overline{EF}, \overline{FG}, \overline{GC}$.

Step 3:   Measure the five angles at the star points.

Step 4:   Calculate the sum of the angle measures.

Investigate

Does the sum of the angles of the inscribed star change as you change the angles by moving points around the circle? (Make sure your figure stays a star.) What if you change the radius of the circle? Compare the measures of these inscribed angles to the measures of the arcs they intercept. (Select two arc endpoints and the circle, then choose ArcAngle in the Measure menu.) How are they related? What's the sum of the measures of the arcs in a circle? Write a paragraph to answer these questions and describe your findings in the space below. (Use a separate sheet of paper, if necessary.)

_____

_____

_____

_____

_____

_____

_____

Present Your Findings: Discuss your findings with your partner or group. To present your findings, you could print a captioned sketch showing your measurements and your conjectures along with any explanation you might have for why your conjecture is true.

Explore More

1. Do your conjectures apply to stars that are not inscribed in a circle?

2. What happens to the angle measures and their sum when you move a point so far around the circle that you no longer have a star? Create a script to do this construction. When you play it back, your five points will be placed on the circle at random, providing you with a puzzle: Can you rearrange the points to make a star?

3. Try this investigation with stars with different numbers of points. Can stars with an even number of points be constructed this way?

Investigation: Inscribed Stars

Student Audience: Middle School/High School

Prerequisites: Students should know, or be introduced to, the terms **inscribe**, **arc**, and **inscribed angle**. It's helpful if students know that the sum of the angles surrounding a point is 360°.

Sketchpad Proficiency: Beginner

Class Time: 20 minutes

Example Sketch: Inscribed Star (Mac) or **5polygns\inscstar.gsp** (Windows)

Construction Tips: Students will most likely be very familiar with how to make five-pointed stars. They'll use this method when they inscribe a star in a circle with the Segment tool. Novices need to be careful that their segments actually share endpoints and that those endpoints are on the circle. By not using point *B* as a star point, you can control the radius of the circle separately from the location of the star points.

Step 3: Select three points to measure an angle: point, vertex, point.

Investigate/Conjecture: Students are asked to write a paragraph before they write their conjectures. This is to encourage them to think about *why* their conjectures might be true before they state them. When students see that the sum of the angle measures is 180°, they'll probably consider that significant and want to relate it to the angles in a triangle. Some may even realize that a triangle is just a three pointed star, and may want to generalize for all stars. Investigating the relationship between arc measure and inscribed angles will offer clues as to why the sum of the angle measures is 180°. Students might make one or more of the following conjectures:

The measure of an inscribed angle in a circle is half the measure of the arc it intercepts.

The sum of the measures of the angles in a five-pointed star inscribed in a circle is 180°.

The first conjecture is a reason for the second. A star intercepts all the arcs of the circumscribing circle with one or more of its angles, depending on how it's constructed. In a five-pointed star, each arc is intercepted by exactly one inscribed angle. The sum of these arc measures is 360°, so the sum of the inscribed angles must be half that, or 180°.

Explore More

1. It turns out that stars need not be inscribed in circles for these conjectures to hold. In a five-pointed star, for example, the inner pentagon has two sets of exterior angles each of whose sum is 360°. These exterior angles are two angles in each of your five triangles. The sum of these ten angles is (2)(360°) = 720°. The sum of the angles in the five triangles is (5)(180°) = 900°. Subtract 720° and you're left with 180° for the star angles.

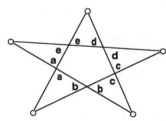

2(a + b + c + d + e) = 2(360) = 720

3. Students will discover a fundamental difference between odd and even-pointed stars. For stars with 6 or more points, different construction methods yield different angle sums because angles may intercept overlapping arcs. Further conjectures students might make include:

    The sum of the measures of the angles in an odd-pointed star is a multiple of 180°.

    The sum of the measures of the angles in an even-pointed star is a multiple of 360°.

 Exploring Geometry

Construction: The Regular Pentagon

The regular pentagon construction is somewhat more complex than constructing other regular polygons like equilateral triangles, square, and hexagons. In this activity, you'll do a compass and straightedge construction of a regular pentagon.

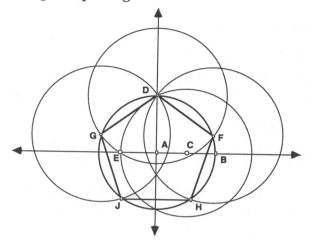

Sketch

Step 1: Construct circle *AB* and $\overleftrightarrow{AB}$.

Step 2: Construct a line perpendicular to $\overleftrightarrow{AB}$ through *A*.

Step 3: Construct $\overline{AB}$ and its midpoint, *C*.

Step 4: Construct circle *CD*, where *D* is the intersection of the perpendicular line and circle *AB*.

Step 5: Construct circle *DE*, where *E* is the intersection of circle *CD* and $\overleftrightarrow{AB}$. A radius of this circle will be one of the sides of your pentagon.

Step 6: Construct sides $\overline{DF}$ and $\overline{DG}$, where *F* and *G* are the intersections of circles *AB* and *DE*.

Step 7: Construct circles *GD* and *FD*.

Step 8: Complete your pentagon with sides $\overline{FH}$, $\overline{HJ}$, and $\overline{JG}$, where *H* and *J* are intersections of circles *GD* and *FD* with circle *AB*.

Step 9: Hide the circles, lines, and points *E* and *C*.

Investigate

How can you use measures to confirm this is a regular pentagon? This is a classical construction using only compass and straightedge. Can you think of an easier way to construct a regular pentagon with Sketchpad using rotations? You can construct a five-pointed star (a pentagram) inside your pentagon by constructing diagonals to alternate vertices. Compare the length of one diagonal to the length of a side of the pentagon. Inside the pentagram there's another pentagon. Investigate relationships between this inner pentagon and your original. Can you come up with a method for constructing a larger pentagram and pentagon outside of your original?

Conjecture: Write any conjectures you make about your figures below.

_____

_____

_____

_____

_____

_____

Construction: The Regular Pentagon

Student Audience: High School

Prerequisites: Students should know the definition of **regular polygons**. Students will discover an example of the **Golden Ratio**.

Sketchpad Proficiency: Experienced User

Class Time: 30-40 minutes

Example Script/Sketch: **5/Pentagon (Inscribed)** (Mac script)and **Pentagon/grams** (Mac sketch) or **5polygns\5inscrib.gss** and **5polygns\pentgram.gsp** (Windows)

Construction Tips

Step 4: Be careful with this tricky point of intersection. Some students will find it easier to construct the point of intersection first, then the circle.

Step 5: Students should study the diagram carefully if they're unsure of what circle to construct. This circle has the same radius as circle *CD*, but not the same as circle *AB*.

Step 7: Make sure students actually use point *D* in the construction, and that they don't just construct circles that pass through *D*.

Step 9: Choose the Circle tool, Select All Circles in the Edit Menu, and Hide Circles in the Display menu. Repeat for lines.

Investigate/Conjecture

If students measure sides and angles, they'll discover that this is a regular pentagon. An easier construction would be to construct a segment and rotate it and one endpoint about the other endpoint by 72°. Repeat to create five vertices of a pentagon. The ratio of a diagonal to a side to the nearest hundredth is 1.62. This is the **Golden Ratio**, Ø. (Students will need to do other activities to appreciate its significance.) The ratio of a side of the large pentagon to a side of the inner pentagon is 2.62, or 1 + Ø. A larger pentagram and pentagon can be constructed by simply constructing lines through the sides of the pentagon.

Construction: Templates for the Platonic Solids

The **Platonic solids** are polyhedra in which all the faces are congruent, regular polygons meeting at each vertex in the same way. You've probably constructed an equilateral triangle. That construction was the first proposition in Euclid's book, *The Elements*. After thirteen books of carefully sequenced constructions and theorems, the grand finale of *The Elements* is Euclid's proof that there are exactly five Platonic solids. The five solids are shown below:

With Sketchpad, you can construct a template for an unfolded polyhedron and print it out on a piece of stiff paper. Then you can cut it out and fold it into the polyhedron, taping together the edges. Each of the solids has more than one possible template. Two examples are shown at right:

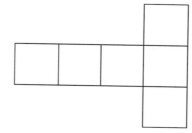
Cube (Hexahedron)

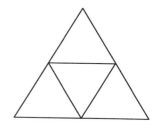
Tetrahedron

Use Sketchpad to create other templates for these and the other Platonic Solids. Once you've created a regular polygon, you can use reflections and/or rotations to repeat it. You could also record scripts for regular polygons and play the scripts repeatedly to create your templates. Hint: for the dodecahedron, create two identical templates with six pentagons each. If you can, print your templates, cut them out, and fold them to see if they work the way you imagined.

Present Your Findings

Compare your templates to those of your partner or group. To present your findings you could:

1. Print captioned sketches with small versions of all the templates you made.
2. Create scripts for all the different templates you made.
3. Construct and decorate platonic solids using the templates you made.

Explore More

1. Make templates for other three-dimensional shapes: cylinders, prisms, etc.
2. Do some research and make templates for semi-regular polyhedra (called Archimedean solids).
3. Do some research to learn more about the Platonic solids. See if you can discover relationships among the number of faces, edges and vertices of the solids.

Construction: Templates for the Platonic Solids

Student Audience: Middle School/High School

Prerequisites: Students should know the terms **polyhedron (polyhedra)**, and **regular polygon**. To create the templates, students should understand **reflections** and **rotations** and know how to perform them with Sketchpad.

Sketchpad Proficiency: Experienced User. Beginners can use the example sketch, **Platonic Templates** (Mac) or **5polygns\platonic\platsol.gsp** (Windows).

Class Time: 50-150 minutes. If you actually had students make templates for all the solids, print them, then build the solids, this could be a several-day project.

Example Scripts/Sketches: Sketches of templates for all the Platonic solids are found in a folder called **Platonics Templates** (Mac) or a directory called **5polgygns\platonic** (Windows). Regular polygons scripts are found in the **Regular Polygons** folder (Mac) or the directory **regpoly** (Windows).

Construction Tips

Below is shown one possible template for each solid. They all have more than one possible template.

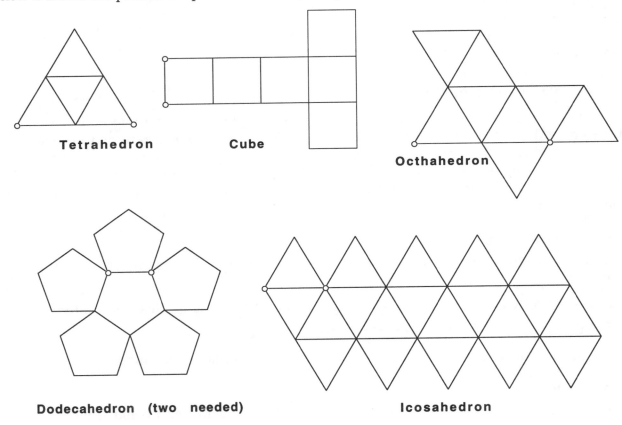

Tetrahedron   Cube   Octhahedron

Dodecahedron (two needed)   Icosahedron

Explore More

3. Students can discover Euler's formula for polyhedra: $F + V = E + 2$, where F stands for faces, V for vertices, and E for edges. This formula applies to all convex polyhedra, not just regular polyhedra.

Chapter 6
Circles

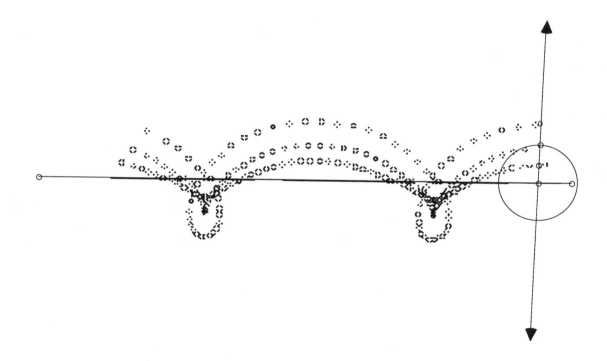

Exploration: Chords in a Circle

Construct a circle and a quadrilateral inscribed in it.
Each of the four sides of the quadrilateral is a **chord**
of the circle (a segment with endpoints on a circle).
Measure the lengths of these chords and the arcs
intercepted by them. Measure the angles. Move the
vertices around the circle and look for relationships
among your measurements.

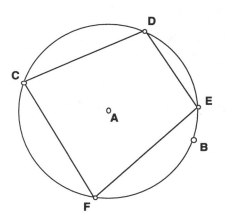

Also, see if you can find a way to use chords to
determine the center of a circle. (You can hide the
center, figure out where it is, then Show All
Hiddens to see if you were right.)

Write as many conjectures as you can in the space below.

_____
_____
_____
_____
_____
_____
_____
_____
_____
_____
_____
_____
_____
_____
_____
_____
_____
_____
_____
_____
_____
_____

Exploration: Chords in a Circle

Student Audience: High School

Prerequisites: Students would probably get more out of this activity if they knew how **arc measure** is defined in a circle. They should know or be introduced to the terms **arc** and **chord**.

Sketchpad Proficiency: Beginner

Class Time: 20-40 minutes (depends on how long you want to allow students to explore. This activity is very open-ended.)

Investigate/Conjecture

Students are not guided in this activity to any particular conjectures, but they come up with some of the following conjectures:

Congruent chords intercept congruent arcs.

The arcs between parallel chords are congruent.

Chords in a circle that are closest to the center are longest. The longest chord in a circle is a diameter.

The perpendicular bisector of any chord in a circle goes through the center.

The measure of an inscribed angle is 1/2 the measure of the arc it intercepts.

If a quadrilateral is inscribed in a circle, its opposite angles are supplementary.

The perpendicular bisectors of chords intersect at the center of the circle. If a circle's center is hidden, it can be found by constructing two non-parallel chords and their perpendicular bisectors. The point of intersection of these chords is the circle's center.

Investigation: Congruent Chords in a Circle

A **chord** is a segment connecting two points on a circle. In this activity, you'll construct congruent chords in a circle and investigate their properties.

Sketch

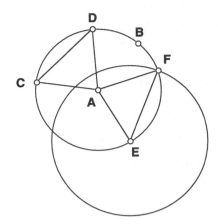

Step 1: Construct circle *AB*.

Step 2: Construct $\overline{CD}$, where *C* and *D* are points on the circle.

Step 3: Construct point *E* on the circle, then construct a circle with center *E* and radius $\overline{CD}$.

Step 4: Construct $\overline{EF}$, where *F* is either point of intersection of the two circles. You've constructed $\overline{EF}$ to be congruent to $\overline{CD}$.

Step 5: Hide the second circle, *EF*.

Step 6: Construct $\overline{AC}, \overline{AD}, \overline{AE}$, and $\overline{AF}$.

Investigate

Measure *CD* and *EF* to confirm that the chords are congruent. Measure central angles ∠*CAD* and ∠*EAF*. Move point *C* or *D* to confirm that the relationship between central angles holds for congruent chords of any length. Measure arcs *CD* and *EF* (arc angle and arc length). Measure the distances from $\overline{CD}$ and $\overline{EF}$ to *A*, the center of the circle. Again, move point *C* or *D* to confirm your findings hold for all congruent chords.

Conjecture: Write your conjectures below.

_____

_____

_____

_____

_____

_____

_____

_____

Present Your Findings: Discuss your findings with your partner or group. To present your findings, you could print a captioned sketch showing your measurements and your conjectures, along with any explanation you might have for why your conjectures are true.

Explore More: Construct the perpendicular bisectors of the two chords in your circle. Do they intersect anywhere special? Construct a third chord, not congruent to the others, and construct its perpendicular bisector. Does this give you an idea for how you can find the center of a circle whose center is missing? Construct another circle. Hide its center, then find it.

Investigation: Congruent Chords in a Circle

Student Audience: High School

Prerequisites: Students should know how **arc measure** is defined in a circle. Arc measure is called ArcAngle by Sketchpad to distinguish it from arc length. They should know or be introduced to the terms **central angle**, **arc** and **chord**.

Sketchpad Proficiency: Beginner

Class Time: 15-30 minutes

Example Sketch: **Congruent Chords** (Mac) or **6circles\congchrd.gsp** (Windows)

Construction Tips

Step 3: Use the command Circle By Center+Radius in the Construct menu.

Investigate/Conjecture

Students should make some of the following conjectures:

The central angles defined by congruent chords are congruent.

Congruent chords intercept congruent arcs.

Congruent chords are equidistant from the center of the circle.

Explore More

The perpendicular bisectors of any chords, congruent or not, intersect at the center of the circle. If a circle's center is hidden, it can be found by constructing two non-parallel chords and their perpendicular bisectors. The point of intersection of these chords is the circle's center.

Investigation: Tangents to a Circle

A line can intersect a circle in zero, one, or two points. A line that intersects a circle in exactly one point—that just touches the circle without going into the circle's interior—is called a **tangent**. The point of intersection is called the **point of tangency**. A line that intersects a circle in two points is called a **secant**. In this investigation, you'll construct a secant, then manipulate it until it becomes a tangent to discover an important property of tangents.

Sketch

Step 1: Construct a circle with center A and radius endpoint B.

Step 2: Construct radius $\overline{AB}$.

Step 3: Construct secant $\overleftrightarrow{BC}$, making sure point C falls on the circle.

Step 4: Measure $\angle ABC$.

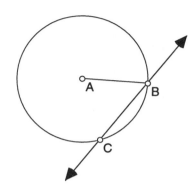

Investigate

Drag point C around the circle toward point B. What happens to $\angle ABC$ as point C gets closer to point B? What's the measure of $\angle ABC$ when point C is right on top of point B? When points B and C coincide, your line intersects the circle in a single point, so it's tangent to the circle. What's the relationship between a tangent and a radius to the point of tangency? Use this relationship to devise a method for constructing a tangent to a circle.

Conjecture: Write your conjecture below, and describe your method of construction.

_____

_____

_____

_____

Present Your Findings

Discuss your results with your partner or group. To present your findings you could:

1. Print a captioned sketch showing several circles with secants that get progressively closer to being tangents. Show the angle measure between the radius and secant for each circle.

2. Create a captioned sketch with instructions, in your own words, for how to do this investigation.

Explore More

See if you can come up with methods for constructing externally or internally tangent circles (circles that intersect in a single point). Write any discoveries you make about these circles on the back of this sheet or on a separate piece of paper.

Investigation: Tangents to a Circle

Student Audience: High School

Prerequisites: The activity introduces the terms **secant** and **tangent**.

Sketchpad Proficiency: Beginner

Class Time: 15-20 minutes

Example Sketch: **Common Tangents** (Mac) or **6circles\commtan.gsp** (Windows)

Construction Tips

This is a very simple construction that elegantly illustrates the concept.

Investigate/Conjecture

As you drag point *C* toward *B*, the angle between the radius and secant approaches 90°. If you drag slowly, it's quite obvious when *C* and *B* coincide. At this point, the angle measure should read 90°, leading students to conjecture:

The angle between a radius and a tangent line through the radius endpoint is 90°.

A line tangent to a circle is perpendicular to a radius at the point of tangency.

However students phrase it, make sure their conjectures stipulate that the tangent and radius share a common point on the circle. Students should now be able to construct tangents by constructing a radius and then constructing a perpendicular line through the radius endpoint.

Explore More

To construct internally or externally tangent circles, first construct a circle and tangent line. Extend the radius to a full line and construct a second circle with center on that line and radius endpoint the same as the first circle (the point of tangency).

You can also have students try to construct two or more circles with a common external or internal tangent. To do this, construct a circle and a tangent. Through a random point on the tangent, construct a perpendicular. Construct a circle with center on this perpendicular and radius endpoint at the point of intersection with the tangent. In the diagram below, circles *AG* and *GF* have a common external tangent. Circles *AB* and *DC* have a common internal tangent. (Circles *GF* and *DC* where constructed after the tangent line.)

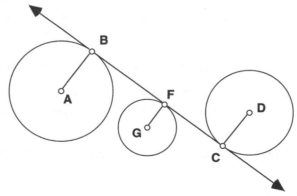

     Exploring Geometry

Investigation: Tangent Segments

In this activity, you'll learn how to construct tangents. Then you'll compare the lengths of the two segments from the common intersection point to the points of tangency.

Sketch

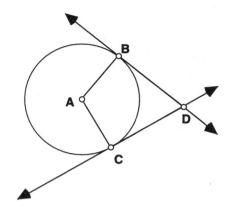

Step 1: Construct circle AB and radius $\overline{AB}$.

Step 2: Construct a line perpendicular to $\overline{AB}$ through B. This line is tangent to the circle.

Step 3: Construct a second radius AC and a tangent through C.

Step 4: Construct $\overline{BD}$ and $\overline{CD}$ to the point of intersection of the tangent lines.

Step 5: Hide the lines.

Investigate

Measure the lengths BD and CD. Move points C, B, or A to see if this relationship holds for all segments tangent to a circle from a point outside the circle.

Conjecture: Write your conjectures below.

_____

_____

Present Your Findings

Discuss your results with your partner or group. To present your findings you could print a captioned sketch showing several circles with pairs of tangent segments. Show measures that illustrate your conjecture.

Explore More

1. Construct $\overline{AD}$. Investigate relationships among the angles and sides of the two triangles formed. Are the triangles congruent? Can you see why?

2. See if you can come up with methods for constructing two or more circles with a common tangent (a line tangent to both circles). Hint: construct the second circle after you've constructed the first circle's tangent.

3. See if you can construct tangent segments given the circle and the point outside of the circle (instead of constructing the point of intersection of two arbitrary tangents as you did in the investigation).

Investigation: Tangent Segments

Student Audience: High School

Prerequisites: Students should the term **tangent**.

Sketchpad Proficiency: Beginner

Class Time: 15-30 minutes

Example Sketches/Script: Tangent Segments, Common Tangents (Mac sketches), and
Tangent Segments 2 (Mac script) or **6circles\tansegs.gsp, 6circles\commtan.gsp,** and **tanseg2.gss** (Windows)

Construction Tips

Step 4: Students may need to adjust point *B* or *C* so that the intersection is visible on the screen.

Investigate/Conjecture

Students should make some of the following conjecture:

Tangent segments to a circle from a point outside the circle are congruent.

Explore More

1. The triangles *ABD* and *ACD* are congruent by Hypotenuse-Leg. (*AB* and *AC* are radii of a circle and $\overline{AD}$ is congruent to itself. Angles *ABD* and *ACD* are right angles.) Thus, $\overline{DB}$ and $\overline{DC}$ are corresponding parts of congruent triangles.

2. This suggestion is an easy way to construct circles with a common tangent: construct the tangent to one circle before you construct the second circle.

3. This is a bigger challenge than number 2. Construct a segment connecting the point and the circle's center. Construct the midpoint. Construct a circle with this center diameter. The tangent segments are constructed to the points of intersection of this circle with the original circle.

Investigation: Circles and Angles

An angle with its vertex at the center of a circle is called a **central angle**. An angle whose sides are chords of a circle and whose vertex is on the circle is called an **inscribed angle**. In this activity you'll investigate relationships among central angles, inscribed angles, and the arcs they intercept.

Sketch

Step 1:   Construct circle *AB*.

Step 2:   Construct $\overline{AC}$ and $\overline{AD}$ to create central angle *CAD*.

Step 3:   Construct $\overline{EC}$ and $\overline{ED}$, where *E* is a point on the circle, to create inscribed angle *CED*.

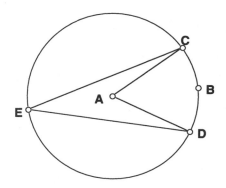

Investigate

Measure ∠*CAD*, ∠*CED*, and arc angle *CD*. Move point *C* or *D*, changing ∠*CED* but keeping it acute. The relationship between the measure of the central angle *CAD* and the arc angle measure of arc *CD* should be clear. Do you see a relationship between the inscribed angle *CED* and the arc it intercepts? By moving *C* or *D* you can confirm that this relationship holds for all inscribed angles. By moving *E*, you can make a conjecture about all inscribed angles that intercept the same arc.

Conjecture: Write your conjectures below or on a separate sheet.

_____

_____

_____

_____

Present Your Findings

Discuss your results with your partner or group. To present your findings you could print a captioned sketch with several circles with central and inscribed angles. Show measures that illustrate your conjectures.

Explore More

1. How would you describe central angle ∠*CAD* when the measure of inscribed angle ∠*CED* is 90°? What kind of arc does ∠*CED* intercept?

2. What if the measure of ∠*CED* is greater than 90°? In circles, it's convenient to talk about central angles with measures greater than 180° because they can intercept arcs that are greater than semicircles. An arc greater than a semicircle is called a **major arc** and must be named by three points: an endpoint, a point on the arc, and the other endpoint. To measure a major arc with Sketchpad, select a circle and three points on it and choose ArcAngle in the Measure menu. Experiment with inscribed angles that intercept major arcs. Do your conjectures still hold?

Investigation: Circles and Angles

Student Audience: High School

Prerequisites: Students should know the terms **chord** and **arc**. The terms **inscribed angle** and **central angle** are introduced in the activity.

Sketchpad Proficiency: Beginner

Class Time: 20-30 minutes

Construction Tips

Step 4: To measure a minor arc, select two points on the circle and the circle itself.

Investigate/Conjecture

As students move C or D, the angles change. Students will see that even as these measures change, the measure of the central angle is always equal to the measure of the arc. The measure of the inscribed angle is half these measures. Students may want to use Calculate to confirm (or discover) this. Take care that $\angle CAD$ doesn't exceed 180°. Moving point E doesn't change the angle. At first his may seem uninteresting, but moving point E allows students to see all the inscribed angles that intercept arc CD. Students should make the following conjectures:

The measure of a central angle in a circle is equal to the measure of the arc it intercepts (definition).

The measure of an inscribed angle in a circle is half the measure of the arc it intercepts.

All inscribed angles that intercept the same arc are equal in measure.

Explore More

1. When the measure of $\angle CED$ becomes 90°, points C, A, and D become collinear. The measure of $\angle CAD$ is 180°. This may be the first time students have had to think about an angle with measure 180°. The inscribed right angle intercepts a semicircle.

2. When the measure of $\angle CED$ exceeds 90°, it intercepts a major arc (an arc with measure greater than 180°). Arcs defined by three points may be minor or major or change from one to the other as you move the points.

 Exploring Geometry

Investigation: More on Circles, Angles, and Arcs

You already know about some relationships among central angles, inscribed angles, and the arcs they intercept. In this activity, you'll discover more relationships that follow from the ones you already know. As you discover them, think about why your conjectures must be true in terms of what you already know about arcs.

Sketch

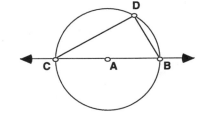

Step 1: Construct circle *AB*.

Step 2: Construct $\overleftrightarrow{AB}$.

Step 3: Construct $\overline{CD}$, where *C* is the other point of intersection of $\overleftrightarrow{AB}$ and the circle and *D* is a point on the circle.

Step 4: Construct $\overline{DB}$.

Investigate: Measure $\angle CDB$ and move point *D* around the circle. What can you say about any angle inscribed in a semicircle?

Conjecture: Write your conjectures below.

_____

_____

_____

Sketch

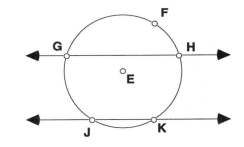

Step 1: Construct circle *EF*.

Step 2: Construct $\overleftrightarrow{GH}$, where *G* and *H* are on the circle.

Step 3: Construct point *J* on the circle and a line through *J*, parallel to $\overleftrightarrow{GH}$.

Step 4: Construct point *K*, the other point of intersection of the parallel line with the circle.

Investigate: Measure arcs *GJ* and *HK*. Move points *G*, *H*, *J*, and *F*. What can you say about arcs intercepted by parallel lines?

Conjecture: Write your conjectures below.

_____

_____

Present Your Findings: Discuss your results with your partner or group. To present your findings you could print a captioned sketch with several circles with central and inscribed angles. Show measures that illustrate your conjectures.

Explore More

Construct a circle and inscribe a quadrilateral in it. Measure the four angles of the quadrilateral. Make a conjecture about opposite angles of a quadrilateral inscribed in a circle.

Investigation: More on Circles, Angles, and Arcs

Student Audience: High School

Prerequisites: Students should know basic relationships among **central angles**, **inscribed angles**, and the **arcs** they intercept.

Sketchpad Proficiency: Beginner

Example Sketch: **More Angles and Arcs** (Mac) or **6circles\angsarcs.gsp** (Windows)

Class Time: 20-30 minutes. You might want to do this investigation in the same class period as Circles and Angles.

Construction Tips

The first construction is a simple construction of a triangle inscribed in a semicircle

Investigate/Conjecture

Students should conjecture:

Any angle inscribed in a semicircle is a right angle.

Construction Tips

The second construction is a simple construction of two parallel lines intercepting a circle.

Investigate/Conjecture

Students should conjecture:

Arcs intercepted by parallel lines are congruent.

Explore More

The opposite angles in an inscribed quadrilateral intercept two arcs that make up the entire circle. Therefore, the sum of the arcs they intercept is 360°, so their sum must be 180°. Hence, opposite angles in a quadrilateral inscribed in a circle are supplementary. (This should reveal to students what type of quadrilaterals can be circumscribed. Such quadrilaterals are called **cyclic**.)

Investigation: The Circumference/Diameter Ratio

In this investigation you'll discover a relationship between the circumference and diameter of a circle.

Sketch

Step 1: Construct $\overleftrightarrow{AB}$.

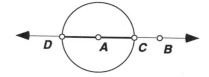

Step 2: Construct a circle AC, where C is a point on the line.

Step 3: Construct diameter $\overline{DC}$.

Step 4: Measure the length of the circle's diameter and the circle's circumference.

Step 5: Select the diameter and circumference measures, in that order, and choose Plot As (x, y) in the Graph menu. You should get axes for a graph. The point you plotted may be off the screen. Drag C to shrink the circle until you can see the plotted point.

Step 6: Select the plotted point and C, in that order, and choose Locus in the Construct menu.

Investigate

The point you plotted is one point on the locus you constructed. Drag C to change the diameter of the circle and observe what happens to the plotted point. What does the locus represent? Construct a second point on the locus and a line through the two points. Measure the line's slope. Is this number familiar? Choose Calculate in the Measure menu. Select the symbol Pi (π) from the Values pop-up menu in the calculator. The symbol π is the Greek letter "Pi." What does it represent? Sketchpad displays an approximation for this number to the nearest thousandth if you've chosen this precision in Preferences. See if you can perform a calculation using your circumference and diameter measures that gives you a value equal to π.

Define: Write a definition of Pi (π) below:

_____

Conjecture: Complete the expressions below.

$C/D =$ _____ , *where* C = *circumference and* D = *diameter of a circle.*

The circumference C *of a circle can be found using the formula* C = _____ , *where* D *represents the diameter.*

The circumference C *of a circle can be found using the formula* C = _____ , *where* r *represents the radius.*

Present Your Findings

Discuss your findings with your partner or group. To present your findings, you could print a captioned sketch showing several circles and the measures of their circumferences and diameters. Also show the circumference/diameter ratio. (Edit the measurement text to make it easy to understand.)

Explore More

Construct an arc on your circle and see if you can come up with formulas for finding arc length.

Investigation: The Circumference/Diameter Ratio

Student Audience: Middle School/High School

Prerequisites: Students need to know the terms **circumference** and **diameter**.

Sketchpad Proficiency: Experienced User

Class Time: 30 minutes

Example Sketch: Circumference (Mac) or **6circles\circdiam.gsp** (Windows)

Construction Tips

There are other ways to construct a circle and a diameter, but this method ensures students will be able to construct a locus for a graph, as point C is free to move along the line.

Investigate/Conjecture

If students construct the locus correctly, they should get a straight-line graph. When they drag point C, the plotted point will move up and down this line. They'll need to construct a second point and a line on this locus so they can measure the slope. Most students will recognize the slope, 3.14, as an approximation for π when they see it. The linear graph demonstrates the direct proportion between a circle's circumference and diameter. Students familiar with this concept may be able to write an equation for the graph: $C = 3.14d$ or $C = \pi d$. If they succeed in using the

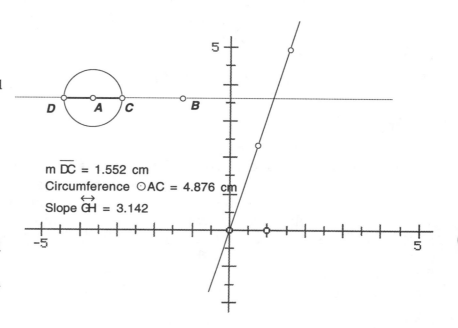

circumference and diameter to calculate a value equal to π, students should discover this definition:

π is the ratio of a circle's circumference to its diameter.

The investigation should make these formulas more relevant to students:

$C = \pi D$, or $C = 2\pi r$.

Discuss how 3.14 is just an approximation for π.

Explore More

1. Students may be able to reason out and test a formula for arc length: $S = (N/360)\pi D$, where N is the arc angle measure.

2. (Not on student activity sheet) Many students are fascinated that π is a number whose decimal part "goes on forever." Some may be interested in researching the history of π and doing a report.

3. (Not on student activity sheet) It takes time, but students may be more convinced of the definition of π by measuring physical objects.

Investigation: Arc Length

How would you calculate the distance around a half-circle? How about a quarter circle? How about the part of a circle intercepted by a 120° central angle? An **arc** is just part of a circle. If you can find the circumference of a circle, and you know what part of the circle an arc is, you can find the length of the arc. In this activity, you'll derive a formula for arc length.

Sketch

Step 1:   Construct a circle *AB*.

Step 2:   Construct radii $\overline{AB}$ and $\overline{AC}$.

Step 3:   Measure ∠*BAC*, the circumference of the circle, and arc length *BC*.

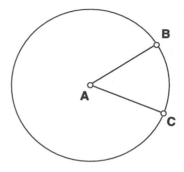

Investigate

Knowing the measure of ∠*BAC* allows you to find what fraction of the circumference is taken by arc *BC*. If the measure of ∠*BAC* is part of a whole, what angle measure represents the whole circle? Use the measure of ∠*BAC*, 360, and the circumference of the circle to build an expression with Calculate that's equal to arc length *BC*.

Conjecture: Complete the expression below.

Arc length S = _____ , *where* N *represents the measure of the central angle and* C *represents the circumference of the circle.*

Present Your Findings

Discuss your findings with your partner or group. To present your findings, you could print a captioned sketch showing a large circle with several arcs and central angles. Show measures and expressions that you build to calculate arc lengths.

Explore More

1. Because Sketchpad doesn't measure angles greater than 180°, the expression you created using central angle ∠*BAC* can only calculate arc lengths of minor arcs. How can you calculate the arc length of a major arc?

2. Change Preferences to measure the central angle in radians instead of degrees. Can you build an expression to measure arc length given the measure of the central angle in radians?

Investigation: Arc Length

Student Audience: High School

Prerequisites: Students need to know the terms arc, circumference, and diameter.

Sketchpad Proficiency: Beginner

Class Time: 20-30 minutes

Example Sketch: **Arc Length** (Mac) or **6circles\arcleng.gsp** (Windows)

Construction Tips

Step 3: Select points B and C and the circle to measure arc length.

Investigate/Conjecture

If the central angle has measure N, then it represents a fraction of $N/360$ of the circle. Students should build a calculation that looks like Angle(BAC)*Circumference(Circle 1)/360 = 0.98, or Angle(BAC)/360*Circumference(Circle 1) = 0.98. Conjectures should read:

Arc Length $S = (N/360)$ C, *where* N *represents the measure of the central angle and* C *represents the circumference of the circle.*

Explore More

As this is a very short investigation, you should have all students try this Explore More. To calculate the length of a major arc, they need only subtract the length of the minor arc from the circumference of the circle. Asking students to think about this will reinforce the idea of an arc being a part, or fraction, of a circle. This is also an opportunity to discuss how to identify major arcs with three points to differentiate them from minor arcs. Students can use arc measures instead of the measures of central angles to calculate arc lengths. Measure major arcs be selecting the circle and three points.

 Exploring Geometry

Problem: Distance in a Circle

How can you find the longest chord going through a given point in a circle? What about the shortest? In this investigation, you'll explore that problem.

Sketch

Step 1:   Construct a circle AB.

Step 2:   Construct $\overrightarrow{CD}$, where C is on the circle and D is in its interior.

Step 3:   Construct $\overline{CD}$ and $\overline{DE}$, where E is the intersection of the ray with the circle.

Step 4:   Hide the ray.

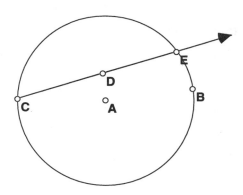

Investigate

Measure CD and DE and calculate the sum $CD + DE$. This is the quantity you wish to maximize and minimize. Move point C around the circle until $CD + DE$ is the greatest you can make it. What can you say about the location of $\overline{CE}$? Now move C so that $CD + DE$ is a minimum. Do you notice anything about the position of $\overline{CE}$ now? Try constructing a line through A perpendicular to $\overline{CD}$ or $\overline{DE}$.

You've investigated the sum of these distances, now investigate the product. Calculate $CD * DE$. Now move point C around the circle. Can you maximize or minimize this product? What can you conjecture about the product? Move D and try this part of the investigation again. Do your conjectures apply regardless of the location of point D?

Conjecture: Write your conjectures below.

_____

_____

_____

_____

_____

Present Your Findings

Discuss your findings with your partner or group. To present your findings, you could print a captioned sketch illustrating your conjectures.

Explore More

Can you explain your product conjecture? (Hint: Construct another ray from the circle through point D then construct segments along this ray with endpoints on the circle and point D. Does the product of these segment lengths behave the same way? Can you see how similar triangles may be involved?)

Problem: Distance in a Circle

Student Audience: High School

Prerequisites: Students need to know the term chord.

Sketchpad Proficiency: Beginner

Class Time: 15 minutes

Example Sketch: Distance in a Circle (Mac) or **6circles\distcirc.gsp** (Windows)

Construction Tips

It's necessary to construct ray $\overrightarrow{CD}$ instead of segment $\overline{CE}$ with point D on it, because you want D to remain fixed as you move point C around the circle.

Investigate/Conjecture

Students are asked to calculate the sum $CD + DE$ instead of simply measuring CE because they are later asked to investigate the product. Also, measuring CD and DE separately gives students the opportunity to recognize the symmetry in the problem: that is, $CD + DE$ is maximized when C is in the two locations that make $\overline{CE}$ a diameter. In one of these two cases CD is minimized and DE is maximized. In the other case, the opposite is true. The sum $CD + DE$ is minimized when a CD and DE are equal. This happens when a line through D and center A is the perpendicular bisector of $\overline{CE}$.

The product $CD * DE$ is constant.

Students should come up with one or more of the following conjectures:

The longest chord through a given point in a circle is a diameter of the circle.

The shortest chord through a given point in a circle is perpendicular to a line through the center and the given point. (The line is the perpendicular bisector of the chord.)

A point in a circle divides all chords that pass through it into two segments, the product of whose lengths is a constant.

Explore More

The last conjecture is the same one discovered in the investigation, Intersecting Chords in a Circle, and can be proved using similar triangles. If two chords, $\overline{AB}$ and $\overline{CD}$, intersect at E, then $\triangle AEC \sim \triangle BED$. Thus, $AE/CE = DE/BE$, and $AE * BE = CE * DE$.

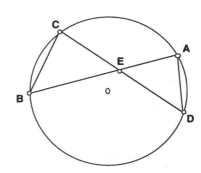

Exploring Geometry

Investigation: Tracing a Cycloid Curve

What's the path of a point on a wheel as the wheel rolls along a road? In this activity, you'll investigate that question.

Sketch

Step 1: Construct a small circle *AB* and radius $\overline{AC}$.

Step 2: Construct a point *D* and a circle with center *D* and radius *AC*.

Step 3: Construct a line through *D* parallel to $\overline{AC}$.

Step 4: Construct a point *E* on this line, inside the circle.

Step 5: With *E* selected, choose Trace Locus in the Display menu.

Step 6: Construct a long horizontal segment, $\overline{FG}$.

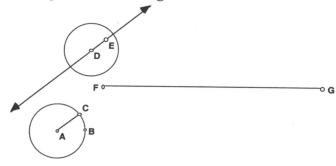

Investigate

Create an Action Button to animate point *D* on $\overline{FG}$ one way at medium speed and point *C* on circle *AB* one way at medium speed. The path that point *E* traces is the path a point inside a wheel would trace as the wheel rolled along the ground. (Imagine the path of a reflector on a bicycle wheel.) This curve is called a cycloid. Move point *E* so that it's on the circle (or construct a second point at the intersection of the circle and line). Animate again. How has the curve changed? Try the animation with point *E* outside the circle. These are all different types of cycloids. In the space below, sketch three different curves traced by point *E* inside, on, and outside the circle:

E **inside circle**   *E* **on circle**   *E* **outside circle**

If your segment is long enough and the circle small enough, the curve will repeat itself. For this reason, a cycloid is called **periodic**. How far does the center of your circle travel in the horizontal direction before the curve starts repeating itself? This distance is called the period of the curve. What does the period depend on? Is the period different if point *E* is outside the circle instead of inside? What's the period of a cycloid produced by a circle with radius 1 cm? On a separate piece of paper, write a paragraph to answer these questions.

Investigation: Tracing a Cycloid

Student Audience: High School Enrichment/College

Prerequisites: None. Cycloids are not generally part of the high school geometry curriculum, but this activity is an easy, informal introduction to this fascinating curve. Advanced math and calculus students can use this activity as a jumping off point for further investigation.

Sketchpad Proficiency: Experienced User

Class Time: 30 minutes

Example Sketch: **Cycloid Tracer** (Mac) or **6circles\cycloid.gsp** (Windows)

Construction Tips

This construction may seem quite roundabout (so to speak) but it's necessary to construct two circles because one circle must have a point animated around it, and thus it can't move. (Objects that are paths for an animation can't themselves be animated.)

Step 1: Circle *AB* should be quite small, especially if students are working on computers with small screens. If the circle is too large, a complete cycle of the curve won't be traced, and students won't recognize the pattern.

Investigate/Conjecture

When the point is on the circle, the cycloid develops a cusp where the point comes to the bottom of its revolution around the circle. This cusp evolves into a loop as the point is moved outside the circle. Student sketches should look something like those below:

E inside circle   **E on circle**   **E outside circle**

If the segment were long enough, the curve would repeat itself over and over. The curve repeats itself after each revolution, in which time the circle has traveled a horizontal distance equal to its circumference. Thus, the period of the curve depends on the circumference of the circle. (It does not depend on the location of point *E* relative to the circle.) The period of the cycloid curve, then, is $2\pi r$, where r is the radius of the circle. Hence, a circle with radius 1 cm would produce a cycloid with period 2π cm.

A cycloid is impossible to construct using Euclidean tools, but Sketchpad's animation feature makes it possible to trace one because animation can locate points as a function of time. If you have a fast computer, you might want to close class with **Life's Highway** (Mac) or **present\lifeshwy.gsp** (Windows). The curve traced in this sketch is not a cycloid (it's a catenary), but kids will find the sketch amusing, and will be able to relate it to the cycloid in terms of the path of a rotating point.

 Exploring Geometry

Chapter 7
Area

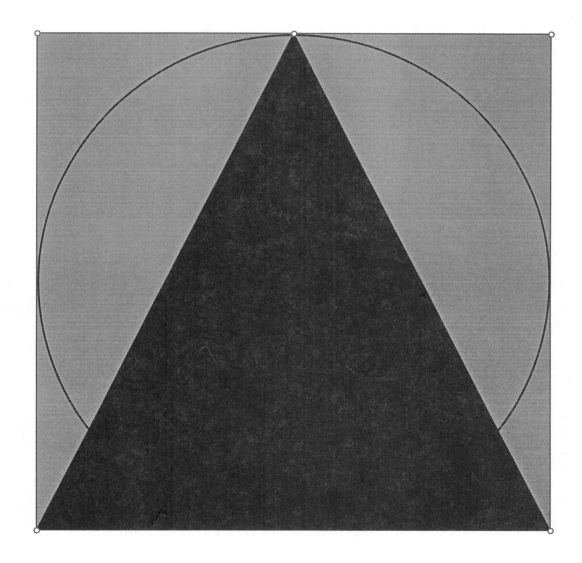

Investigation: Area of Parallelograms

You'll discover a relationship between the areas of rectangles and parallelograms by investigating a process called **shearing**. This will give you a formula for area that you can generalize for all parallelograms.

Sketch

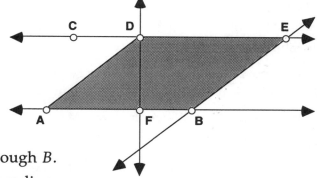

Step 1:   Construct $\overleftrightarrow{AB}$ so that it appears horizontal.

Step 2:   Construct C and a line through C parallel to $\overleftrightarrow{AB}$.

Step 3:   Construct $\overline{AD}$ where D is on the parallel line.

Step 4:   Construct a line parallel to $\overline{AD}$ through B.

Step 5:   Construct E, the intersection of these lines, and construct polygon interior $ADEB$.

Step 6:   Construct a line through D, perpendicular to $\overleftrightarrow{AB}$, and the point of intersection, F, of this line and $\overleftrightarrow{AB}$.

Investigate

Measure the area of parallelogram $ADEB$. Move point D along its line so that $ADEB$ looks like a rectangle. How would you calculate this area? Now move point D to make your parallelogram more and more slanted. Transforming a parallelogram in this way without changing its base or height is called **shearing**. Does the area change? Why or why not? What remains constant when you move point D? What do you have to move to change the area of the parallelogram? How could you cut a parallelogram into two pieces that could be put together into a rectangle with the same area? Measure DF and AB. Calculate with these measures to create an expression that gives the area of the parallelogram.

Conjecture

In the space below, write a formula for the area of a parallelogram, a description of how you discovered the formula, and a description of the relationship between the area of a rectangle and the area of a parallelogram that's not a rectangle.

_____

_____

_____

_____

Present Your Findings

Compare and discuss your results with your partner or group. To present your findings you could print a sketch that shows several different parallelograms that have the same base and height. Type comments that describe why their areas are equal.

Explore More

Create a sketch of a parallelogram in which a triangle can be cut from one part of the parallelogram and pasted somewhere else to make a rectangle.

Investigation: Area of Parallelograms

Student Audience: Middle School/High School

Prerequisites: Students should know how to find the area of a rectangle and should know the terms **area**, **rectangle** and **parallelogram**. They should know the terms **height** and **base** as they apply to parallelograms. No previous understanding of the concept of **shearing** is required, but it should be discussed further after the investigation.

Sketchpad Proficiency: Beginner

Class Time: 20 minutes. You might try having students do this investigation, Area of Triangles, and Area of Trapezoids in one or two trips to the computer lab.

Example Sketch: **Parallelogram Area** (Mac) or **7area\pararea.gsp** (Windows)

Construction Tips

Step 1: Press and hold down the Shift key to constrain the segment to 15° intervals, making it easy to construct a horizontal segment.

Step 3: Make sure students construct $\overline{AD}$ to a new point *D*. They must not use existing point *C*, as dragging *C* will change the height of the parallelogram.

Investigate/Conjecture

When *D* is dragged to make *ADEB* look like a rectangle, points *F* and *A* coincide. Students should know that the area of the rectangle can be found by multiplying *AB* (or *DE*) times *DF*. As they drag *D*, they should see that the area remains constant. Likewise, *DF* remains constant, whereas *DA* increases. To change the area of the parallelogram, students would have to change *AB* or the height of the parallelogram by dragging *C* (or the line through *C*). This visual information should help students recognize that the base and height determine the area of a parallelogram. To measure *AB*, students could either construct a segment $\overline{AB}$ and measure its length, or simply measure the distance between *A* and *B*. This is also true for *DF*. The area is the product of *AB* and *DF*.

Students should recognize that the area of a parallelogram is found the same way as the area of a rectangle, since any parallelogram, including a rectangle, with the same base and height will have the same area. In the case where *D* is located above $\overline{AB}$, students should notice that triangle *AFD* could be removed from the parallelogram and moved to the other side, forming a rectangle with base *AB* and height *DF*. (They are asked to actually do this in the Explore More part of this investigation.)

Explore More

The parallelogram's interior should be constructed in two parts: the right triangle on one side and the remaining trapezoid with the two right angles.

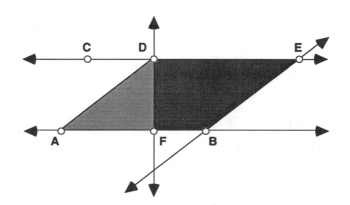

Investigation: Area of Triangles

The area of a triangle is very closely related to the area of a parallelogram. In this investigation you'll discover this relationship and come up with a formula for calculating the area of a triangle.

Sketch

Step 1: Construct $\overline{AB}$ so that it appears horizontal.

Step 2: Construct C and a line through C parallel to $\overline{AB}$.

Step 3: Construct $\overline{AD}$ and $\overline{DB}$ where D is on the parallel line.

Step 4: Construct polygon interior ADB.

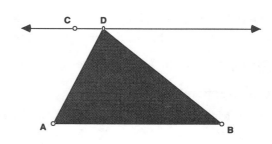

Investigate

Measure the area of $\triangle ADB$. Move point D along its line. Does the area change? Why or why not? What distances remain constant when you move point D? What do you have to move to change the area of the triangle? Construct a line through B parallel to $\overline{AD}$. Construct E, the point of intersection of this line and $\overleftrightarrow{CD}$. $ADEB$ is a parallelogram. How does the area of this parallelogram compare to the area of $\triangle ADB$? Measure the distance from D to $\overline{AB}$ and the length of $\overline{AB}$. Calculate with these measures to create an expression that gives the area of the $\triangle ADB$. What's a word that describes the distance from D to $\overline{AB}$?

Conjecture

In the space below, write a formula for the area of a triangle, a description of how you discovered the formula, and a description of the relationship between the area of a triangle and the area of a parallelogram.

_____

_____

_____

_____

_____

_____

_____

Present Your Findings

Compare and discuss your results with your partner or group. To present your findings you could print a sketch that shows several different triangles that have the same base and height. Add comments that describe why their areas are equal.

Explore More

Show that the area of the triangle can be calculated using different bases and heights.

Investigation: Area of Triangles

Student Audience: Middle School/High School

Prerequisites: Students should know how to find the area of a parallelogram.

Sketchpad Proficiency: Beginner

Class Time: 20-30 minutes. You might try having students do investigations Area of Parallelograms, Area of Trapezoids, and Area of Triangles in one or two trips to the computer lab.

Example Sketch: **Triangle Area** (Mac) or **7area\triarea.gsp** (Windows)

Construction Tips

Step 3: Make sure students construct $\overline{AD}$ to a new point D. They must not use existing point C, as dragging C will change the height of the triangle.

Investigate/Conjecture

When D is dragged, the area of the triangle remains unchanged. The height and the length of the base of the triangle remain constant. (The lengths of the other two sides change, but this doesn't affect the area.) By constructing a parallel line through B, students form a parallelogram which they should recognize as being comprised of two identical triangles. (As an alternative here, you could have students rotate the triangle 180° about the midpoint of $\overline{BD}$ to create the parallelogram. While this is a more involved construction, it may better reinforce the notion that the triangles making up the parallelogram are identical.) Students who already know that the area of a parallelogram can be found by multiplying base times height can conjecture that the area of a triangle is half that. Students are asked to measure the distance from D to $\overline{BD}$, rather than constructing an altitude. (Sketchpad measures the perpendicular distance from a point to a segment the same way as it measures the distance from a point to a line. If the point is not over the segment, the distance is measured to a line that would be created by extending the segment.) Question students to check that they understand that this distance is the height of the triangle. If students make the connection between a base and its corresponding height, they should be able to use any of the sides as bases and calculate the area three ways.

Explore More

Students can do this easily without constructing altitudes if they measure distances from each vertex to each opposite side. You may want students to construct altitudes anyway to reinforce the idea that the formula for the area of a triangle applies whether the height is measured inside or outside the triangle.

Investigation: A Triangle Area Problem

In this investigation, you'll divide a triangle into regions and explore the relationship among these areas.

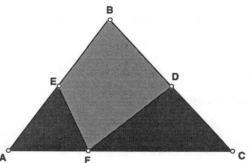

Sketch

Step 1: Construct △*ABC*.

Step 2: Construct *D* and *E*, the midpoints of $\overline{BC}$ and $\overline{AB}$.

Step 3: Construct $\overline{DF}$ and $\overline{EF}$, where *F* is any point on $\overline{BC}$.

Step 4: Construct the polygon interiors of triangles *AEF* and *FDC* and quadrilateral *BEFD*.

Investigate

Without measuring, can you guess how the areas of the triangles are related to the area of the quadrilateral? Move point *F* back and forth along $\overline{AC}$ to see if that gives you any ideas. Think about special cases, such as when *F* is at the midpoint, or at *A* or *C*. When you've made your conjecture, measure the areas and calculate to confirm it.

Conjecture

Write your findings below, along with any explanation you may have for why your conjecture is true.

_____

_____

_____

_____

_____

_____

_____

Present Your Findings

Compare and discuss your results with your partner or group. To present your findings you could print a sketch that shows several copies of your triangle with *F* in different locations to illustrate your conjecture. Include measures and add comments that illustrate what the relationship among the areas is and why.

Explore More

Here's another challenging area problem:

Construct a square. Find two segments from one of the vertices that divide the square into three equal areas. Where should the other endpoints of these segments be located?

Investigation: A Triangle Area Problem

Student Audience: Middle School/High School

Prerequisites: Students should know how to find the area of a triangle.

Sketchpad Proficiency: Beginner

Class Time: 15-30 minutes

Example Sketch: Δ **Area Problem** (Mac) or **7area\triarprb.gsp** (Windows)

Construction Tips

Step 3: Make sure F is on $\overline{AC}$.

Step 4: Give the triangles a different shade than the quadrilateral to distinguish among the shapes to be compared.

Investigate/Conjecture

At first, you don't want students to measure. See if they can figure it out. The shaded triangles each have half the height of the large triangle *ABC*. The sum of their bases is the base of the larger triangle, so together, they make up half the area of the larger triangle. Thus, the quadrilateral must make up the other half, and must be equal in area to the sum of the areas of the small triangles. This will be easiest for students to see when they try special cases: When *F* is at the midpoint of $\overline{AC}$, students may notice that the small triangles are identical, each with 1/4 the area of the large triangle. When *F* is dragged to *A* or *C*, one of the small triangles disappears, leaving the other with base $\overline{AC}$ and height half that of the large triangle.

Explore More

The two segments share an endpoint at a vertex of the square. The other endpoints should be one third of the distance away from the opposite vertex along the opposite sides.

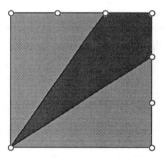

Exploration: Triangle Area/Perimeter

Is it possible to construct two, non-congruent triangles that have both equal areas and perimeters? Use Sketchpad to investigate this question. Use the space below to describe your findings, or print a sketch with comments that describe your findings.

Sketch

If possible, draw and label two non-congruent triangles that have equal area and perimeter in the space below. (Or print your sketch and attach it to this paper.) If you find it's not possible, illustrate why.

Conjecture

In the space below, write a description of what you did in this investigation. If you created two non-congruent triangles with equal areas and perimeters, describe how you did it and describe any relationships you find between the two triangles.

_____

_____

_____

_____

_____

_____

_____

_____

_____

_____

Exploration: Triangle Area/Perimeter

Student Audience: Middle School/High School

Prerequisites: Students need to know how to find the area and perimeter of a triangle.

Sketchpad Proficiency: Beginner

Class Time: 30-40 minutes, depending on how long you allow students to explore

Example Sketches: **Triangle Area** and **Δ Given Perimeter** (Mac) or **7area\triarea.gsp** and **7area\triperim.gsp** (Windows)

Construction Tips: To measure area and perimeter, students need to construct the interiors of the triangles. No Sketch steps are offered to guide students through this exploration. Let them start by manipulating freely constructed triangles. They'll soon discover that it's difficult to do this carefully enough to get a triangle to have a given area and perimeter. They'll start to think of ways to keep the area or the perimeter constant. If they don't come up with something themselves, suggest the following method for keeping the area of one triangle constant while changing its perimeter.
This method is used in the sketch **Triangle Area** (Mac) or **7area\triarea.gsp** (Windows).

Step 1:   Construct a triangle *ABC* and its interior. Measure its area and perimeter.

Step 2:   Construct $\overline{DE}$, a point *F*, and a line through *F*, parallel to $\overline{DE}$. (*DE* should not equal *AC*.)

Step 3:   Construct $\overline{DG}$ and $\overline{EG}$ to create triangle *DGE*. (Don't use *F* in the triangle!)

Step 4:   Construct the interior of Δ*DGE* and measure its area and perimeter.

Step 5:   Move the line until the area of Δ*DGE* is equal to the area of Δ*ABC*.

Step 6:   Point *G* can now be moved to change the perimeter of Δ*DGE* without changing its area.

It's also possible to hold the perimeter of the second triangle constant and manipulate it to change its area. This method is employed in the sketch **Δ Given Perimeter** (Mac) or **7area\triperim.gsp** (Windows).

Step 1:   Construct Δ*ABC*, and its interior. Measure its area and perimeter.

Step 2:   Construct $\overline{DE}$, measure its length, and drag *E* until *DE* is equal to the perimeter of Δ*ABC*.

Step 3:   Construct $\overline{DF}$, $\overline{FG}$, and $\overline{GE}$, where *F* and *E* are on $\overline{DE}$. $\overline{DF}$ will be one side of the triangle. *FG* and *GE* will serve as lengths for the other two sides.

Step 4:   Construct a circle with center *D* and radius *FG*. Construct a circle with center *F* and radius *GE*.

Step 5:   Construct *H*, one intersection of these circles.

Step 6:   Construct the interior of Δ*DHF*. Its perimeter is already equal to the perimeter of Δ*ABC*. Move points *G* and *F* and see if you can make the areas equal. (A side investigation: Trace the locus of *H*. Drag *G*. What's the locus of *H*? Answer: an ellipse.)

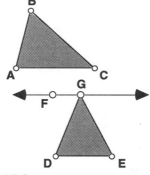

Investigation: A Square Within a Square

A median of a triangle connects a vertex with the midpoint of the opposite side. The three medians in a triangle intersect in a single point. In this investigation, you'll connect the vertices of a square with midpoints of sides in a special order so that the intersections create a square within your square. You'll discover that this inside square has an interesting relationship to the outside square.

Sketch

Step 1: Construct square *ABCD*. Use any method you like, or use a script.

Step 2: Construct midpoints *E, F, G,* and *H*.

Step 3: Construct $\overline{AG}, \overline{BF}, \overline{CE},$ and $\overline{DH}$, in order as shown.

Step 4: Construct the four points of intersection of these segments.

Step 5: Construct the polygon interior of the inside square.

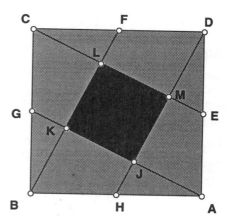

Step 6: Construct the polygon interior of the outside square and give it a lighter shade so that both squares are visible.

Investigate

Without measuring, can you guess what the relationship is between areas of the larger and smaller squares? Measure these areas and calculate the ratio to confirm your guess. How do the areas compare? Change the size of your original square to see if this applies to all squares. Can you explain why this is true?

Conjecture: Write your conjectures below.

_____

_____

_____

_____

_____

Present Your Findings

Compare and discuss your results with your partner or group. To present your findings you could print a captioned sketch that illustrates your conjectures.

Explore More

1. Here's a way to visually demonstrate your conjecture: Print your sketch. Cut out the nine pieces into which the outside square is divided. Rearrange these pieces into squares, congruent to the inside square, to illustrate your conjecture.

2. Try this investigation with a regular hexagon. There are actually three different inside hexagons you can investigate.

3. How do points *K* and *J* divide segment $\overline{AG}$?

4. Compare the ratio of the sides of the squares to the ratio of their areas.

Investigation: A Square Within a Square

Student Audience: Middle School/High School

Prerequisites: Students should have some idea of how the areas of squares and triangles are found.

Sketchpad Proficiency: Beginner

Class Time: 15-30 minutes

Example Sketch: **Square w/in Square** (Mac) or **7area\sqinsq.gsp** (Windows)

Construction Tips

Labels in students' constructions need not match the labels in the diagram, but it's important they construct the correct segments so that they don't get two segments going to the same midpoint.

Investigate/Conjecture

Students are likely to guess a four-to-one relationship between the larger and smaller square. (The involvement of midpoints will suggest a power of two.) In fact, the larger square has five times the area of the smaller. This can be explained by the following reasoning:

The inner square is surrounded by four right triangles congruent to $\triangle ABG$. Each such triangle has area of 1/4 the original square, but they overlap one another by small right triangles like $\triangle HJA$. Triangle ABG can be thought of as being comprised of a medium sized right triangle, $\triangle ABK$, and the small right triangle BGK. Triangle BGK is congruent to $\triangle AHJ$ which can be seen to have 1/4 the area of $\triangle ABK$. So $\triangle BGK$ has area 1/5 that of $\triangle ABG$. Since the large right triangles each have 1/4 the area of the square and there are four of them, their total area is the area of the square. But subtracting the four small triangles that overlap (and were thus counted twice) we see that the area surrounding the inner square is 4/5 the total area.

Explore More

2. The ratios of the outside hexagon area to the three inside hexagons are 7/4, 13/3, and 13/1.

3. GK is 1/5 of GA. $KJ = JA = 2/5$ of GA.

4. The ratio of AB to KJ is the square root of 5.

Investigation: A Triangle Within a Triangle

In this activity you'll investigate the area relationship between a triangle and a triangle within it made by connecting each vertex with a trisection point on the opposite side.

Sketch

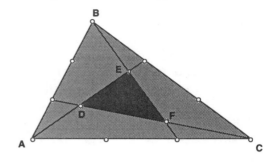

Step 1:   Construct $\triangle ABC$.

Step 2:   Open the script **Segment Trisector** (Mac) or **1lineang\trisect.gss** (Windows).

Step 3:   Play the script on points A, B, and C, selected in that order, to trisect $\overline{AB}$. Play it again on B, C, and A and C, A, and B to trisect $\overline{BC}$ and $\overline{AF}$. Hide the labels of these trisection points.

Step 4:   Going clockwise around the triangle from A to B to C, construct a segment from A to the first point clockwise past B, a segment from B to the first point clockwise from C, and a segment from C to the first point clockwise from A.

Step 5:   Construct points of intersection D, E, and F, the vertices of the inner triangle formed by the segments of step 4.

Step 6:   Construct the polygon interiors of the outside triangle and the inner triangle. Make the outside triangle a lighter shade.

Investigate

Before you measure, can you guess the relationship between the larger and smaller area? Measure the areas. Can you tell what the ratio is? Calculate the ratio of the larger area to the smaller. Surprised? Manipulate your triangle to confirm the areas are always in this ratio. Measure some lengths and look into why this is true.

Conjecture: Write your conjectures below.

_____

_____

_____

Present Your Findings

Compare and discuss your results with your partner or group. To present your findings you could print a captioned sketch that illustrates your conjectures.

Explore More

1. Investigate whether or not the large and small triangles are similar.

2. Try this investigation again subdividing the sides of the triangle in fourths.

3. Try this investigation on a quadrilateral.

4. Create a triangle outside your original triangle by extending each side by a distance equal to the length of the side in a pinwheel fashion. For example, rotate $\overline{AB}$ and B 180° about point A. Rotate $\overline{BC}$ and C 180° about B, and so on. Compare areas of your outer and your original triangles.

Investigation: A Triangle Within a Triangle

Student Audience: High School

Prerequisites: Students should have some idea of how the areas of a triangle is found.

Sketchpad Proficiency: Experienced User

Class Time: 20-40 minutes

Script Needed and Example Sketch: Segment Trisector (Mac script) and Δ **Within a** Δ (Mac sketch) or **1lineang\trisect.gss** and **7area\triintri.gsp** (Windows)

Construction Tips

Step 3: The script **Segment Trisector** (Mac) or **1lineang\trisect.gss** (Windows) requires three points to be selected. The first two points selected are the endpoints of the segment.

Step 4: This instruction sounds a little complicated, but students should have not trouble if they follow the diagram. If students do choose the wrong trisection points, their results will be different.

Investigate/Conjecture

Students are likely to guess a six-to-one or nine-to-one ratio between the larger and smaller square. (The trisection will suggest a multiple of three.) In fact, the larger square has seven times the area of the smaller. A proof gets complicated, but an unsubstantiated explanation, based on the diagram below, might go like this:

The inner triangle is surrounded by three triangles like Δ*ADC* that have equal areas. These triangles have six times the area of little triangles like Δ*FCG*. Triangles *FGC* and *HDA* have equal areas, so the area of Δ*HDA* is 1/7 the area of Δ*HAC*. The three large triangles like Δ*HAC* each have area 1/3 the area of the large triangle, so the sum of the areas of these three triangles is the area of the large triangle. Therefore, the three little triangles where these large triangles overlap have total area equal to the area of the inner triangle. Since each of these little triangles has area 1/7 of the overlapping triangles, the area of the inner triangle is 1/7 the area of the outer triangle.

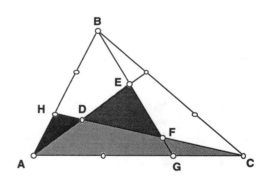

Explore More

1. The triangles are not similar. It's possible for the outer to be acute and the inner to be obtuse.

2. Dividing the triangle sides in fourths yields an inner triangle whose area is 4/13 the outer triangle.

3. Dividing the sides of a quadrilateral in thirds yields an inner quadrilateral whose area is 2/5 the outer.

4. This method yields an outer triangle with area 7 times the original.

Investigation: Maximum Area Rectangles

If you wanted to enclose a field with a fence, typically you'd find out the dimensions of the field and determine how much fence you needed. But suppose the process were reversed. Suppose you started out with a given amount of fence and you wanted to use it to enclose the biggest possible rectangular field. What rectangle shape would you choose? In other words, what type of rectangle has the most area for a given perimeter? You'll discover the answer in this investigation. Or, if you have a hunch already, this investigation will help confirm your hunch and give you more insight into it.

Sketch

Step 1: Construct $\overline{AB}$.

Step 2: Construct $\overline{AC}$ on $\overline{AB}$.

Step 3: Construct perpendiculars to $\overline{AB}$ through points A and C.

Step 4: Construct circle CB.

Step 5: Construct point D where this circle intersects the perpendicular.

Step 6: Construct a line through point D, parallel to $\overline{AB}$.

Step 7: Construct point E and polygon interior $ACDE$ to complete the rectangle.

Step 8: Measure the area and perimeter of this polygon and measure distances AC and AE.

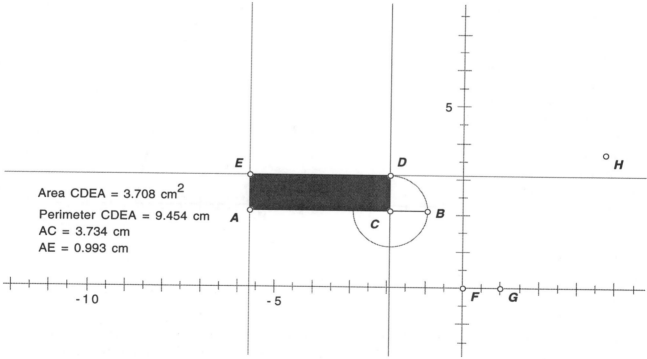

Area CDEA = 3.708 cm^2

Perimeter CDEA = 9.454 cm

AC = 3.734 cm

AE = 0.993 cm

Investigate

So far you should have a figure similar to the one above, but without the graph. You'll get to that in a minute. First, drag point C back and forth. How does this affect the area and perimeter of the rectangle? Without measuring, can you see how AB is related to the perimeter of the rectangle? Explain why this rectangle has a fixed perimeter.

Investigation: Maximum Area Rectangles

Student Audience: High School

Prerequisites: Students should know the terms **rectangle**, **square**, **area**, and **perimeter**.

Sketchpad Proficiency: Experience User

Class Time: 30-40 minutes

Example Sketch: **Max Area Rectangle** (Mac) or **7area\maxarea.gsp** (Windows)

Construction Tips

Step 3: These perpendiculars can both be constructed at the same time: select the two points and segment.

Step 7: Students need not construct segments *EA*, *ED*, and *DC* as long as they construct the polygon interior.

Step 8: Simply click anywhere on the polygon to select it and measure its area and perimeter. Select two points to measure distances.

Investigate/Conjecture

As students drag point *C*, they should notice that the area of the rectangle changes but its perimeter remains constant. Because *CB* and *CD* are radii of the same circle, the sum of two sides of the rectangle, *AC* + *CD*, is equal to *AB*. Thus, *AB* is half the perimeter of the rectangle. As long as this length is kept constant, the perimeter of the rectangle will be constant.

Students are likely to observe, before they create a graph, that maximum area is achieved when the rectangle is a square. It's worthwhile to see this played out graphically. When students construct the locus of point *H*, they'll see a parabola. The area, given by the y-coordinate of point *H*, is maximum when point *H* is at the vertex of the parabola.

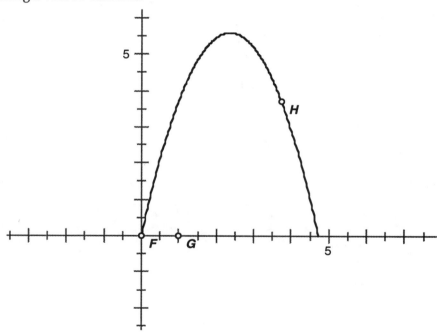

Explore More

1. The square has the maximum area of any quadrilateral for a given perimeter.

2. Regular polygons have maximum area for a given perimeter. Polygons with more sides are more efficient. The circle is the closed planar figure that gives maximum area for a given perimeter.

3. The area of the rectangle can be represented by the equation $A = x[(1/2)P - x]$. The graph is a parabola with roots 0 and $(1/2)P$. So the x-value of the maximum point is $(1/4)P$. Since the side length of the maximum area rectangle is 1/4 the rectangle's perimeter, the rectangle must be a square.

Exploring Geometry

Investigation: Maximum Area Rectangles (continued)

As you drag point C, observe what rectangular shape gives the greatest area. What shape do you think that is? You can explore this relationship graphically. Select the Measures AC and Area CDEA in that order. Choose Plot As (x, y) in the Graph menu. You should get axes and a point H as shown. The vertical axis represents the area of the rectangle and the horizontal axis corresponds to the length of one side. If you drag point C, you'll see point H move to correspond to different side lengths and perimeters. To see a graph of all possible areas for this rectangle, select point H and point C, in that order, and choose Locus in the Construct menu. It should now be easy to position point C so that point H is at a maximum value for the area of the rectangle.

Conjecture

On a separate paper, write a paragraph about your construction, answering the questions posed in the Investigate section above. Then make a conjecture about what type of rectangle encloses the maximum area for a given perimeter.

Present Your Findings

Compare and discuss your results with your partner or group. To present your findings you could print a captioned sketch showing your graph and measures that illustrate your conjecture.

Explore More

1. Your construction limited your investigation to rectangles. But do you think other, nonrectangular quadrilaterals might yield even greater area for a given perimeter than the special rectangle you found? Investigate with a quadrilateral drawn freehand using the segment tool.

2. Investigate area/perimeter relationships in other polygons. Can you make a conjecture about what kinds of polygons yield the greatest area for a given perimeter?

3. What's the equation for the graph you made? Let AC be x and let AB be (1/2)P, where P stands for perimeter (a constant). Write an equation for area, A, in terms of x and P. What value for x (in terms of P) gives a maximum value for A?

Investigation: The Area of a Trapezoid

A **trapezoid** is a quadrilateral with exactly two parallel sides. In this investigation you'll measure various parts of a trapezoid and use the Calculate command to see if you can come up with a formula for the area of a trapezoid.

Sketch

Step 1:   Construct $\overline{AB}$ and point C not on $\overline{AB}$.

Step 2:   Construct a line parallel to $\overline{AB}$ through C.

Step 3:   Construct $\overline{CD}$, where D is on the parallel line.

Step 4:   Construct $\overline{AC}$ and $\overline{DB}$.

Step 5:   Construct polygon interior *ABDC*.

Step 6:   Construct E and F, the midpoints of $\overline{AC}$ and $\overline{BD}$.

Step 7:   Construct lines through E and F, perpendicular to $\overline{AB}$.

Step 8:   Construct G, H, J, and K where these lines intersect $\overline{AB}$ and $\overleftrightarrow{CD}$.

Step 9:   Measure all lengths in the trapezoid, including its height *(HG or JK)*. Measure its area.

Investigate

Without measuring the area of the rectangle *GHJK*, can you see how it compares to the area of the trapezoid? Use Calculate to see if you can come up with an expression using the parts of the trapezoid that gives you its area. Don't just try things at random; think of combinations that would make sense.

When you find a formula that seems to work, make sure you try moving parts of your trapezoid to see if your formula works for *all* trapezoids.

Conjecture: Using b_1 and b_2 for bases and *h* for height, complete the formula below.

The area of a trapezoid is found by the formula $A = $ _____

Present Your Findings: Compare and discuss your results with your partner or group. To present your findings you could:

1. Print a captioned sketch showing measures that illustrate your conjecture.

2. Write a report describing the things you tried when you were looking for the area formula. Include things you tried that didn't work, and try to explain why they didn't work.

Explore More

1. Construct a midsegment of a trapezoid, connecting midpoints of the non-parallel sides (sometimes called the median). Can you use the length of the midsegment to invent a new area conjecture?

2. Rotate the trapezoid interior 180° about E or F so that the original and image together form a long parallelogram. How does this illustrate the area formula conjecture?

3. Construct a triangle inside your trapezoid whose area is always half the area of the trapezoid. Is there more than one way to do this?

Investigation: The Area of a Trapezoid

Student Audience: High School

Prerequisites: Students should know the terms **height** and **base** as they refer to a trapezoid. They should know how to find the areas of a rectangle, a parallelogram, and a triangle.

Sketchpad Proficiency: Beginner

Class Time: 20-40 minutes

Example Sketch: **Trapezoid Area** (Mac) or **7area\traparea.gsp** (Windows)

Construction Tips

Step 7: These perpendiculars can both be constructed at the same time: select the two points and segment.

Step 9: Encourage students to measure legs, if only to show that they don't figure in the area formula. Height can be measured as *HG* or *JK*, or can be measured as the distance from *C* or *D* to $\overline{AB}$.

Investigate/Conjecture

The areas of the rectangle *GHJK* and trapezoid *ACDB* are equal. Imagine $\triangle GAE$ rotated into the space occupied by $\triangle HCE$ and $\triangle BKF$ rotated into $\triangle JDF$. The heights of the rectangle and trapezoid are the same. The base of the rectangle is the average of the bases of the trapezoid. Students should experiment until they get an expression like:

Distance(G to H)*(Length(Segment m)+Length(Segment j))/2 = 4.45

Students are likely to write the formula in a variety of ways, but they should be equivalent to:

$$A = (1/2)(b_1 + b_2)h$$

Explore More

1. $A = mh$, where m is the length of the midsegment, gives the area of the trapezoid. The length of the midsegment is the average of the lengths of the bases.

2. The lengths of the bases of the long parallelogram formed this way are each $b_1 + b_2$. So the area of this parallelogram is $(b_1 + b_2)h$. The area of the trapezoid is half that.

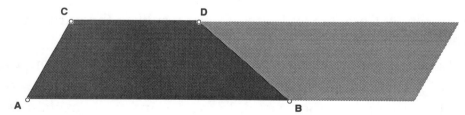

3. In the figure in the activity, $\triangle GCK$ would have half the area of the trapezoid.

Problem: Dividing Land

When farmers Clarence and Myrtle died, they left their two daughters their land with instructions to divide it equally. One daughter, Ella, was considerably brighter (and more conniving) than her sister, Jo. The land, unfortunately, was shaped as an irregular quadrilateral, and it wasn't immediately obvious how to divide it equally. Ella first tried to get Jo to agree to split it down the diagonal $\overline{AC}$ shown, with Ella getting region ACD and Jo getting region ABC. Even Jo could see that was a bad deal, so she called a lawyer.

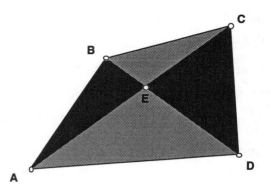

Ella then offered to split the land with both diagonals. Ella would take two regions: AED and BEC, leaving Jo with ABE and CED. This sounded good to Jo, but her lawyer checked it out and reported that the sums of the respective regions were still not equal. "Ah," said Ella, "but the products of our regions *are* equal!" This stumped Jo and her lawyer (who was none too bright either) and she agreed to the deal out of sheer awe for Ella's discovery.

Investigate

Model this problem with Sketchpad. Is Ella's claim true for all quadrilaterals? Does that mean that this was a fair way to divide the land? Why or why not? See if you can show why Ella's conjecture is true. Write your findings in the space below.

_____

_____

_____

_____

_____

_____

_____

_____

_____

_____

Explore More

See if you can come up with a way to divide an irregular quadrilateral using only two segments so that the four regions can be shared equally.

Problem: Dividing Land

Student Audience: High School

Prerequisites: Students should know how to find the area of a triangle.

Sketchpad Proficiency: Beginner

Class Time: 10-30 minutes, depending on how long you give students to try to figure out why this works

Example Sketch: Dividing Land (Mac) or **7area\diviland.gsp** (Windows)

Construction Tips

Students may be tempted to construct two self-intersecting polygons to compare areas, but they need to construct four separate regions to compare products.

Investigate/Conjecture

Students will find the the products of the areas are, indeed, equal. But that doesn't mean it's a fair way to divide the land. The only fair way, of course, would ensure that the sums of the areas were equal. The product relationship can be explained as follows:

Draw altitudes $\overline{BF}$ and $\overline{DG}$. The area of $\triangle ABE$ is $(1/2)(AE)(BF)$. The area of $\triangle CED$ is $(1/2)(CE)(DG)$. The area of $\triangle BEC$ is $(1/2)(CE)(BF)$ and the area of $\triangle AED$ is $(1/2)(AE)(DG)$. The product of the areas of $\triangle ABE$ and $\triangle CED$ is $(1/2)(AE)(BF)(1/2)(CE)(DG)$. The product of the areas of $\triangle BEC$ and $\triangle AED$ is $(1/2)(CE)(BF)(1/2)(AE)(DG)$, which is the same as the product of the areas of $\triangle ABE$ and $\triangle CED$.

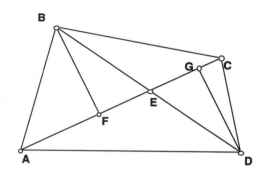

Explore More

Divide the quadrilateral as shown, by connecting midpoints of opposite sides. It even works for convex quadrilaterals.

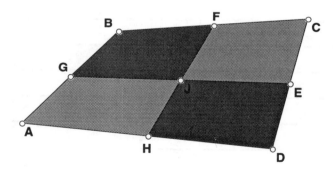

Investigation: Area of Regular Polygons

A **regular polygon** has equal sides and angles. Any regular polygon can be divided into congruent triangles. In this investigation you'll discover a relationship between the area of a triangle and the area of a regular polygon. You'll also derive a formula for finding the area of a regular polygon.

Sketch

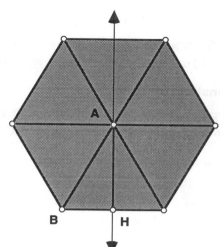

Step 1: Use the script **6/Hexagon (Inscribed)** (Mac) or **regpoly\6inscrib.gss** (Windows) to construct a regular hexagon. Construct its interior.

Step 2: Construct segments from its center to each vertex. (Each of these segments is called a **radius**.)

Step 3: Construct a line through the center, perpendicular to one of the sides.

Step 4: Construct a segment $\overline{AH}$ along this line, from the center to the point of intersection with the side. This segment is called an **apothem**.

Step 5: Hide the line.

Investigate

How many triangles were formed when you constructed the radii of the hexagon? The apothem is the height of one of these triangles. How would you find the area of this triangle? If you knew the area of this triangle, how would you calculate the area of the hexagon? Measure the length of one side and the length of the apothem. Use Calculate to create an expression using these lengths that give the area of the hexagon. Measure the area to confirm you've built a correct expression. Measure the perimeter of the hexagon. Use Calculate to create another expression for the area of the hexagon, this time using the perimeter and the length of the apothem. Make sure your expressions work even if you change the size or position of your hexagon.

Conjecture: Write a formula for the area of any regular polygon using *a* for apothem, *s* for the length of one side, and *n* for the number of sides:

$$A = \underline{\hspace{6cm}}$$

What's the perimeter of a regular polygon in terms of s and n? Write a formula for the area of a regular polygon using a for apothem and p for perimeter:

$$A = \underline{\hspace{6cm}}$$

Write a description of how you derived your formulas for the area of a regular polygon and how this area is related to the area of a triangle.

_____

_____

_____

_____

Investigation: Area of Regular Polygons

Student Audience: High School

Prerequisites: Students should know how to find the area of a triangle.

Sketchpad Proficiency: Beginner

Class Time: 20-30 minutes

Script Needed/Example Sketch: **6/Hexagon (Inscribed)** (Mac script) and **Regular Hexagon Area** (Mac sketch) or **regpoly\6inscrib.gss** and **7area\reghexar.gsp** (Windows)

Construction Tips

Step 1: This script requires two points to be selected as "givens." One point is the center of the hexagon. (If students don't use the "Inscribed" script, they won't have the center they need.)

Investigate/Conjecture

The radii of the hexagon form six congruent triangles. The area of one of these triangles is 1/2 the length of the base (the side of the polygon) times the height (the apothem of the polygon). The area of the hexagon could be found by just multiplying the area of one triangle by six. Students should be able to generalize this method for all regular polygons. An *n*-gon can be divided into *n* triangles. The area of the *n*-gon is just the area of one of these triangles times *n*. Students should write versions of the following formulas:

$A = (1/2)(s)(a)(n)$, where s is the length of one side, a is the length of the apothem, and n is the number of sides.

$A = (1/2)(a)(p)$, where a is the length of the apothem and p is the perimeter. (This formula is derived by substituting p for $(s)(n)$.)

Explore More

Students should notice that the perimeter of a 17-gon is pretty close to the circumference of the circumscribing circle and the apothem is close to the radius.
So students might conjecture that the area of a circle is given by the formula
$A = (1/2)(C)(r)$, where C is the circumference and r is the radius of the circle. Substituting $2\pi r$ for C, we get the more familiar formula, $A = \pi r^2$.

Exploring Geometry

Investigation: Area of Regular Polygons (continued)

Present Your Findings

Discuss your results with your partner or group. To present your findings you could:

1. Create and print a sketch that shows several different regular polygons and how their areas can be calculated. Include comments that explain your reasoning.

2. Record a script that constructs a regular polygon with an apothem and calculates an expression for its area. Add comments to the script to make a presentation that describes how to find the area of a regular polygon.

Explore More

Play the script **17-gon (Inscribed)** (Mac) or **regpoly\17gon.gss** (Windows). Construct the circumscribing circle. How do the perimeter and circumference compare? Construct a radius and an apothem. How do the lengths of these segments compare in a regular polygon with many sides? Can you use these observations to come up with a formula for the area of a circle?

Problem: Boarding Up the Bathroom Window

A man had a square window on the south side of his mountain cabin. In the winter, too much light came through it, so he decided to board up part of it. Always looking for a stylish solution, he settled on forming a smaller square by joining midpoints of the sides as shown and boarding up the corners. This let in half as much light as before. (Can you see why?)

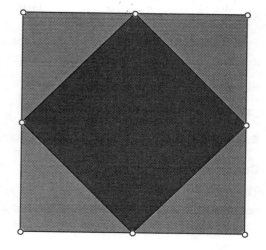

Now he wants to do the same thing with a hexagonal window in his bathroom. After he joins midpoints and boards up the corners, what fraction of the light will come through?

Use Sketchpad to find an answer to the problem. In the space below, draw a picture of the window and explain your answer.

Problem: Boarding Up the Bathroom Window

Student Audience: High School

Prerequisites: Students should have a basic understanding of area. To explain their answer, they'll need to know about relationships in 30-60 right triangles.

Sketchpad Proficiency: Beginner

Class Time: 20-30 minutes

Example Sketch: **Hexagon Window** (Mac) or **7area\hexwindw.gsp** (Windows)

Construction Tips

The easiest way to construct the first hexagon is to use the script **6/Hexagon (By Edge)** (Mac) or **regpoly\6byedge.gss** (Windows). The inner hexagon can be constructed easily by connecting midpoints.

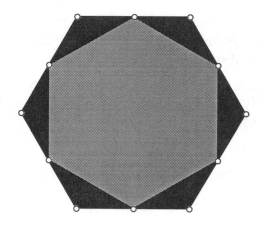

Investigate/Conjecture

The inner hexagon has 3/4 the area of the larger. (So the window will let in 3/4 as much light.) Students who know about relationships in special right triangles can explain this as follows:

The ratio of the areas of the hexagons is the same as the ratio of the areas of triangles NPR and FAR. The ratio of these areas is the square of the ratio of their sides. Let $FP = 1$. $RP = \sqrt{3}$ and $FA = 2$. So the ratio of the sides of triangles NPR and FAR is $\sqrt{3}/2$, and the ratio of their areas is 3/4.

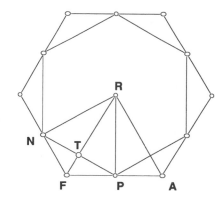

©1996 by Key Curriculum Press   Exploring Geometry

Demonstration: The Area of a Circle

The formula for the area of a circle can be derived from the formula for the area of a regular polygon. You'll experiment with a sketch that demonstrates this.

Sketch

Step 1:   Open the sketch **To a Circle** (Mac) or **7area\polycirc.gsp** (Windows).

Step 2:   Drag (or animate) point "Drag" along its segment. Observe how the polygon and the measures change.

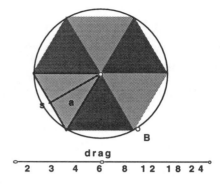

drag

2   3   4   6   8   12   18   24

a*s*6/2 = 14.21   a = 2.03 cm
Area(Circle 1) = 17.18 square cm   r = 2.34 cm

Investigate

One expression you'll see in this sketch is a*s*n/2, where a is the length of the apothem, s is the length of one side of the polygon, and n will vary depending on the number of sides your polygon has. What quantity does this expression represent? (Hint: the apothem is the height of one triangle.) What does s*n represent? Using p for perimeter, can you write another expression for the area of a regular polygon? As the number of sides in the polygon increases, the length of the apothem approaches what circle quantity? What circle quantity does the perimeter of the polygon approach? Can you rewrite the polygon area formula, a*p/2 to represent the area of a circle? What's the formula for the circumference of a circle?

Conjecture: In the space below, write a paragraph answering the questions above. Then use your answers to come up with an equation for the area of a circle.

_____

_____

_____

_____

_____

_____

_____

Present Your Findings: Compare and discuss your results with your partner or group. To present your findings you could add captions to this sketch that explain how you derived your formula for the area of the circle.

Explore More

1.   Use Calculate to confirm that your formula for the area of a circle works.

2.   Print the sketch with the 18-gon showing. Cut out the circle wedges and arrange them into a shape approximating a rectangle. What are the approximate dimensions of the "rectangle"?

Demonstration: The Area of a Circle

Student Audience: High School

Prerequisites: Students should know how to find the area of a regular polygon.

Sketchpad Proficiency: Beginner

Class Time: 15-30 minutes. You might want to do this activity in the same class period as Area of a Regular Polygon.

Example Sketch: To a Circle (Mac) or **7area\polycirc.gsp** (Windows)

Construction Tips

Students don't need to construct anything in this activity. They will manipulate the pre-made sketch.

Investigate/Conjecture

The expression $a*s*n/2$ represents the area of the polygon. The expression $s*n$ represents the perimeter of the polygon (s is the length of one side and n is the number of sides). So $a*p/2$ is another expression that would give the area of the polygon. As the number of sides in the polygon increases, the length of the apothem approaches the radius of the circle. The perimeter of the polygon approaches the circumference of the circle. An equation for the area of a circle could be $r*C/2$ (r takes the place of a and C takes the place of p in the polygon area formula). Circumference is given by the formula, $C = 2\pi r$. Substituting, we get the familiar formula for the area of a circle:
$A = \pi r^2$.

Explore More

2.   The dimensions of this rectangle are πr (half the circumference) by r. Thus, the area is πr^2.

Investigation: New Area Formulas

Space scientists have discovered a capsule from an extraterrestrial civilization. Within they found mysterious writings which noted intergalactic linguists translated into the area formulas below. Use Sketchpad to determine if all four formulas always work.

Translations

1. To find the area of a triangle, use $A = mh$, where m is the length of the midsegment of the triangle and h is the height of the triangle.

2. To find the area of a trapezoid, use $A = mh$, where m is the length of the midsegment of the triangle and h is the height of the triangle.

3. To find the area of a rhombus, use $A = rs$, where r and s are the lengths of the diagonals.

4. To find the area of a kite, use $A = rs$, where r and s are the lengths of the diagonals.

Sketch

Make sure you construct your trapezoid and rhombus so that they'll remain a trapezoid and a rhombus when you manipulate them.

Investigate

Construct polygon interiors and measure the areas. Now measure other quantities (heights, midsegments, etc.) and use Calculate to test the formulas. Which work? Which don't? Why? Make sure you manipulate your figures to confirm that the formulas that work always work.

Conjecture: In the space below, write explanations for why the formulas do or don't work. Use algebra and what you know about the standard area formulas for these shapes. Correct any formulas that don't work.

_____

_____

_____

_____

_____

_____

_____

Present Your Findings: Compare and discuss your results with your partner or group. To present your findings you could print a captioned sketch showing the shapes and their new area formulas. Include explanation for why they work.

Explore More

See if you can come up with other new area formulas for these or other shapes.

Investigation: New Area Formulas

Student Audience: High School

Prerequisites: Students should know standard ways of finding the areas of triangles, trapezoids, and rhombuses. Students should know the term midsegment. (A midsegment connects midpoints of two sides in a triangle or of the legs of a trapezoid. Many books use the terms midline for triangles and median for trapezoids. These terms cause confusion that can be avoided by using the term midsegment.)

Sketchpad Proficiency: Experienced User

Class Time: 30-50 minutes

Example Sketch: **Alternate Areas** (Mac) or **7area\altareas.gsp** (Windows)

Construction Tips

Students are not given any construction steps, the assumption being that they have enough Sketchpad experience to construct these figures. Possible construction steps are summarized below:

To construct a trapezoid, start with a segment and a point not on the segment. Construct a parallel line through the point, then construct segments from your original segment to the line. Hide the line and construct the second base.

To construct a rhombus, construct a segment and its midpoint. Construct a perpendicular through the midpoint. Construct a random point on this line, mark the segment mirror, and reflect the point across the segment. Connect the four points, hide the line, and construct the second diagonal. (One advantage of this construction method is that it reinforces the property that diagonals of a rhombus are perpendicular bisectors of one another.

Investigate/Conjecture

The first two formulas work. The formula for the area of a rhombus should be $(1/2)(r)(s)$.

1. In the triangle, the length of a midsegment is 1/2 the length of the base to which it's parallel. Substitute m for $(1/2)(b)$ in the standard formula, $A = (1/2)(b)(h)$ and get $A = mh$.

2. In the trapezoid the length of the midsegment is the average of the lengths of the bases. Substitute m for $(1/2)(b_1 + b_2)$ in the standard formula, $A = (1/2)(b_1 + b_2)h$, and get $A = mh$.

3. In the rhombus, a diagonal r divides the rhombus into congruent triangles. The height of one of these triangles is $(1/2)(s)$, so the area of this triangle is $(1/2)(r)[(1/2)(s)]$. The area of the two triangles, then, is $(1/2)(r)(s)$.

4. In the kite, the same argument holds as for the rhombus. The area should be $(1/2)(r)(s)$.

©1996 by Key Curriculum Press   Exploring Geometry

Investigation: Archimedes' Tombstone

In this activity, you'll construct the figure that the famous Greek mathematician, Archimedes, requested be put on his tombstone. You'll discover some relationships that made this figure so fascinating to the great mathematician.

Sketch

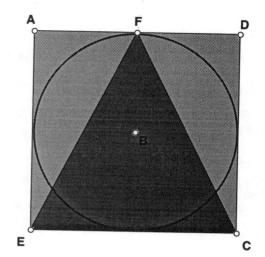

Step 1: Use the script **4/Square (Inscribed)** (Mac) or **regpoly\4inscrib.gss** (Windows) to construct square *ADCE* with center *B*.

Step 2: Construct *F*, the midpoint of $\overline{AD}$.

Step 3: Construct circle *BF*.

Step 4: Construct $\overline{EF}$ and $\overline{CF}$.

Step 5: Construct polygon interiors of square *ADCE* and triangle *FCE*.

Investigate

Measure the areas of the square, the circle, and the triangle. Drag *A* until the area of the square is as close to 4.000 sq. in. as you can make it. What are the areas of the circle and triangle? Do you recognize this value of the area of the circle? Calculate the ratios of the area of the square to the area of the circle and the area of the circle to the area of the triangle. Do these ratios remain the same for any sized square? Complete the statement below:

Area$_{square}$ to Area$_{circle}$ to Area$_{triangle}$ is _____ to _____ to _____.

Explore More

1. When each of the figures (square, circle, and isosceles triangle) is revolved about the vertical axis of symmetry, it generates a solid of revolution (cylinder, sphere, and cone). Calculate the volumes of these solids and complete the statement of proportionality below:

   Volume$_{cylinder}$ to Volume$_{sphere}$ to Volume$_{cone}$ is _____ to _____ to _____.

2. Do some research and write a report on Archimedes' life.

Investigation: Archimedes' Tombstone

Student Audience: High School

Prerequisites: Students should know how to find the areas of a triangle, a circle, and a square.

Sketchpad Proficiency: Beginner

Class Time: 20-30 minutes

Script Needed: **4/Square (Inscribed)** (Mac) or **regpoly\4inscrib.gss** (Windows)

Construction Tips

You might have students construct the square from scratch. If they do, make sure they also construct the center.

Investigate/Conjecture

Students should complete the statement to read:

$\text{Area}_{\text{square}}$ to $\text{Area}_{\text{circle}}$ to $\text{Area}_{\text{triangle}}$ is 4 to π to 2.

Explore More

The ratios of the volumes come out 2π to $(4/3)\pi$ to $(2/3)\pi$, which reduces to 3 to 2 to 1. No wonder Archimedes was so enamored to this figure!

Chapter 8
The Pythagorean Theorem

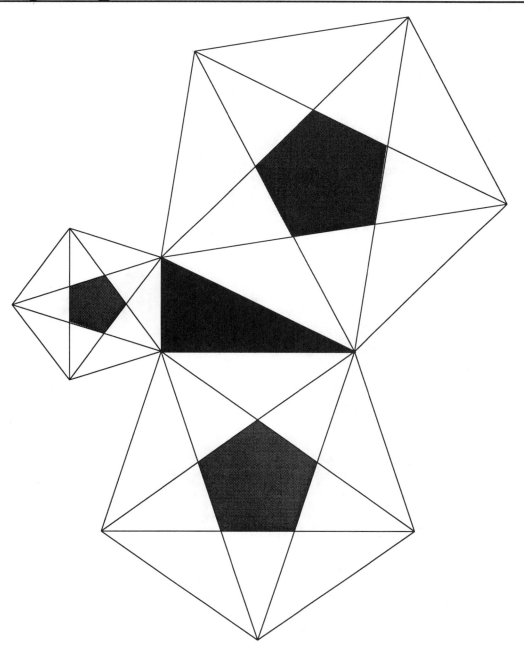

Investigation: The Pythagorean Theorem

In this investigation you'll create a script for constructing a square, then construct squares on the sides of a right triangle. The areas of these squares illustrate perhaps the most famous relationship in mathematics—the Pythagorean Theorem.

Sketch

Record a script for constructing a square:

Step 1: Construct ray *AB* and perpendicular lines through *A* and *B*.

Step 2: Construct circle *AB*.

Step 3: Construct *C*, the intersection of the circle and perpendicular line.

Step 4: Construct a line through *C*, perpendicular to $\overleftrightarrow{AC}$.

Step 5: Construct *D*, the fourth vertex of the square, at the intersection of perpendicular lines.

Step 6: Hide the ray, lines, and circle and construct segments as needed. Construct the polygon interior of the square.

Start with a blank sketch and construct a right triangle:

Step 7: Construct $\overline{AB}$.

Step 8: Construct a line perpendicular to $\overline{AB}$, through *A*.

Step 9: Construct $\overline{AC}$ with *C* any point on the perpendicular.

Step 10: Construct $\overline{BC}$. Hide the line.

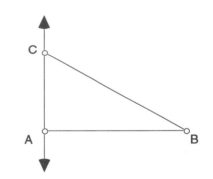

Investigate

Play your square script on the two endpoints of each side of your right triangle. If your script constructs the square to fall into the triangle, undo and select the points in the opposite order.

Measure the areas of the squares and look for a relationship among these areas. Can you translate this discovery into a relationship among the sides of the right triangle?

Use Calculate to confirm your findings.

Drag the vertices of the triangle to confirm that this relationship holds for all right triangles.

Investigation: The Pythagorean Theorem

Student Audience: High School

Prerequisites: Students should know what a **right triangle** and a **square** are and should know terms like **hypotenuse** and **leg**. Students should know how to find the **area of a square**.

Sketchpad Proficiency: Experienced User

Class Time: 30-45 minutes

Example Script/Sketch: 4/Square (By Edge) (Mac Script) and **Pythagorean Theorem** (Mac Sketch) or **regpoly\4byedge.gss** and **8pythag\pytheorm.gsp** (Windows)

Construction Tips: This construction involves recording a script for constructing a square and playing this script on the sides of a right triangle. You can speed things up by having students use a pre-made script such as **4/square (By Edge)** (Mac) or **regpoly\4byedge.gss** (Windows). This script starts with a ray so that it will be reversible; that is, selecting given points in different order yields different squares. This is important—if students use an irreversible script they'll have one or more squares falling inside the triangle. If a student's script constructs the square the "wrong way," have them undo and try again, selecting the givens in the opposite order. But don't spend half the period trying to help students get their squares going the "right" way. the investigation can still be carried out (the Pythagorean Theorem still works) if squares fall inside the triangle.

Investigate/Conjecture: If areas are displayed with precision greater than tenths place, students may not do the mental math to notice that the areas of the squares on the legs add up to the area of the square on the hypotenuse. Guide them to this conjecture by suggesting they try to get one or two of the sides to be an integer length. When they perform some calculations with the measures, they'll discover:

The sum of the areas of the squares constructed on the legs of a right triangle is equal to the area of the square constructed on the hypotenuse.

Some students already familiar with the Pythagorean Theorem are likely to write: $a^2 + b^2 = c^2$ as their conjecture. Have them express the theorem in words. You may want to have students label their diagrams to correspond to this familiar formula.

Explore More

1. Some other similar shapes can be tried on the sides of the right triangle with the construction students already have. For example, select the vertices of the square in the "wrong" order when you construct the Polygon Interior to get an X shape instead of a square. The sum of the areas of these shapes on the legs will equal the area of the shape on the hypotenuse. Students can play scripts for other regular polygons on the sides of a right triangle. See the sketch **Unsquare Pythagoras** (Mac) or **8pythag\unsquare.gsp** (Windows) to see how the Pythagorean Theorem can be generalized to other similar shapes.

2. Students should play their square script on a scalene triangle to show that the Pythagorean Theorem applies only to right triangles, thus demonstrating the converse of the theorem.

3. This is a variation on 1 above. The triangles constructed are similar, thus, the sum of the areas of the small triangles is equal to the area of the triangle on the hypotenuse.

One visual proof of the Pythagorean Theorem is demonstrated by the sketch **Shear Pythagoras** (Mac) or **8pythag\shear.gsp** (Windows) and is further explained in the demonstration activity of the same name. The **8-Pythagorean Theorem** folder (Mac) or **8pythag** directory (Windows) contains several demonstrations of the theorem.

Investigation: The Pythagorean Theorem (continued)

Conjecture: Write the Pythagorean Theorem in your own words below.

_____

_____

Present Your Findings

Discuss your results with your partner or group. To present your findings you could:

1. Print a captioned sketch that shows a right triangle with squares on the sides. Show measures that illustrate the Pythagorean Theorem.

2. Create and add comments to a script that constructs a right triangle with squares on the sides.

Explore More

1. Try constructing other similar shapes on the sides of a right triangle to see if the Pythagorean Theorem can be generalized to shapes other than squares. Try equilateral triangles, regular pentagons, or hexagons. (Use scripts that create these shapes "by edge.")

2. See if the Pythagorean Theorem works for any triangles besides right triangles. Make more conjectures.

3. Construct a line through the right angle vertex, perpendicular to the hypotenuse. Construct the point of intersection of this line and the hypotenuse. Reflect this point across each of the legs. Reflect the right triangle vertex across the hypotenuse. Use these points and the vertices of the original right triangle to construct triangles on the sides of your right triangle. What can you say about these triangles? Does the Pythagorean Theorem apply?

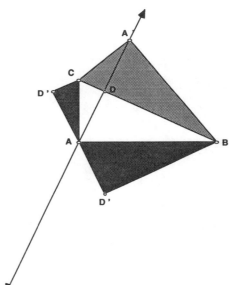

Demonstration: Visual Proof of the Pythagorean Theorem

In this activity you'll do a visual demonstration of the Pythagorean Theorem based on Euclid's proof. By **shearing** the squares on the sides of a right triangle you'll create congruent shapes without changing the areas of your original squares.

Sketch

Step 1: Open the sketch **Shear Pythagoras** (Mac) or **8pythag\shear.gsp** (Windows). You'll see a right triangle with squares on the sides.

Step 2: Measure the areas of the squares.

Step 3: Drag point *A*, then point *B*, onto the line that's perpendicular to the hypotenuse. Note that as the squares become parallelograms their areas don't change.

Step 4: Drag point *C* so that the large square deforms to fill in the triangle. The area of this shape doesn't change either. It should appear congruent to the shape you made with the two smaller parallelograms.

Step 5: Change the shape of the triangle and try the experiment again.

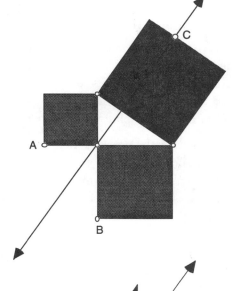

Investigate

You should now have two shapes. One shape was formed from the two squares on the legs of the right triangle. The other shape was formed from the square on the hypotenuse. What can you say about these shapes?

Conjecture: Write your conjectures below.

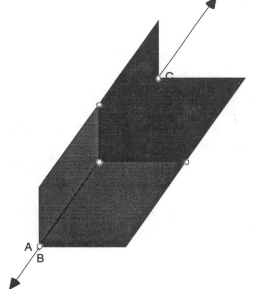

_____

_____

_____

_____

_____

_____

_____

_____

_____

Explore More

Once you've manipulated the squares so that you have congruent shapes, you can Copy and Paste the shape that's on the hypotenuse. Drag the copy over the shape on the legs and see that it fits perfectly.

Demonstration: Visual Proof of the Pythagorean Theorem

Student Audience: High School/College/Teacher Education

Prerequisites: Students will appreciate this more if they already have some experience with the Pythagorean Theorem.

Sketchpad Proficiency: Beginner

Class Time: 20-30 minutes

Sketch Needed: Shear Pythagoras (Mac) or **8pythag\shear.gsp** (Windows)

Demonstration Tips

You can demonstrate and talk about this sketch in a whole class presentation using an overhead projector, or students can play with the sketch independently, in which case you may want to reproduce the activity sheet for them. If students aren't familiar with the Pythagorean Theorem, this demonstration is unlikely to lead to new insights, but it does offer a nice visual proof along the lines of Euclid's proof of the theorem and is intriguing to play with or watch.

Because neither the squares' heights nor bases (the sides of the triangle) change as the squares are sheared into parallelograms, their areas remain constant (*bh* is a formula students should be familiar with; it works for any parallelogram, including squares). Showing all hiddens may help you figure out how the figure is constructed. (Shearing is technically defined as translating each point on a figure in a direction parallel to an axis by a distance proportional to the point's distance from the axis. This is an example of Cavelieri's principle applied in two dimensions, which states that if you distort a figure without changing the lengths of any of its cross sections parallel to a given axis, you won't change the figure's area. Cavalieri's principle applies to volumes and cross sectional areas in three dimensions.)

Use keyboard commands for undo and redo to rapidly repeat the demonstration.

Step 2: You may want students to calculate the sum of the areas on the legs to confirm that it's equal to the area on the hypotenuse.

Investigate/Conjecture

Assuming students already know the Pythagorean Theorem, they can restate it here in terms relevant to the demonstration:

The sum of the areas of the squares on the legs of a right triangle is equal to the area of the square on the hypotenuse.

The squares on the sides of a right triangle can be sheared, without changing their areas, so that a shape on the legs is congruent to a shape on the the hypotenuse.

Explore More

There are a variety of investigations students can do in relation to the Pythagorean Theorem. Have students experiment with the sketch **Unsquare Pythagoras** (Mac) or **8pythag\unsquare.gsp** (Windows), or have them try circles, equilateral triangles, or other similar figures on the sides of right triangles. The folder **8-Pythagorean Theorem** (Mac) or directory **8pythag** (Windows) has several demonstrations related to the Pythagorean Theorem.

 Exploring Geometry

Investigation: Dissection Proof of the Pythagorean Theorem

A dissection proof is done by cutting a figure into pieces and rearranging the pieces to demonstrate some property. Many proofs of the Pythagorean Theorem involve cutting up the squares on the sides and rearranging them to fit in the square on the hypotenuse.

Sketch

Step 1:   Construct a right triangle *ABC*.

Step 2:   Use a script to construct squares on the sides.

Step 3:   Find the center of the square on the large leg by constructing the diagonals. Hide the diagonals.

Step 4:   Construct a line through this center, parallel to the hypotenuse.

Step 5:   Construct another line through the center, this time perpendicular to the hypotenuse.

Step 6:   Construct points where these lines intersect the sides of the square.

Step 7:   Construct four polygon interiors in this square as shown, using the center as one vertex.

Step 8:   Construct the polygon interior of the square on the small leg of the triangle.

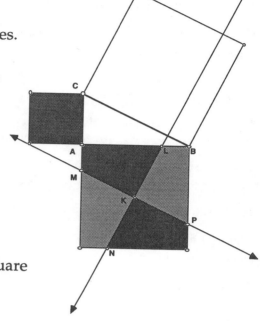

Investigate

You now have five pieces: four in the large square plus the one small square. Can these five pieces be rearranged to fit in the square on the hypotenuse? Select these polygon interiors and choose Cut in the Edit menu. Now choose Paste. The pieces will now be free, and you can move them around. Drag them into the square on the hypotenuse and arrange them so they fill this square without gaps or overlapping. What does this demonstrate? Will this work for any size or shape of right triangle? Use Undo to go back to before you cut the pieces. Change the triangle and repeat the experiment.

Conjecture: In the space below, state the Pythagorean Theorem in terms of the dissection you did.

_____

_____

_____

Present Your Findings: Compare and discuss your results with your partner or group. To present your findings, print a captioned sketch showing the dissection proof.

Explore More: Do some research into other dissection proofs of the Pythagorean Theorem. Many cultures had dissection proofs of the theorem long before Pythagoras' time. U. S. President Garfield even came up with an original dissection proof.

Investigation: Dissection Proof of the Pythagorean Theorem

Student Audience: High School/College/Teacher Education

Prerequisites: This investigation could be used to introduce the Pythagorean Theorem.

Sketchpad Proficiency: Experienced User

Class Time: 20-30 minutes

Example Sketch: **Dissected Pythagoras** (Mac) or **8pythag\dissect.gsp** (Windows)

Construction Tips: Students are given minimal construction instructions in this activity. They should be familiar enough with Sketchpad to construct, for example, a right triangle with no instructions.

Step 1: Construct a segment, construct a line perpendicular to one endpoint. Construct a segment on this line and hide the line. Construct the hypotenuse of the triangle.

Step 2: Students need a script that constructs a square given the endpoints of a side. The script **4/Square (By Edge)** (Mac) or **regpoly\4byedge.gss** (Windows) will do the job.

Step 3: The diagonals are not shown in the figure. The large side in the figure here is $\overline{AB}$. Students should not make their initial triangle isosceles, though they can later investigate that case.

Step 4: In the figure, this is the line through K, parallel to $\overline{BC}$.

Investigate/Conjecture: Students must make sure they select only the interiors before cutting. The pieces can be arranged in the square on the hypotenuse as shown:

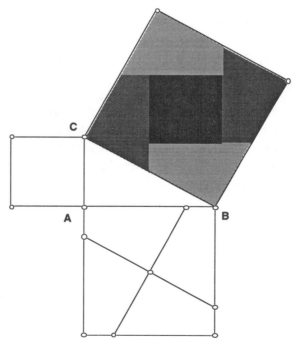

Students should state the Pythagorean Theorem in terms of square areas:

The sum of the areas of the squares on the legs of a right triangle is equal to the area of the square on the hypotenuse.

Investigation: Pythagorean Triples

Is the converse of the Pythagorean Theorem true? That is, if you have three numbers that work in The Pythagorean Theorem and you make a triangle with those lengths, will it be a right triangle? That's what you'll find out in this investigation. (As a bonus, you'll learn how to use Sketchpad to construct a segment of a given length.)

Sketch

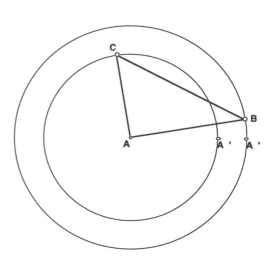

Step 1: Make sure the distance unit in Preferences is set to cm.

Step 2: Construct point A and use the Transform menu to Translate it 4 cm (at any angle).

Step 3: Construct circle AA' and $\overline{AB}$ where B is on the circle.

Step 4: Hide the circle and point A'. You've now constructed a segment ($\overline{AB}$) with fixed length 4 cm.

Step 5: Translate A 3 cm and construct circle AA'.

Step 6: Construct $\overline{AC}$ where C is any point on the circle. Hide the circle and A'.

Step 7: Construct $\overline{BC}$.

Step 8: Measure AC and AB (3 cm and 4 cm respectively) and BC. Edit their measures to read "$AC = $" etc. Also measure $\angle BAC$.

Investigate

Use Calculate to create expressions for AB^2, AC^2, BC^2 and $AB^2 + AC^2$. Drag point B or C until $AB^2 + AC^2 = BC^2$. What does BC equal? What's the measure of $\angle BAC$? When three whole numbers work in the Pythagorean Theorem, we call them a **Pythagorean triple**. The Pythagorean triple you just discovered is the most famous one. Some other Pythagorean triples include 5, 12, and (?); 8, (?), and 17; and (?), 24, and 25. Still more triples can be derived by finding multiples of these. When three numbers work in the Pythagorean Theorem, is the triangle a right triangle?

Conjecture: In the space below, write the converse of the Pythagorean Theorem. Then write a list of at least three Pythagorean triples.

_____

_____

_____

Pythagorean triples: _____

Present Your Findings: Compare and discuss your results with your partner or group. To present your findings you could print a captioned sketch showing several triangles formed by Pythagorean triples.

Explore More: Show that multiples of triples are themselves triples by constructing a 3-4-5 triangle, for example, and dilating it by any scale factor. Is the new triangle still a right triangle?

Investigation: Pythagorean Triples

Student Audience: High School

Prerequisites: Students should be familiar with the **Pythagorean Theorem** and should know what a converse is.

Sketchpad Proficiency: Experienced User

Class Time: 30-40 minutes

Example Sketch: **3-4 Triangle** (Mac) or **8pythag\34tri.gsp** (Windows)

Construction Tips

Step 1: Preferences is found in the Display menu. Students should probably show distance and calculation measurements to tenths precision to mask rounding errors Sketchpad introduces. These errors may mask the whole number relationships in this activity.

Step 8: Double-click on a measure with the Text tool to edit it.

Investigate/Conjecture

Students expressions will look like AB*AB, AC*AC, and AB*AB + AC*AC. When students drag point B or C until the Pythagorean Theorem applies, they'll get 5 cm for BC (or very close to it). At this point, $\angle BAC$ will be 90°. Three, four, and five work in the Pythagorean Theorem, as 9 + 16 = 25. Students should write something like the following for the converse of the Pythagorean Theorem:

If the sum of the areas of the squares of two sides of a right triangle is equal to the area of the square of the third side, then the triangle is a right triangle.

Besides 3-4-5, students should identify the following Pythagorean triples and some multiples of them:

5-12-13, 8-15-17, 7-24-25

Explore More

Dilation doesn't change the shape of a figure. Any multiple of a 3-4-5 right triangle will still be a right triangle.

Investigation: The Isosceles Right Triangle

An isosceles right triangle is a special triangle with several special properties. These properties result in shortcuts that make it easy to find unknown measures of parts of isosceles right triangles.

Sketch

Step 1: Construct circle AB and $\overline{AB}$.

Step 2: Construct a line perpendicular to $\overline{AB}$ through A.

Step 3: Construct $\overline{AC}$ where C is the intersection of the circle and line. Hide the circle and line.

Step 4: Construct $\overline{BC}$.

Step 5: Measure AC, AB, and CB.

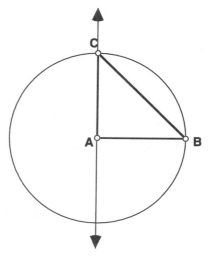

Investigate

AC and AB, of course, should be equal. Can you guess what the measures of angles ACB and ABC are without measuring them? Measure them if you wish to confirm your conjecture. Now, there's a special relationship between the length of the hypotenuse in an isosceles right triangle and the length of one leg. Use Calculate to find the ratio CB/AB. Do you recognize this number? (It's rounded to whatever precision you're displaying.) If not, try multiplying it by itself in the Calculate dialog. Manipulate your triangle to make it bigger or smaller. Does CB/AB change? What is this ratio?

Conjecture: Write your conjectures below.

_____

_____

_____

Present Your Findings: Compare and discuss your results with your partner or group. To present your findings you could print a captioned sketch showing several isosceles right triangles and measures of their sides, along with the ratios of the hypotenuse to one side.

Explore More

1. Continue with this sketch to construct a square out of an isosceles right triangle.

2. Do some research into the discovery by the society of the Pythagoreans of the square root of 2.

Investigation: The Isosceles Right Triangle

Student Audience: High School

Prerequisites: Students should be familiar with the **Pythagorean Theorem** and should know the term **isosceles**. Students should have experience with square roots.

Sketchpad Proficiency: Beginner

Class Time: 20-30 minutes

Example Sketch/Script: **Isosceles Rt.** Δ (Mac sketch) and **Iso. Rt.** Δ (Mac script) or **8pythag\isorttri.gsp** and **8pythag\isorttri.gss** (Windows)

Construction Tips

There's nothing tricky about this construction.

Investigate/Conjecture

Since ∠CAB is 90° and the other two are equal and must add up to 90°, they must be 45°. When students calculate the ratio of the hypotenuse to a leg, they'll see it's 1.41 (assuming precision for distances is set to hundredths in Preferences). They may recognize this as the square root of two. If they use Calculate to multiply this ratio by itself, they'll get exactly two. This ratio of hypotenuse to leg is the square root of two for any isosceles right triangle. Students should write the following conjecture:

The length of the hypotenuse of an isosceles right triangle is $\sqrt{2}$ times the length of a leg.

Explore More

1.   Students need only reflect *A* across $\overline{BC}$. They can create a larger square consisting of four triangles by reflecting across legs instead of across the hypotenuse. These squares are worthy of further investigation. For example, how does the length of a diagonal of a square compare to the length of a side? (This is how the Pythagoreans are said to have discovered irrational numbers.)

Investigation: A Special Right Triangle—30-60-90

The 30-60 right triangle—formed by taking half of an equilateral triangle—has many special properties. You'll discover some of these in this investigation. Knowing these properties makes many problems easy to solve quickly.

Sketch

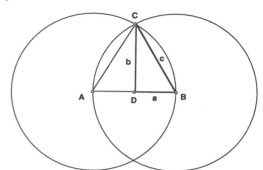

Step 1: Construct $\overline{AB}$.

Step 2: Construct circles AB and BA.

Step 3: Construct $\overline{AC}$ and $\overline{CB}$, where C is one point of intersection of the circles.

Step 4: Construct D, the midpoint of $\overline{AB}$.

Step 5: Construct $\overline{CD}$ and $\overline{DB}$.

Step 6: Hide the circles, A, $\overline{AB}$, and $\overline{AC}$.

Step 7: Relabel $\overline{DB}$, $\overline{DC}$, and $\overline{CB}$ as a, b, and c respectively. (Relabel the triangle vertices as well, if you want them to correspond to opposite sides.)

Investigate

Before you measure, can you guess the relationship between a and c? Measure a, b, and c. Use Calculate to find c/a and b/a. Drag B to change the size of your triangle. Do the ratios c/a and b/a change? Do you recognize this number b/a when it's rounded to the hundredths place? Try multiplying it by itself.

Conjecture: In the space below, write your conjectures. Explain how you could find two sides of any 30-60 right triangle given the length of just one side.

_____

_____

_____

_____

_____

_____

Present Your Findings

Compare and discuss your results with your partner or group. To present your findings you could print a captioned sketch showing several 30-60 right triangles and measures of their sides, along with the ratios that illustrate your conjectures.

Explore More

1. Construct an equilateral triangle and the three medians. How many 30-60 right triangles have you formed?

2. Open the sketch **Graph Paper (Cartesian)** (Mac) or **8pythag\grafcart.gsp** (Windows). Scroll to quadrant IV (the lower right corner). Can you make an equilateral triangle in this quadrant using the graph paper intersections (called lattice points) for vertices? How close can you get?

Investigation: A Special Right Triangle—30-60-90

Student Audience: High School

Prerequisites: Students should be familiar with the **Pythagorean Theorem** and should know the term **equilateral**. Students should have experience with square roots.

Sketchpad Proficiency: Beginner

Class Time: 20-30 minutes

Example Sketch: **30-60 Rt. Δ** (Mac) or **8pythag\3060rttr.gsp** (Windows)

Construction Tips

Steps 1-3: These steps are unnecessary if students use a script to construct an equilateral triangle.

Step 7: Click on a segment with the text tool to display its label. The default labels for these segments will be lower case somewhere in the middle of the alphabet. To edit a label, double-click on the label with the text tool.

Investigate/Conjecture

The construction itself should give away the fact that the short leg is 1/2 the hypotenuse. The ratio c/a is 2. The ratio b/a will be displayed as 1.73, if hundredths is the precision chosen in Preferences. Students may or may not recognize that as an approximation for the the square root of three. Multiplying it by itself will give 3. Students should write the following conjecture:

The length of the hypotenuse in a 30-60 right triangle is twice the length of the shortest side. The length of the long side is $\sqrt{3}$ times the length of the shortest side.

Explore More

1. There are 6 small ones and 6 medium-sized (half the equilateral triangle) ones: 12 altogether.

2. An equilateral triangle can't be constructed on lattice points, but students will do some deep thinking when they try.

Construction: The Square Root Spiral

An irrational number like the square root of two has a point that corresponds to it on a ruler, but you could never find that point precisely by dividing your ruler into fractional parts. Interestingly, you can construct square roots with compass and straightedge (or with Sketchpad). In this activity, you'll construct a square root spiral and use it to create a chart of approximate square roots.

Sketch

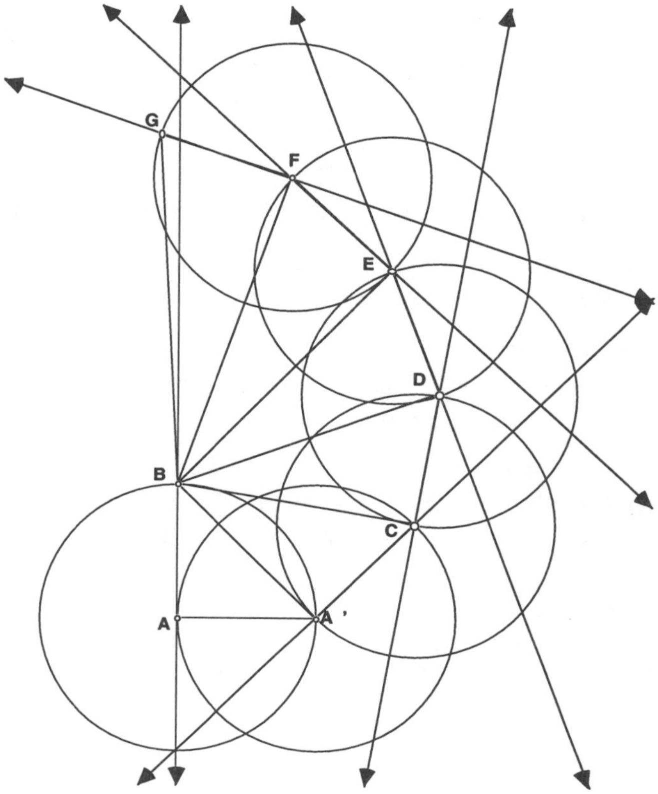

Step 1: Construct point *A* and translate it 1 in., 0° to create *A'*.

Step 2: Construct $\overline{AA'}$ and a line through *A*, perpendicular to $\overleftrightarrow{AA'}$.

Step 3: Construct circle AA' and $\overline{AB}$, where *B* is the intersection of the line and the circle.

Step 4: Construct $\overline{A'B}$.

Before you go on, use the Pythagorean Theorem to find the exact value of *A'B*: (in radical form, not an approximation).
A'B = _____.

Step 5: Construct a line through *A'*, perpendicular to $\overline{A'B}$.

Step 6: Construct a circle $A'A$ and $\overline{A'C}$, where *C* is the intersection of circle $A'A$ and the line.

Step 7: Construct $\overline{BC}$.

What's the length of *A'C*? *A'C* = _____.

Use the Pythagorean Theorem to find an exact value (radical form) of *BC*. *BC* = _____.

Step 8: Continue around constructing perpendiculars and circles with radius 1 inch to construct $\overline{BD}$, $\overline{BE}$, $\overline{BF}$, and $\overline{BG}$ with lengths $\sqrt{4}$, $\sqrt{5}$, $\sqrt{6}$, and $\sqrt{7}$ respectively. Hide the circles and lines.

Investigate

Measure the lengths *BA*, *BA'*, *BC*, *BD*, *BE*, *BF*, and *BG* and complete the chart below:

$$BA = \sqrt{1} = 1 \qquad BA' = \sqrt{2} \approx 1.41 \qquad BC = \sqrt{3} \approx \text{_____}$$

$$BD = \text{_____} \approx \text{_____} \qquad\qquad BE = \text{_____} \approx \text{_____}$$

$$BF = \text{_____} \approx \text{_____} \qquad\qquad BG = \text{_____} \approx \text{_____}$$

Explore More: Continue your spiral until you've made a complete revolution around *B*. To get a sense of how accurately Sketchpad is calculating these square roots, take Sketchpad's measure for $\sqrt{9}$ and multiply it by 10,000. Is Sketchpad accurate to at least seven decimal places? How far out do you have to go to find error?

Construction: The Square Root Spiral

Student Audience: High School

Prerequisites: Students should be familiar with the **Pythagorean Theorem** and should have experience with square roots.

Sketchpad Proficiency: Experienced User

Class Time: 30-40 minutes

Example Sketch/Script: **Square Roots** (Mac sketch) and **Square Root of n** (Mac script) or **8pythag\sqrts.gsp** and **8pythag\sqrtofn.gss** (Windows)

Construction Tips: Make sure points of intersection are properly constructed.

Steps 1: Make sure Preferences are set to display distances in inches.

Step 4: After this step, students should calculate $A'B$ using the Pythagorean Theorem (not using Sketchpad's Calculate or Measure options). They should get $A'B = \sqrt{2}$.

Step 5: Students could record a recursive script for steps 5 through 7 and play it to depth 4 to carry out step 8. But this is likely to complicate the investigation more than potential time savings would warrant. (See Explore More explanation below.)

Step 6: This is where students need to be careful about points of intersection. Students who have trouble constructing circle $A'A$ with the freehand tool can select the points in order and construct the circle using the command Circle By Two points in the Construct menu.

Step 7: The length $A'C$ is equal to 1, as $A'C$ is a radius of a circle and thus equal to AA'. Students should use the Pythagorean Theorem to get $BC = \sqrt{3}$.

Step 8: Choose the Circle tool, Select All Circles in the Edit Menu, and Hide Circles in the Display menu. Repeat for lines.

Investigate/Conjecture

Make sure Preferences are set to display lengths to the thousandths precision. The chart students fill out should look like the one below:

$$BA = \sqrt{1} = 1 \qquad BA' = \sqrt{2} \approx 1.414 \qquad BC = \sqrt{3} \approx 1.732$$
$$BD = \sqrt{4} = 2 \qquad\qquad\qquad\qquad BE = \sqrt{5} \approx 2.236$$
$$BF = \sqrt{6} \approx 2.449 \qquad\qquad\qquad BG = \sqrt{7} \approx 2.646$$

Explore More: To continue the spiral, a recursive script can really come in handy. Assuming you record the steps 5-7, the last thing you should do before you stop recording is to select the givens and click Loop. In this case, you should select, in order, C, $\overline{BC}$, A', and B. Then click Loop and then Stop. Select those objects in the same order again and play the script on them to whatever recursion depth you like. The script **Square Root of n** (Mac) or **8pythag\sqrtofn.gss** (Windows) when played to redursion depth n will yield a spiral whose last segment has length $n + 3$.

Sketchpad will display the length of the $\sqrt{9}$ segment as 3.000. Multiplying this by 10,000 will give 30000.000. So Sketchpad's measure for these square roots is good at least to seven decimal places. Multiplying by 10,000 again will give 300000000.000, suggesting Sketchpad has measured accurately to 11 decimal places. However, multiplying again introduces an calculation error in the 8th decimal place for some reason. (Interestingly, the digits in the error always make a power of 2. A computer idiosyncrasy.)

 Exploring Geometry

Chapter 9
Similarity

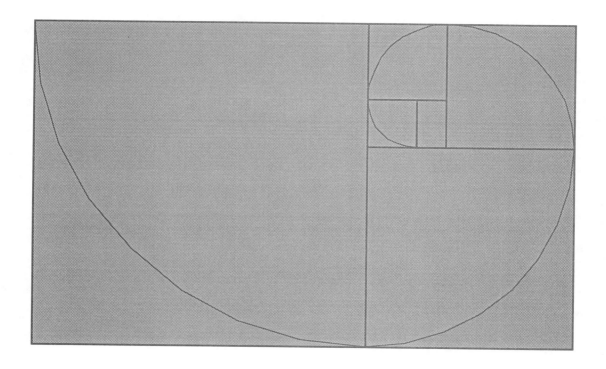

Investigation: The Golden Rectangle

The Golden Ratio appears often in nature: in the proportions of nautilus shells, for example, and proportions in our bodies and faces. A rectangle whose sides are in the Golden Ratio is called a **Golden Rectangle**. If you cut a square off a Golden Rectangle, you're left with a smaller rectangle similar to the first (and thus, also golden). If you add a square to the long side of a Golden Rectangle, you get another, larger Golden Rectangle. In a Golden Rectangle, the ratio of the short side to the long side is equal to the ratio of the long side to the sum of the sides. Because Golden Rectangles are somehow pleasing to us, they're used often in architecture, especially the classical architecture of ancient Greece. In this activity you'll find an approximation for the Golden Ratio and construct a Golden Rectangle.

Sketch

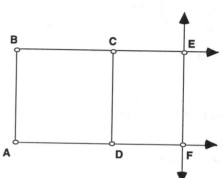

Step 1: Construct a square *ABCD*. (Use a "by edge" script or construct from scratch.)

Step 2: Extend two sides by constructing rays $\overrightarrow{AD}$ and $\overrightarrow{BC}$.

Step 3: Construct *E* on $\overrightarrow{BC}$ and a line through *E*, perpendicular to $\overrightarrow{AD}$.

Step 4: Construct *F*, the intersection of the line and $\overrightarrow{AD}$.

Step 5: Measure *BE*, *EF*, and *FD*.

Investigate: First, you might want to see if you're among those who find a Golden Rectangle pleasing. Move point *E* until rectangle *ABEF* looks "just right." Make it your idea of the perfect rectangle. (You may want to construct its interior to aid your visual judgment.) Now you can see how close your "perfect" rectangle is to being golden. Calculate *BE/EF* and *EF/FD*. Are these ratios close to equal? If so, then rectangles *ABEF* and *CEFD* are close to similar (and golden). Move *E* until these ratios are equal (or as close to equal as possible). The ratio *BE/EF* is an approximation of the Golden Ratio.

Conjecture: Complete the conjecture below.

The value of the Golden Ratio is approximately _____.

Continue with the following steps to actually construct a Golden Rectangle.

Sketch

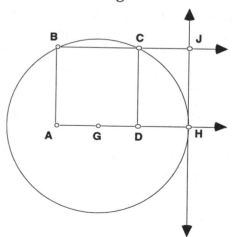

Step 6: Undo in your construction until, *F*, the line through *E*, and *E* are gone.

Step 7: Construct *G*, the midpoint of $\overline{AD}$.

Step 8: Construct circle *GC*.

Step 9: Construct *H*, the intersection of $\overrightarrow{AD}$ and the circle.

Step 10: Construct a line perpendicular to $\overrightarrow{AD}$ through *H*.

Step 11: Construct *J*, the intersection of this line and $\overrightarrow{BC}$.

Investigation: The Golden Rectangle

Student Audience: High School/College/Teacher Education

Prerequisites: It would be useful for students to have some experience with ratios in geometry, such as in similar triangles or polygons. Students will be more impressed with this activity if they've already learned something about Golden Rectangles and their significance. A fun activity is to have students take a poll to choose the most "popular" rectangle in a group of rectangles, one or two of which are golden. Golden Rectangles tend to win hands down (see *Discovering Geometry*, page 475).

Sketchpad Proficiency: Experienced User

Class Time: 30-50 minutes

Example Sketch/Script: **Golden Rectangle** (Mac sketch) and **3-Point Curve** (Mac Script) or **9-10sim\goldrect.gsp** and **9-10sim\3ptcurve.gss** (Windows)

Construction Tips: This is a many-step construction but should have few pitfalls if followed carefully.

Step 1: Make sure students position *A* and *B* vertically, with *A* below *B* as shown. This becomes important if they choose to do Explore More number 2. Students can use the script **4/Square (By Edge)** (Mac) or **regpoly\4byedge.gss** (Windows), or their own script.

Step 5: If students haven't constructed these segments, they'll have to select two points and choose Distance to measure the lengths. (This is usually easier anyway because the measure text contains the endpoint labels.)

Investigate/Conjecture: Students should fill in the conjecture.

The value of the Golden Ratio is approximately 1.62.

This is the value Sketchpad gives, rounded to the hundredths place. Students may not be able to get the ratios exactly equal, so they may write values between 1.61 and 1.63.

Construction Tips

Step 7: Make sure students select the segment and not the ray that overlaps it. Repeated clicking on overlapping objects will cycle selection through the objects. If you select the wrong thing, just click again.

Investigate/Conjecture

BJ is equal to *HD* + *JH* because *BJ* = *BC* + *CJ*, and *BC* = *JH* and *CJ* = *HD*.
BJ/*JH* = *JH*/*HD* ≈ 1.62, the Golden Ratio.

Explore More

1. To find the golden ratio using the quadratic formula, let the short side of a golden rectangle be 1 and the long side be *x*. The proportion $(1 + x)/x = x/1$ must hold. Cross multiplying and gathering terms on one side gives $x^2 - x - 1 = 0$. Completing the square or using the quadratic formula will yield the exact value of the Golden Ratio: $(1 + \sqrt{5})/2$. The other root, $(1 - \sqrt{5})/2$, is the reciprocal, as well as the conjugate, of the Golden Ratio.

3. The ratio of the length of a diagonal to the length of one side in a regular pentagon is the Golden Ratio.

4. See Euclid's *The Elements*, Book 2 Proposition II, *On Growth and Form*, by Sir D'Arcy Thompson, and *Mathematical Snapshots*, by H. Steinhaus.

 Exploring Geometry

Construction: The Golden Rectangle (continued)

Investigate

ABJH is a Golden Rectangle, as is *CJHD*. Hide the lines and circles that you don't need, and supply segments you may still need to complete the rectangle.

Measure *BJ*, *JH*, and *HD*. Calculate *HD + JH*.

How does *BJ* compare to *HD + JH*? Why?

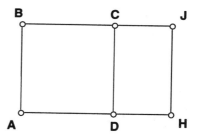

_____

_____

_____

_____

Confirm that these rectangles are golden by calculating *BJ/JH* and *JH/HD*.

Conjecture: Complete the ratios below.

$$\frac{}{BJ} = \frac{BJ}{} = \frac{JH}{HD}$$

Present Your Findings

Discuss your results with your partner or group. To present your findings you could:

1. Print a captioned sketch that shows the hiddens used in the construction as well as a clean copy of the Golden Rectangle. Write captions that explain the steps of the construction. Show measures that illustrate the Golden Ratio.

2. Create and add comments to a script that creates a Golden Rectangle.

Explore More

1. Let the short side of a Golden Rectangle have length 1 and the long side length *x*. Use the quadratic formula to calculate an exact value for the Golden Ratio.

2. Record a script of the construction. While recording, construct an arc with center *C* and endpoints *B* and *D* in the figure above. Select points *D* and *H* and click Loop on the script. Stop recording. This recursive script will construct rectangles within rectangles. Play it at depth 4 to produce the Golden Spiral shown here.

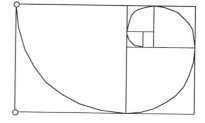

3. Construct a regular pentagon and one diagonal. Calculate the ratio of the length of a diagonal to the length of one side. How does this ratio compare to the Golden Ratio?

4. Do some research and write a report on the Golden Ratio.

Investigation: Similar Polygons

Figures are **similar** if they look the same. They have the same shape, but not necessarily the same size. In this investigation you'll use the Dilate command in the Transform menu to discover principles of **similarity**. You'll use your discoveries to come up with a definition of similar polygons.

Sketch

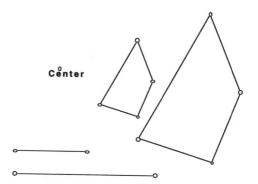

Step 1: Construct any polygon.

Step 2: Construct a point outside the polygon and mark it as center in the Transform menu.

Step 3: Construct two segments of different lengths. Select them and choose Mark Ratio in the Transform menu.

Step 4: Select your entire polygon and dilate by the marked ratio.

Investigate

How do your two figures compare to one another? They're not congruent (why not?). But we say they're similar. Measure the ratio of the segments you marked as ratio. Measure the ratios of the sides of your polygon. How do these ratios compare? Is knowing that sides are proportional enough to know the figures are similar? How do the corresponding angles in these figures compare? Change one of the segments that define your scaling ratio to see other similar polygons.

Conjecture: Write a definition of **similar polygons** below.

_____

_____

Present Your Findings

Discuss your findings with your partner or group. To present your findings, you could print a captioned sketch showing similar polygons, the ratio of corresponding lengths, and measures of corresponding angles.

Explore More

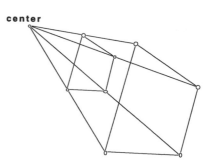

1. To learn more about what a dilation does, construct segments from each vertex of your original polygon to the point marked as center. What other point does each of these segments pass through? How does the distance from a dilated image to the center compare to the distance from a point to the center?

2. See if you can construct a pair of similar triangles without the Dilate command.

3. Construct two non-similar polygons whose corresponding angles are congruent.

4. Construct two non-similar polygons whose corresponding sides are proportional but whose corresponding angles are not equal.

Investigation: Similar Polygons

Student Audience: High School

Prerequisites: Students should know what **congruent polygons** are and have experience with **ratios**.

Sketchpad Proficiency: Beginner

Class Time: 20-40 minutes

Construction Tips

Step 3. The selection order determines whether the dilation will shrink or enlarge the figure. If you select the short segment then the long one, you've marked a ratio less than one and dilations by this ratio will shrink figures.

Investigate/Conjecture

Students will note that the figures are not the same size (so they're not congruent), but they are the same shape. Informally, this is what it means for polygons to be similar. The ratios of corresponding sides will all be the same and corresponding angles will all be equal. This activity, by itself, is probably not enough to guide students to a good definition, but through good questioning you can guide them to the following definition:

Similar polygons are polygons with the same shape: their corresponding sides are proportional and their corresponding angles are congruent.

Explore More

1. The ratio of these distances is the scale factor of the dilation. For example, the image of a point dilated by a 2/1 scale factor is twice as far from the center of dilation as the original point.

3. Example:

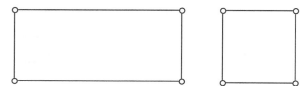

4. Example:

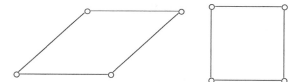

 Exploring Geometry

Investigation: Similar Triangles—AA Similarity

There are several shortcuts to the definition of similar polygons to show that two triangles are similar. In this activity you'll investigate examples where you need information about only a few corresponding parts in a pair of triangles to determine that they are similar.

Sketch

Step 1: Construct $\triangle ABC$ and line $\overleftrightarrow{DE}$.

Step 2: Select D and choose Mark Center in the Transform menu. Select, in order, C, B, and A and choose Mark Angle in the Transform menu.

Step 3: Rotate $\overleftrightarrow{DE}$ by the marked angle.

Step 4: Mark E as center and mark $\angle BCA$.

Step 5: Rotate $\overleftrightarrow{DE}$ again by the new marked angle.

Step 6: Construct F, the point of intersection of these two rotated lines. Hide the lines and replace them with segments.

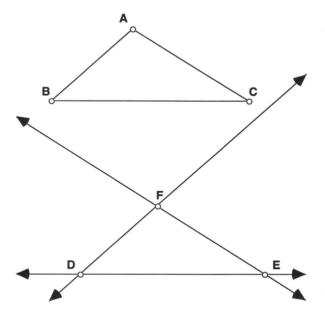

Investigate

You constructed angles D and E to be congruent to angles B and C respectively. Without measuring, how do you think angles A and F compare? Why? Confirm your guess by measuring the three pairs of angles. Do the triangles appear similar? Test this by measuring the ratios of corresponding side lengths. Move points around to confirm that your findings apply to any pair of triangles constructed this way. Is it enough to know that two pairs of corresponding angles are equal to determine that the triangles are similar?

Conjecture: Write an **AA Similarity Conjecture** in your own words below.

_____

_____

Present Your Findings

Discuss your findings with your partner or group. To present your findings, you could print a captioned sketch showing several examples of triangles that are similar by AA similarity. Show angle measures and ratios of corresponding lengths.

Explore More

1. Construct two parallel lines and two non-parallel transversals. The transversals should intersect to form similar triangles. How do you know these triangles are similar?

2. Investigate AA or AAA similarity for quadrilaterals.

Investigation: Similar Triangles—AA Similarity

Student Audience: High School

Prerequisites: Students should know the definition of **similar polygons**.

Sketchpad Proficiency: Experienced User

Class Time: 20-40 minutes

Construction Tips

Step 2: Selection order is important in marking angles to serve as angles of rotation. A brief animation will show which way a rotation by this angle will go.

Step 3: Rotate the line only—not the points.

Investigate/Conjecture

Angles B and L must also be congruent because their measures must be $180 - (m\angle A + m\angle C) = 180 - (m\angle D + m\angle E)$. The triangles are similar, but students should confirm this by measuring ratios of corresponding sides. Students should conjecture:

If two angles in one triangle are congruent to two angles in another triangle, then the triangles are similar.

Explore More

1. The figures below were constructed as follows: Construct $\overleftrightarrow{AB}$ and C not on $\overleftrightarrow{AB}$. Construct a line through C parallel to $\overleftrightarrow{AB}$. Construct lines $\overleftrightarrow{AD}$ and $\overleftrightarrow{BD}$ and points of intersection E and F. Point D can be between the lines, as shown at left, or outside the lines, as shown at right. In either case, $\triangle ABD \sim \triangle FED$ by AA similarity.

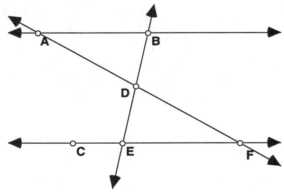 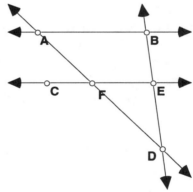

2. As the examples in the teacher comments for the investigtion Similar Polygons illustrate, knowing angles of quadrilaterals is not enough to establish similarity. (A square and a rectangle can have four pairs of equal angles and not be similar.)

Investigation: Similar Triangles—SSS Similarity

The definition of similar polygons says that polygons are similar if and only if the angles are equal and sides are proportional. In this activity, though, you'll discover that in triangles it's enough just to know that sides are proportional.

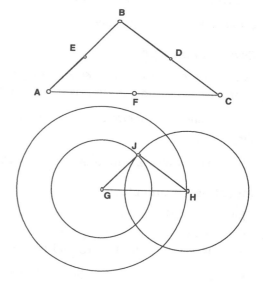

Sketch

Step 1: Construct △*ABC*.

Step 2: Construct *D*, *E*, and *F*, the midpoints of sides $\overline{BC}$, $\overline{AB}$, and $\overline{AC}$.

Step 3: Construct $\overline{AE}$, $\overline{BD}$, and $\overline{CF}$.

Step 4: Construct *G* and a circle with center *G* and radius *CF*.

Step 5: Construct $\overline{GH}$, where *H* is on the circle. Hide the circle.

Step 6: Construct a circle with center *G* and radius *AE* and a circle with center *H* and radius *BD*.

Step 7: Construct $\overline{GJ}$ and $\overline{HJ}$, where *J* is the intersection of these circles. Hide the circles.

Investigate

The smaller triangle you've constructed has proportional corresponding sides. (Why?) Do the two triangles appear similar? Measure angles to determine if they are similar. Make sure to manipulate your original triangle to show that this construction yields similar triangles given any triangle. In this example, you needed only construct three pairs of proportional sides to create similar triangles. Do you think if you constructed a triangle with sides 1/3 the sides in another triangle the triangles would be similar? You can try this using the script **Segment Trisector** (Mac) or **1lineang\trisect.gss** (Windows) Does knowing that corresponding sides are proportional ensure that the triangles are similar?

Conjecture: Write an **SSS Similarity Conjecture** in your own words below.

_____

_____

Present Your Findings

Discuss your findings with your partner or group. To present your findings, you could print a captioned sketch showing several examples of triangles that are similar by SSS similarity. Show angle measures and ratios of corresponding lengths.

Explore More

1. Construct △*DEF* by connecting midpoints in your original triangle. Is △*DEF* ~ △*ABC*?

2. Investigate SSSS similarity in quadrilaterals.

Investigation: Similar Triangles—SSS Similarity

Student Audience: High School

Prerequisites: Students should know the definition of **similar polygons**.

Sketchpad Proficiency: Experienced User

Class Time: 20-40 minutes

Construction Tips

Step 4: Students need to make sure they select the shorter segment, $\overline{CF}$, and not $\overline{CA}$. Repeated clicking alternates selection through overlapping objects.

Step 5: Constructing circles by center and radius is a handy Sketchpad method for duplicating segment lengths.

Step 7: The circles ensure that $GJ = AE$ and $HJ = CD$.

Investigate/Conjecture

The smaller triangle was constructed so that its sides are 1/2 the length of their corresponding sides in the large triangle. By measuring the angles, students can determine that these triangles are similar. When students manipulate the original triangle, the smaller triangle will change to remain similar.

Make sure that students understand they've investigated only one case—the case where the sides of one triangle were 1/2 the sides of the other. Time permitting, allow students to investigate triangles with sides in a 1/3 ratio using the script **Segment Trisector** (Mac) or **1lineang\trisect.gss** (Windows). They can try a 1/4 ratio too (find midpoints again). Students should conjecture:

If three sides in one triangle are proportional to the corresponding sides in another triangle, then the triangles are similar.

Explore More

1. Triangles *DEF* and *ABC* are similar. In fact, triangles *DEF* and *GHJ* are congruent

2. There's no such thing as SSSS similarity in quadrilaterals. A rhombus and square can have proportional sides and not be similar.

Investigation: Similar Triangles—SAS Similarity

It seems that many congruence tests (SSS, for example) also work to test for similarity. You just require sides to be proportional instead of equal. In this investigation, you'll explore an example to see if SAS is sufficient information to determine similarity.

Sketch

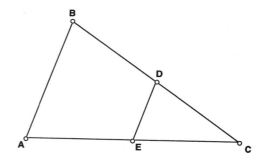

Step 1: Construct △*ABC*.

Step 2: Construct *D* and *E*, the midpoints of sides $\overline{BC}$ and $\overline{AC}$.

Step 3: Construct $\overline{DE}$.

Investigate

In triangles *BAC* and *DEC*, what pair of sides do we know are proportional from our construction?

$$\text{------} = \text{------} = \frac{1}{2}$$

We also know ∠*C* is congruent to itself. Do triangles *BAC* and *DEC* appear similar? Measure the other angles and pair of sides to determine whether the triangles are similar. Manipulate △*ABC* to confirm your findings apply to any pair of triangles constructed this way. This is an example of **SAS similarity**. Now try it for a ratio other than 1/2: Mark *C* as center in the Transform menu. Dilate points *D* and *E* by some scale factor other than 1/2. Construct $\overline{D'E'}$. Is △*D'E'C* similar to triangles *BAC* and *DEC*?

Conjecture: Write an **SAS Similarity Conjecture** in your own words below.

_____

_____

Present Your Findings

Discuss your findings with your partner or group. To present your findings, you could print a captioned sketch showing several examples of triangles that are similar by SAS similarity. Show angle measures and ratios of corresponding lengths.

Explore More

1. Construct polygon interiors and compare the areas of triangles *ABC* and *DEC*. Are the areas in the same ratio as the sides?

2. Investigate similarity in quadrilaterals. What's the least amount of information needed to determine quadrilaterals are similar?

Investigation: Similar Triangles—SAS Similarity

Student Audience: High School

Prerequisites: Students should know the definition of **similar polygons**.

Sketchpad Proficiency: Beginner

Class Time: 20-40 minutes

Construction Tips

Step 2: Students can construct these midpoints simultaneously by selecting both segments before choosing Point At Midpoint.

Investigate/Conjecture

In triangles *BAC* and *DEC*, *EC/AC* = *DC/BC* = 1/2, by the construction. Angle *C* is congruent to itself. By measuring the other angles, students can establish that the triangles are similar. This is only one example of SAS similarity, and students should try other ratios using dilations before they conjecture:

If two sides in one triangle are proportional to the corresponding sides in another triangle and the angles between them are equal, then the triangles are similar.

Explore More

1. If the sides are in a 1/2 ratio, the ratio of the areas will be 1/4, the square of the ratio of the sides. Students investigate this in the activity Proportions With Area.

2. ASASA and SASAS, for example, are enough to determine similarity in quadrilaterals. Students are likely to discover other combinations.

Investigation: The Geometric Mean

What comes next in the number sequence: 2, 6, 18, 54, 162, ...? If you guessed 486, you noticed that each number in the sequence is just the previous term multiplied by three. Or you may have noticed that there was a constant ratio between successive terms: $54/18 = 18/6 = 6/2 = 3$. A sequence with a constant ratio is called a geometric sequence and each term is the **geometric mean** or mean proportional between the terms on either side of it. For example, 6 is the geometric mean of 2 and 18 because $2/6 = 6/18$. In this activity, you'll discover what a geometric mean is geometrically, and you'll learn how to construct a geometric mean between two lengths.

Sketch

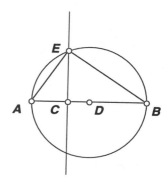

Step 1:   Construct $\overline{AB}$ and C on $\overline{AB}$. You will construct the geometric mean between the lengths AC and CB.

Step 2:   Construct the midpoint, D, of $\overline{AB}$.

Step 3:   Construct circle DA.

Step 4:   Construct a line through C, perpendicular to $\overline{AB}$.

Step 5:   Construct $\overline{AE}$ and $\overline{EB}$, where E is the intersection of the line and the circle.

Investigate

What kind of triangle is $\triangle ABE$? Hint: It's inscribed in a semicircle. There are three triangles in your figure. Are they similar? Why? Write the similarity relationships below and write an explanation of why it's true on a separate paper.

$$\underline{\hspace{3cm}} \sim \underline{\hspace{3cm}} \sim \underline{\hspace{3cm}}$$

From your similar triangles, can you figure out which distance is the geometric mean between AC and CB? Measure some distances in the triangle and use Calculate to confirm your conjecture. Write a proportion below:

$$\frac{AC}{\underline{\hspace{2cm}}} = \frac{\underline{\hspace{2cm}}}{CB}$$

Conjecture: Write your conjectures on a separate paper.

Present Your Findings: Discuss your findings with your partner or group. To present your findings, you could print a captioned sketch showing measures and proportions that illustrate the geometric mean.

Explore More

1. See if you can find a geometric mean in a regular pentagram (five-pointed star).

2. There are two other geometric means in your triangle. Can you find them?

3. Calculate the product $(AC)(CB)$. Select measures CE and this product and choose Plot As (x, y) in the Graph menu. Construct the locus of this plotted point and point E. Describe the graph.

Investigation: The Geometric Mean

Student Audience: High School

Prerequisites: Students are introduced to the terms **geometric mean** and **mean proportional**. They need to know how to identify similar triangles and proportions in them.

Sketchpad Proficiency: Beginner

Class Time: 20-40 minutes

Example Sketch/Script: **Geometric Mean** (Mac sketch) and **Geometric Mean Script** (Mac script) or **9-10sim\geomean.gsp** or **9-10sim\geomean.gss** (Windows)

Construction Tips

Step 3: Make sure this circle used point *A* to define its radius and isn't just "passing through."

Investigate/Conjecture

Because it's inscribed in a semicircle, $\triangle ABE$ is a right triangle. Triangles *ACE*, *ECB*, and *AEB* are similar by AA similarity because they're all right triangles and triangles *ACE* and *ECB* share angles *A* and *B* respectively with $\triangle AEB$.

Students should write the ratio: $AC/EC = EC/CB$. They can conjecture:

The length of the altitude drawn to the hypotenuse of a right triangle is the geometric mean between the lengths of the two segments into which it divides the hypotenuse.

Explore More

1. In the pentagram at right, *JK* is the geometric mean between *JL* and *KL*. In fact, $JL/JK = JK/KL =$ the Golden Ratio.

2. In the figure on the student activity sheet, $AC/AE = AE/AB$ and $BC/EB = EB/AB$.

3. Students should get a graph like that shown below. The graph is of the function $y = x^2$, where *x* is the length of the geometric mean. In other words, if *x* is the geometric mean between two numbers *a* and *b*, then $ab = x^2$.

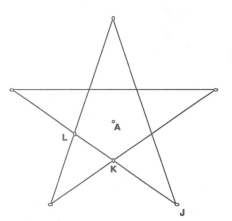

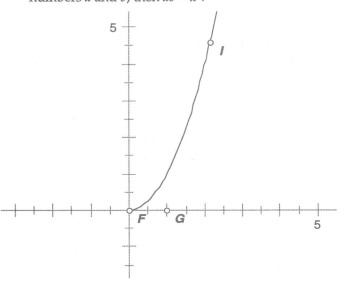

     Exploring Geometry

Investigation: Intersecting Chords

Properties of chords combine with properties of similar triangles to yield some interesting results. You'll discover some of these in this investigation.

Sketch

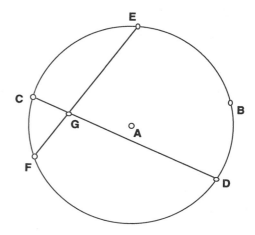

Step 1: Construct circle AB.

Step 2: Construct $\overline{CD}$ and $\overline{EF}$, where C, D, E, and F are on the circle.

Step 3: Construct G, the intersection of $\overline{CD}$ and $\overline{EF}$.

Step 4: Measure CG, GD, EG, and FG.

Investigate

Use Calculate to find a proportion among these four measures: ———— = ————

Move C, D, E, and F around the circle to confirm that this proportion holds for any pair of intersecting chords.

Now cross-multiply to write an equation of two equal products: ————— = —————

Use Calculate to confirm you've written the correct equation.

Conjecture: Write your conjectures below.

_____

_____

_____

Present Your Findings

Discuss your findings with your partner or group. To present your findings, you could print a captioned sketch showing measures and calculations that illustrate your conjecture.

Explore More

1. Can you prove your conjecture? Construct two chords to create triangles. The proof is based on these triangles.

2. Investigate relationships between the angles formed by the intersecting chords and the arcs they intercept.

Investigation: Intersecting Chords

Student Audience: High School

Prerequisites: Students should know what **chords** in a circle are and should have experience with **ratio** and **proportion**. Understanding of similar triangles is necessary to explain students' discovery.

Sketchpad Proficiency: Beginner

Class Time: 20-30 minutes. This activity could be done in the same class period as Secant Segments.

Construction Tips

Step 3: Students may need to move the endpoints of their chords so that they intersect.

Step 4: If students select points and measure distances, they won't need to construct segments to measure lengths.

Investigate/Conjecture

Students are asked to write proportions first because they should be easier to identify. They should write either $CG/FG = GE/GD$ or $CG/GE = FG/GD$. Cross-multiplying gives $(CG)(GD) = (FG)(GE)$. Students should write the following conjecture:

If two chords intersect in a circle, they divide each other into two segments with lengths whose products are equal.

Explore More

1. Triangles *FGC* and *DGE* are similar by AA. (They have a pair of vertical angles and angles *F* and *D* intercept the same arc.)

2. An angle and its vertical angle intercept two arcs. The average of the measures of these arcs is the measure of the angles.

Investigation: Secant Segments

Properties of chords and secants in circles combine with properties of similar triangles to yield some interesting results. You'll discover some of these in this investigation.

Sketch

Step 1:   Construct circle *AB*.

Step 2:   Construct $\overrightarrow{CD}$ and $\overrightarrow{CE}$, where *D*, and *E* are on the circle.

Step 3:   Construct *F* and *G*, the other intersections of $\overrightarrow{CD}$ and $\overrightarrow{CE}$ with the circle.

Step 4:   Measure *CD*, *CF*, *CE*, and *CG*.

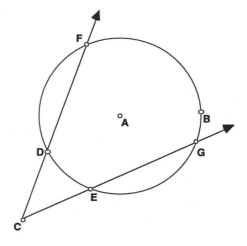

Investigate

Use Calculate to find a proportion among these four measures: ————— = —————

Move *C*, *D*, and *E* to confirm this proportion holds for segments formed by any pair of secants.

Now cross-multiply to write an equation of two equal products: _____ = _____.

Use Calculate to confirm you've written the correct equation.

Conjecture: Write your conjectures below.

_____

_____

_____

Present Your Findings

Discuss your findings with your partner or group. To present your findings, you could print a captioned sketch showing measures and calculations that illustrate your conjecture.

Explore More

1. Can you prove your conjecture? Construct $\overline{FE}$ and $\overline{DG}$ to create triangles. The proof is based on these triangles.

2. Move point *E* around the circle until it coincides with *G*. What can you say about a secant and a tangent with a common endpoint?

3. Investigate relationships between the angle formed by the secant segments and the two arcs they intercept.

Investigation: Secant Segments

Student Audience: High School

Prerequisites: Students should know what **secants** in a circle are and should have experience with **ratio** and **proportion**. Understanding of similar triangles is necessary to explain students' discovery.

Sketchpad Proficiency: Beginner

Class Time: 15-30 minutes. This activity could be done in the same class period as Intersecting Chords.

Construction Tips

Step 2: Points D and E should be on the same side of the circle as C if students figures (and measures) are to match the figure in the activity. In other words, students shouldn't construct rays through the circle to far points on the circle.

Investigate/Conjecture

Students are asked to write proportions first, because they should be easier to identify. They should write either $CG/CF = CE/CG$ or reciprocals. Cross-multiplying gives $(CD)(CF) = (CE)(CG)$. Students should write the following conjecture:

If two secant segments in a circle share an endpoint outside the circle, then the product of the length of one secant segment and the length of its external part is equal to the product of the length of the other secant segment and the length of its external part.

Explore More

1. Triangles CFE and CGD are similar by AA. (They have a common angle and angles F and G intercept the same arc.)

2. In the case that $\overline{CE}$ is tangent, $(CD)(CF) = (CE)^2$.

3. The measure of the angle is half the difference between the arcs it intercepts.

Problem: Modeling a Similar Triangle Problem

Similar triangles have many problem-solving applications. In this activity, you'll model one type of problem that can be solved using similar triangles: finding a distance that can't be measured directly.

Sketch

Step 1: Construct $\overleftrightarrow{AB}$, point C, and a line parallel to $\overleftrightarrow{AB}$ through C. Make these lines thick and imagine they're the banks of a river. You wish to find the distance across the river. (And you can't just measure it—it's a river. So stay away from that Measure menu!)

Step 2: Construct D and a line perpendicular to the banks of the river. D is a large tree and you situate yourself at E, directly across the river from the tree.

Step 3: You walk a few meters and stick a pole in the bank at point F. (Construct $\overline{EF}$, where F is on the bank.)

Step 4: You walk some convenient distance further (construct $\overline{FG}$, where G is on the bank) then make a right turn (construct a line through G perpendicular to the bank).

Step 5: You walk until your pole (point F) lines up with the tree (point D). (Construct $\overrightarrow{DF}$ and H at the intersection of $\overrightarrow{DF}$ and the line through G.)

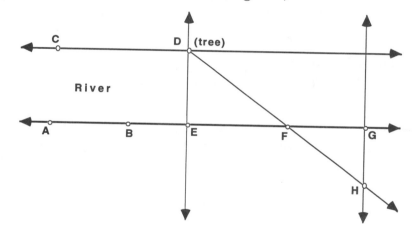

Investigate

Triangle DEF is similar to △HGF. (Why?) DE is the distance you wish to find, and you can measure EF, FG, and GH. Write a proportion in terms of these lengths:

$$\frac{DE}{\rule{2cm}{0.4pt}} = \text{------}$$

Now measure EF, FG, and GH. Use Calculate to find DE. Measure DE to confirm your calculation. You can move the banks of the river or the location of various points to confirm that this method will work under different circumstances.

Explore More

See if you can come up with other ways to model this problem with Sketchpad using similar triangles.

Problem: Modeling a Similar Triangle Problem

Student Audience: High School

Prerequisites: Students should know how to identify similar triangles and write proportions from them.

Sketchpad Proficiency: Beginner

Class Time: 20-30 minutes. With Sketchpad-savvy students, this activity could be done in the same class period as Modeling a Similar Triangle/Mirror Problem.

Example Sketch: **Similar Δ Problem** (Mac) or **9-10sim\simtripr.gsp** (Windows)

Construction Tips

The construction steps are described here in the context of the story, so students need to think about how to model what they're reading with Sketchpad. They should read all the text of each step before constructing anything.

Step 2: E is the point of intersection of the perpendicular line and $\overleftrightarrow{AB}$.

Step 4: Note that a convenient distance FG would be equal to EF. This makes it a congruent triangles problem instead of a similar triangles problem, and makes it easier to solve. Don't tell students this. See if they notice themselves. If students ask why anyone would want to solve it with similar triangles, suggest there may be obstacles that make congruent triangles impractical in a real-world situation.

Step 5: Students may make the mistake of "walking" along this line by constructing $\overline{GH}$ where H is a random point on the line. If they read on, they'll realize they should have constructed H at the intersection of $\overrightarrow{DF}$ and the line.

Investigate/Conjecture

Angles DEF and HGF are right angles and angles GFH and EFD are vertical angles, so the triangles are similar by AA similarity. Students should write a proportion equivalent to $DE/EF = HG/GF$.

When students measure these lengths, it should occur to them that the measures are not realistic to the problem. (No river is likely to be 1.37 cm wide.) Suggest students think of a reasonable scale for their drawing, e.g., 1 cm = 10 m.

Explore More

Another way to model this problem is shown here:

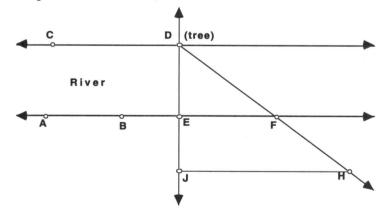

Problem: Modeling a Similar Triangles/Mirror Problem

Because reflections make equal angles, mirrors are useful devices for indirect measurement using similar triangles. In this activity, you'll use Sketchpad to model a problem that can be solved with a mirror and similar triangles.

Sketch

Step 1: Construct horizontal line $\overleftrightarrow{AB}$ and hide points A and B.

Step 2: Construct C on $\overleftrightarrow{AB}$ and a line through C, perpendicular to $\overleftrightarrow{AB}$.

Step 3: Construct $\overline{CD}$ on this line and hide the line. $\overline{CD}$ represents you. (Your eye is located at point D.)

Step 4: Construct E on $\overleftrightarrow{AB}$ and a line through E, perpendicular to $\overleftrightarrow{AB}$.

Step 5: Construct $\overline{EF}$ on this line and hide the line. $\overline{EF}$ represents a flagpole or some other vertical height you wish to measure.

Step 6: Reflect F and $\overline{EF}$ about $\overleftrightarrow{AB}$.

Step 7: Construct $\overrightarrow{F'G}$, where G is on $\overleftrightarrow{AB}$ between C and E.

Step 8: Construct $\overline{FG}$.

Investigate

Imagine point G is a small mirror on the ground. Ray $F'G$ represents the ray along which the reflection of the top of the flagpole can be seen in the mirror. Light from point F reflects off the mirror G at an angle equal to the angle with which it struck the mirror. You want to position yourself so that you can see the top of the flagpole in the mirror. Move point C (your feet) so that D (your eye) is on $\overrightarrow{F'G}$. At this point, $\angle FGE = \angle DGC$. (Why?) Now you have similar triangles. (Which ones, and why?) You could measure the distance from the ground to your eye, DC, your distance from the mirror, CG, and the distance from the mirror to the flagpole, GE. That means you can set up a proportion to find the height of the flagpole, EF. Complete this proportion:

$$\frac{EF}{\rule{1.5cm}{0.4pt}} = \text{-------}$$

Now measure DC, CG, and GE. Edit these measures to read simply, "$DC =$ " etc. Use Calculate to build an expression equal to EF. Measure EF to confirm your calculation. If you're off just a bit, it's probably because D can't be located exactly on $\overrightarrow{F'G}$. You can relocate the mirror and try again from different positions. You can even change your height or the flagpole's height to change the problem.

Explore More

See if you can come up with other ways to model this problem with Sketchpad using similar triangles. Hint: if you use shadows, you can solve the problem without any mirrors.

Problem: Modeling a Similar Triangle/Mirrors Problem

Student Audience: High School

Prerequisites: Students should know how to identify similar triangles and write proportions from them.

Sketchpad Proficiency: Beginner

Class Time: 20-30 minutes. With Sketchpad-savvy students, this activity could be done in the same class period as Modeling a Similar Triangle Problem.

Example Sketch: **Mirror Problem** (Mac) or **9-10sim\mirrorpr.gsp** (Windows)

Construction Tips

The construction steps are described here in the context of the story, so students need to think about how to model what they're reading with Sketchpad. They should read all the text of each step before constructing anything.

Step 1: Hold down the Shift key to constrain lines to 15° intervals (making it easy to construct a horizontal line).

Step 5: EF should be longer than CD. Otherwise, in a real problem EF could be measured directly.

Step 6: Mark $\overleftrightarrow{AB}$ mirror in the Transform menu. Select F and $\overline{EF}$ and choose Reflect in the Transform menu.

Investigate/Conjecture

Angles FGE and F'GE are congruent by reflection, so when D is positioned on $\overline{F'G}$, ∠DGC is a vertical angle with ∠F'GE and is thus congruent to it and ∠FGE. We say that "the angle of incidence is equal to the angle of reflection." So ΔDGC ~ ΔFGE by AA similarity (they both have a right angle). Students should write a proportion equivalent to EF/CD = EG/CG.

Explore More

Another way to model this problem using shadows instead of mirrors is shown here. $\overline{DH}$ and $\overline{FG}$ represent parallel rays of light from the sun. Segments EG and CH represent shadows.

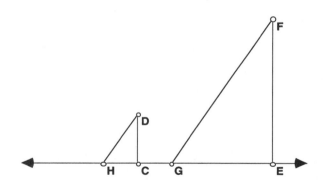

©1996 by Key Curriculum Press

Construction: Subdividing a Segment

In this activity, you'll learn a method for dividing a segment into three or more equal parts.

Sketch

Step 1: Construct $\overline{AB}$. This is the segment that you'll divide into three parts.

Step 2: Select point A and use the Transform menu to translate it 1 in. at an angle of 30°. (This distance and angle are arbitrary.)

Step 3: Translate this new point the same distance and angle to create point A''. Repeat to create a third new point, A'''.

Step 4: Construct a segment from point A''' to point B.

Step 5: With this new segment still selected, select points A' and A'' and construct parallel lines to $\overline{A'''B}$.

Step 6: Construct the points of intersection of these lines with $\overline{AB}$. These points subdivide $\overline{AB}$ into three equal parts.

Step 7: Hide the lines, points A', A'' and A''', and $\overline{A'''B}$.

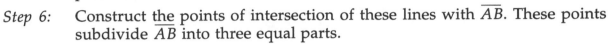

Investigate

Move points A and B and note that the points you constructed continue to divide $\overline{AB}$ equally. You can measure to confirm your observation. To see how it works, you might try showing your hiddens, then manipulating the construction. Why do these lines divide the segment equally?

_____

_____

_____

_____

_____

Explore More

1. Use this procedure to divide a segment into five equal parts.

2. See if you can find other methods to subdivide a segment. Some methods might work only for a particular number of parts, four or eight, for example.

Construction: Subdividing a Segment

Student Audience: High School

Prerequisites: In order to explain why this construction works, students need to know that a line parallel to a side in triangle divides the other sides proportionately.

Sketchpad Proficiency: Beginner

Class Time: 15-30 minutes

Example Script: **Segment Trisector** (Mac) or **1lineang\trisect.gss** (Windows)

Construction Tips

Step 2: Make sure Preferences are set to display distances in inches.

Investigate/Conjecture

If students already know that a line parallel to one side of a triangle divides the other sides proportionately, then the explanation is trivial. The lines divide $\overline{AA'''}$ in a 1:1:1 ratio because these points were constructed to be equally spaced. Thus the lines parallel to $\overline{A'''B}$ divide $\overline{AB}$ in a 1:1:1 ratio as well.

If students didn't already know this, they could explain it in terms of similar triangles. Angles $A'CA$, $A''DA$, and $A'''BA$ are corresponding angles formed by a transversal and parallel lines. Triangles $A'CA$, $A''DA$, and $A'''BA$ all share $\angle A$, so they're similar to one another. The ratios of sides AA', AA'', and AA''' are 1:2:3 so the ratios of AC, AD, and AB are also 1:2:3. Thus $AC:CD:DB = 1:1:1$.

Explore More

2. A segment can easily be divided into an even number of parts by repeatedly constructing midpoints.

Art: Spacing Fenceposts in Perspective

When you look at a long line of telephone poles or fence posts disappearing in the distance, the farther away the posts are the shorter they appear to be. They also appear closer together. In this activity, you'll learn to draw fenceposts in perspective so that their spacing appears realistic.

Sketch

Step 1: Construct horizontal line $\overleftrightarrow{AB}$. This is your horizon line and point B will be your vanishing point.

Step 2: Construct vertical segment $\overline{CD}$. This is your first fencepost (or telephone pole.)

Step 3: Construct $\overline{CB}$ and $\overline{DB}$.

Step 4: Construct E on $\overline{CB}$ and a line through E, parallel to $\overline{CD}$.

Step 5: Construct diagonals $\overline{CF}$ and $\overline{DE}$.

Step 6: Construct $\overline{GB}$, where G is the intersection of the diagonals.

Step 7: Construct ray $\overrightarrow{CH}$, where H is the intersection of $\overline{GB}$ and the line through E.

Step 8: Construct $\overline{EF}$. $\overline{EF}$ is your second fencepost.

Step 9: Construct J where $\overrightarrow{CH}$ intersects $\overline{DB}$. This is the foot of your third fencepost.

Step 10: Construct a line through J parallel to $\overline{EF}$.

Step 11: Construct $\overrightarrow{EK}$, where K is the intersection of this line and $\overline{GB}$.

Step 12: Construct $\overline{JL}$, where L is the intersection of $\overleftrightarrow{JK}$ and $\overline{CB}$. $\overline{JL}$ is your third fencepost.

Step 13: Construct M, the intersection of $\overrightarrow{EK}$ and $\overline{DB}$. M is the foot of your fourth fencepost.

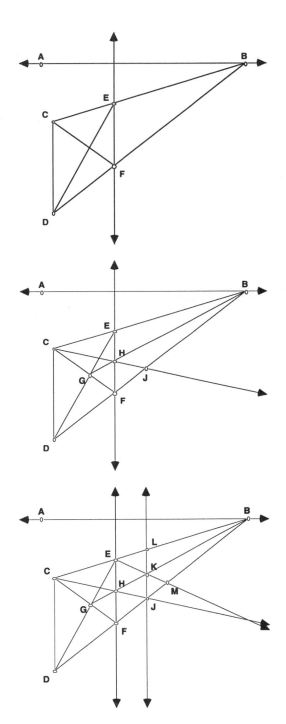

Art: Spacing Fenceposts in Perspective

Student Audience: Any

Prerequisites: None. Experience drawing with perspective may help students understand why fencepost may not be equally spaced when drawn in perspective. Ask them to think about their own experience— have them imagine a fence receding in the distance—before doing the activity.

Sketchpad Proficiency: Experienced User

Class Time: 30-40 minutes

Example Sketch: **Fenceposts** (Mac) or **9-10sim\fencpost.gsp** (Windows)

Construction Tips

Follow the steps in the activity carefully and sequentially to ensure that your fenceposts obey the rules of perspective when you move them.

Steps 1-2: Hold down the Shift key while drawing the horizon line and the first fencepost to make it easy to make horizontal and vertical lines.

Step 8: Make sure students don't make the mistake of constructing a ray to $\overline{DB}$ that just happens to pass through H. Point H must be the control point of the ray, with J being the point where the ray intersects $\overline{DB}$.

Investigate/Conjecture

When the second post is located halfway between the first post and the vanishing point, the third post will be located a third of the way between the second post and the vanishing point. The fourth post will be a fourth of the way between the third post and the vanishing point, and so on. In general, if the ratio of (post 2 to vanishing point)/(post 1 to post 2) is x, then the ratio (post 3 to vanishing point)/(post 2 to post 3) will be $x + 1$, (post 4 to vanishing point/post 3 to post 4) will be $x + 1 + 1$, and so on. No matter how many posts you construct, you'll never reach the vanishing point.

Exploring Geometry

Art: Spacing Fenceposts in Perspective (continued)

Step 14: Construct two or three more fence posts in this manner. Hide all lines, rays, and segments except your fenceposts and horizon line $\overleftrightarrow{AB}$. Make your fenceposts thick lines. Hide all points except *A*, *B*, *C*, *D*, and *E* (these are the points you can drag to manipulate your picture).

Step 15: Your static sketch may not look like much, but drag the first post and various points to see the effect on your sketch. Can you imagine you're a bird swooping down on some abandoned telephone poles in the desert? What happens if you lift the poles so their bases are above the horizon line?

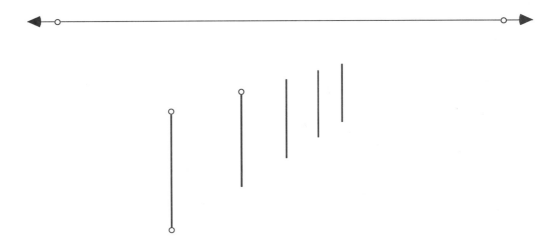

Investigate

There are many relationships among the distances in this sketch. Show the top points of the posts. Investigate relationships between the distance from one top point to the next and the distance from that top point to the vanishing point. To begin to see relationships, start with the special case where the second post is halfway between the first post and the vanishing point. Where is the third post located relative to the second post and the vanishing point? Would it be possible to reach the vanishing point if you just kept constructing posts? Write your findings below.

_____

_____

_____

_____

_____

_____

Investigation: Proportions with an Angle Bisector in a Triangle

Quick! Where does an angle bisector intersect the opposite side in a triangle? Did you guess the midpoint? A quick check will show this only works in special cases. In this activity, you'll discover a proportion relationship of angle bisectors in triangles

Sketch

Step 1: Construct $\triangle ABC$.

Step 2: Construct the bisector of $\angle BAC$.

Step 3: Construct D where the bisector intersects $\overline{BC}$.

Step 4: Measure $AB, BD, DC,$ and AC.

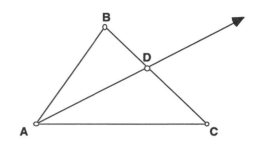

Investigate

Is D the midpoint of $\overline{BC}$? Construct the midpoint. Under what conditions will D and the midpoint coincide? How do BD and CD compare when AB is greater than AC? How do they compare when AC is greater than AB? Does this give you an idea for a possible proportion? Use Calculate to test ratios involving AB, AC, BD, and CD to see if you can create equal ratios (a proportion). Write the proportion below:

$$\frac{\quad\quad}{} = \frac{\quad\quad}{}$$

Manipulate your triangle to make sure your proportion holds for any triangle.

Conjecture: Write your conjectures below.

_____

_____

_____

_____

Present Your Findings

Compare and discuss your results with your partner or group. To present your findings you could print a captioned sketch showing several triangles with angle bisectors and measures that illustrate your conjectures. Make sure to include special cases such as when the angle bisector goes through the midpoint of the opposite side.

Explore More

See if you can use your conjecture to subdivide a segment into a given ratio, say 2 to 3.

Investigation: Proportions with an Angle Bisector in a Triangle

Student Audience: High School

Prerequisites: None

Sketchpad Proficiency: Beginner

Class Time: 20-30 minutes

Construction Tips

Step 2: Select three points (point, vertex, point) to enable the Angle Bisector command in the Construct menu.

Step 4: If students measure distances between points, they won't need to construct segments and measure lengths.

Investigate/Conjecture

Students construct the midpoint to see, first of all, that an angle bisector doesn't necessarily go through the midpoint of the opposite side. In fact, it only does in an isosceles triangle. The can see that as a side is made longer, the intersection of the angle bisector goes away from it and vice versa. This should suggest a proportion. Students should write a proportion equivalent to $AB/BD = AC/CD$. Students should conjecture:

An angle bisector in a triangle divides the opposite side in the same ratio as the lengths of the sides of the bisected angle.

Explore More

Construct a triangle with sides in a 2/3 ratio. Bisect the angle formed by these sides.

Investigation: Parallel Lines in a Triangle

When you cut through a triangle with a line parallel to a side, you create similar triangles. In this activity you'll investigate proportions that result from these similar triangles.

Sketch

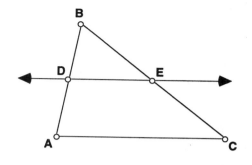

Step 1: Construct △*ABC*.

Step 2: Construct *D* on $\overline{AB}$ and a line through *D*, parallel to $\overline{AC}$.

Step 3: Construct $\overline{DE}$, where *E* is the point of intersection of the line and $\overline{BC}$.

Step 4: Measure *AD*, *DB*, *AB*, *CE*, *EB*, *CB*, *DE*, and *AC*. Edit these measures so they're easy to identify.

Investigate

Triangle *ABC* is similar to triangle *DBE*. (Why?) These similar triangles give you three equal ratios involving the sides of the triangles. Write these ratios below.

$$ \underline{\hspace{3em}} = \underline{\hspace{3em}} = \underline{\hspace{3em}} $$

There's another proportion involving the segments into which the parallel line divides the sides of the triangle. Use Calculate to discover a proportion involving *BD*, *DA*, *BE*, and *EC*. Write this proportion below.

$$ \underline{\hspace{3em}} = \underline{\hspace{3em}} $$

Conjecture: Write your conjectures below.

_____

_____

_____

_____

Present Your Findings

Compare and discuss your results with your partner or group. To present your findings you could print a captioned sketch showing several triangles with parallel lines and measures that illustrate your conjectures. Make sure to include special cases such as when the parallel line goes through the midpoints of the sides.

Explore More

1. Show how the proportions involving *BD*, *DA*, *BE*, and *EC* can be derived using algebra and the similar triangles' proportions.

2. Can you show that the converse of your conjecture is true? That is, can you show that if a line divides the sides of a triangle proportionally, then it's parallel to the third side?

Investigation: Proportional Segments by Parallel Lines

Student Audience: High School

Prerequisites: Students should know how to identify similar triangles and write proportions from them.

Sketchpad Proficiency: Beginner

Class Time: 15-30 minutes

Construction Tips

Step 4: Double-click on a measure with the Text tool to edit it. Students should edit measures like "Distance(A to D) = " to read simply "AD = ".

Investigate/Conjecture

These triangles are similar by AA similarity. They share $\angle B$ and $\angle ADE = \angle A$ because they're corresponding angles. Students should write proportions equivalent to: $BD/BA = BE/BC = DE/AC$. Students should also discover that $BD/DA = BE/EC$. A common mistake students make is to confuse the ratios and think that $DE/AC = BD/DA = BE/EC$. Sketchpad's measures immediately dispel that misconception.

Explore More

1. In the proportion $BA/BD = BC/BE$, replace BA with $BD + DA$ and replace BC with $BE + EC$. Subtract BD/BD from the left side and BE/BE from the right side. That leaves $DA/BD = EC/BE$.

2. If the line divides the sides proportionately, then it creates similar triangles by SAS similarity. Thus the corresponding angles are equal and the line must be parallel to the base.

 ©1996 by Key Curriculum Press

Construction: A Pantograph

A pantograph is a simple mechanical device that uses two pens to copy and enlarge or reduce drawings or maps. Thomas Jefferson even made one hoping he could use it to write more than one letter at a time. In this activity, you'll construct a pantograph and investigate how it works.

Sketch

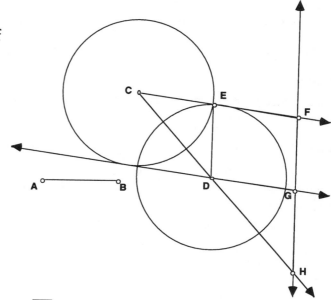

Step 1: Construct $\overline{AB}$. (This is not part of the pantograph, but it's a control segment that will make your pantograph adjustable.)

Step 2: Construct $\overrightarrow{CD}$.

Step 3: Construct circles with centers C and D and radius AB.

Step 4: Construct $\overrightarrow{CE}$ where E is one of the intersections of these circles as shown.

Step 5: Construct $\overline{CE}$ and $\overline{DE}$.

Step 6: Construct $\overline{EF}$, where F is any point past E on $\overrightarrow{CE}$.

Step 7: Construct a line through F parallel to $\overline{DE}$.

Step 8: Construct a line through D parallel to $\overline{EF}$.

Step 9: Construct $\overline{DG}$, where G is the intersection of the lines in steps 6 and 7.

Step 10: Construct $\overline{FH}$, where H is the intersection of $\overleftrightarrow{FG}$ and $\overrightarrow{CD}$.

Step 11: Hide the circles, lines, and rays so that your pantograph consists only of segments. This is more or less what a physical pantograph would look like.

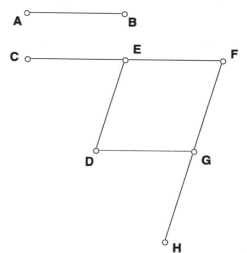

Step 12: Choose Trace Locus for points D and H.

Investigate

In an actual pantograph, point C is fixed and a stylus is attached at D. A pen is attached at point H. As the stylus at D is moved around some figure, the whole apparatus moves around C and the pen at H traces a scaled copy of the figure.

Construction: A Pantograph

Student Audience: High School

Prerequisites: To explain how a pantograph works, students need to know about proportions in similar triangles.

Sketchpad Proficiency: Experienced User

Class Time: 30-40 minutes

Example Sketch: **Pantograph** (Mac) or **9-10sim\pantgrph.gsp** (Windows)

Construction Tips

This is a multi-step construction, but students shouldn't have any trouble if they follow the directions (and diagram) carefully.

Investigate/Conjecture

If students sign their names with point D, they'll see a copy of it traced by point H. The copy traced by point H will be larger than the original traced by point D. When $CE = EF$, point H will trace an image twice as large as the figure traced by D. This can be explained with similar triangles. Triangles CED and CFH are similar by AA similarity. (The share angle F and angles CED and CFH are corresponding angles.) Since $CE = EF$, $CE/CF = CD/CH = 1/2$. To make the pantograph trace an image 3/2 the original, F needs to be moved so that $CF/CE = 3/2$.

Construction: A Pantograph (continued)

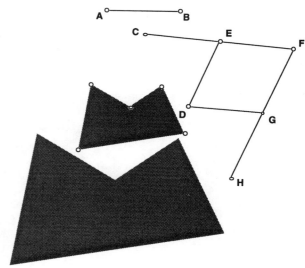

Move point *D* and observe the locus of point *H*. (Try signing your name with point *D*.) Can you see how the path of *H* is related to where you drag *D*? To really see how a pantograph works (and why it's useful) you need to do some more construction: Construct some polygon interior. Now carefully drag *D* around the perimeter of the polygon. What does *H* trace?

Now investigate how the constructed polygon and the one traced by *H* are related: Measure *CE* and *EF* and adjust *F* so these lengths are equal. Mark *C* as center and Dilate your polygon with a scale factor of 2/1. Move the original, if necessary, so that the polygons don't overlap. Now drag *D* around the original polygon. Did *H* trace the perimeter of the larger polygon?

A pantograph works on the principle of similar triangles. As you move *D*, the ratio of *CH*/*CD* doesn't change. Why not? What similar triangles determine this ratio? (You may want to construct $\overline{CH}$ to help you answer this question.) How do you know these triangles are similar? Write an explanation of how a pantograph works below.

_____

_____

_____

_____

_____

_____

_____

_____

You can change the ratio *CD*/*CH* by changing *CE* (adjust $\overline{AB}$) or *EF* (move point *F*). Adjust your pantograph to trace an image 3/2 the original size, or some other ratio.

Present Your Findings

Compare and discuss your results with your partner or group. To present your findings you could print a captioned sketch with instructions for using the pantograph and a brief explanation of how it works.

Explore More

Build an actual pantograph out of old wooden rulers, small bolts, and wing nuts.

Investigation: Proportions with Area

In this exploration you'll discover a relationship between the areas of similar figures.

Sketch

Step 1: Construct segments $\overline{AB}$ and $\overline{CD}$, where $\overline{AB}$ is longer than $\overline{CD}$.

Step 2: Construct any polygon and its interior.

Step 3: Construct a point outside the polygon and mark it as center.

Step 4: Select $\overline{AB}$ and $\overline{CD}$ and mark AB/CD as ratio in the Transform menu. While they're still selected measure their ratio.

Step 5: Dilate the polygon by the marked ratio. (If $\overline{AB}$ is longer than $\overline{CD}$, the image should be bigger than the original.)

Step 6: Measure the ratio of a side on the dilated polygon with the corresponding side on the original polygon.

Step 7: Repeat step 6 using a different side. What is this ratio?

Step 8: Measure the areas of the polygons. Calculate the ratio of the area of the dilated polygon to the area of the original.

Step 9: Select, in order, the measure of the ratio of the side lengths and the calculation of the ratio of the areas. Choose Plot As (x, y) in the graph menu, then choose Trace Point in the Display menu.

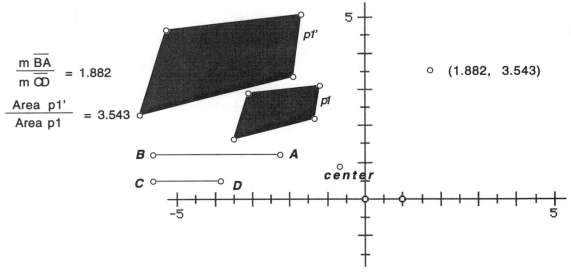

$$\frac{m\ \overline{BA}}{m\ \overline{CD}} = 1.882$$

$$\frac{Area\ p1'}{Area\ p1} = 3.543$$

○ (1.882, 3.543)

Investigate

Drag point B to experiment with different scale factors. The point you plotted will trace out a graph of the side-length ratio vs. the ratio of the areas of the figures. Does your graph give you some idea of what the relationship is between the side-length ratio and the area ratio in similar figures? Measure the coordinates of the plotted point. To see relationships, it's easiest to try nice numbers. Move B so that the side-length ratio (the x-coordinate) is 2. What's the area ratio? What's the area ratio when the side-length ratio is 3? What happens to the figure when the side-length ratio is 1? Do you see a relationship between the ratio of the sides and the ratio of the areas? Use Calculate on one or both of these ratios and collect data in a table to confirm your conjecture.

Investigation: Proportions with Area

Student Audience: Middle School/High School

Prerequisites: Students need to understand the concepts of **area** and **ratio**. **Dilate** may be a new term needing explanation.

Sketchpad Proficiency: Experienced User

Class Time: 30 minutes

Construction Tips

Step 1: Polygons are made up of sides, but in Sketchpad you need to select a polygon's vertices to construct a polygon interior.

Steps 2-3: Dilate means the same thing as scale. When you dilate objects, you shrink or stretch them toward or away from a center of dilation by some scale factor.

Investigate/Conjecture

Students may recognize the graph traced by the plotted point as that of half a parabola, implying the side-length ratio is proportional to the square of the area ratio. The relationship may be more obvious if they measure the coordinates of the plotted point and observe the graph includes points (1, 1), (2, 4), and (3, 9). Students should conjecture:

The ratio of the areas of two similar polygons is equal to the square of the ratio of the lengths of corresponding sides.

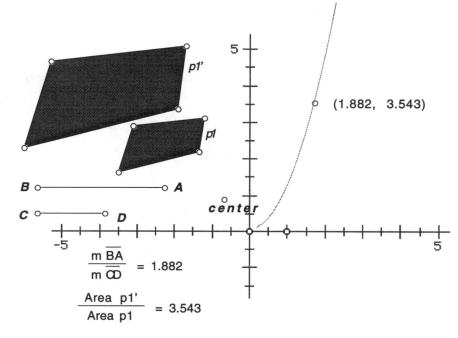

$$\frac{m\ \overline{BA}}{m\ \overline{CD}} = 1.882$$

$$\frac{Area\ p1'}{Area\ p1} = 3.543$$

Note that students aren't likely to see this relationship with Sketchpad when length ratios are not whole numbers. Ask what area ratio they would expect if the length ratio were 3/2. You might want to guide students to a conjecture like:

If the ratios of corresponding sides in two similar polygons is a/b, then the ratio of their areas is $(a/b)^2$.

Students can confirm this conjecture by using Calculate to square the ratio of lengths (or to find the square root of the ratio of areas).

Explore More

The relevance of this concept can be brought home by asking students, "Why do you think all insects are relatively small?" Hint that it has to do with area vs. length ratios. (Insects are small because they have to carry their skeletons outside their bodies. Their skeletons have area, not just length. For an insect to get twice as long, its skeleton has to get four times as big and heavy.)

The ratio of the volumes of similar solids will be the cube of the ratio of corresponding lengths.

Investigation: Proportions with Area (continued)

Conjecture: Write a conjecture below.

_____

_____

_____

_____

Present Your Findings

Discuss your findings with your partner or group. To present your findings, you could:

1. Print a captioned sketch showing scaled polygons, the ratio of corresponding lengths, and the ratio of their areas.

2. Send a demonstration over the network to your classmates and/or teacher.

Explore More

How does the ratio of the volumes of similar solids compare to the ratio of their surface areas and corresponding lengths? Investigate by calculating the volume and surface area of two boxes, one twice as long, wide, and tall as the other.

Chapter 10
Trigonometry

Investigation: Trigonometric Ratios

Trigonometric ratios are relationships between sides and angles of right triangles. In this investigation you'll discover some of these relationships and create a table of trigonometric ratios for some specific angles.

Sketch

Step 1: Construct $\overline{AB}$ and a line perpendicular to $\overline{AB}$ through point B.

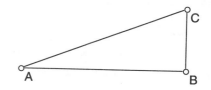

Step 2: Construct $\overline{BC}$ on the line and hypotenuse $\overline{AC}$ to create right triangle ABC.

Step 3: Hide the line.

Step 4: Measure $\angle CAB$ and ratios BC/AC, AB/AC, and BC/AB.

Investigate

Drag point B, the vertex of the right angle. Notice that the measure of $\angle BAC$ doesn't change. (If you drag either of the other two points, the angles will change.) Notice, too, that while the lengths of all the sides change, all of the ratios you measured remain constant. If you change the angle, the ratios will change, but for a given angle in any right triangle the ratios will be constant. These constant ratios are called trigonometric ratios and have names **sine**, **cosine**, and **tangent**. $\overline{BC}$ is the side opposite $\angle CAB$, $\overline{AB}$ is the side adjacent to $\angle CAB$, and $\overline{AC}$ is the hypotenuse of the right triangle. The abbreviated names of the ratios are as follows:

BC/AC = Opposite Side/Hypotenuse = sin $\angle CAB$

AB/AC = Adjacent Side/Hypotenuse = cos $\angle CAB$

BC/AB = Opposite Side/Adjacent Side = tan $\angle CAB$

Edit the ratios to read "Sin A," "Cos A," and "Tan A." Drag point C to create different angles, and tabulate entries in 5° intervals from 0° to 90°. (Get as close to 5° multiples as you can.) A partial table (with angles displayed to thousandths precision) is shown below. You'll probably need to build three separate tables so you can see all the entries.

Angle(CAB)	5.042	10.008	14.948	20.014	24.989	29.982
Sin A	0.088	0.174	0.258	0.342	0.422	0.500
Cos A	0.996	0.985	0.966	0.940	0.906	0.866
Tan A	0.088	0.176	0.267	0.364	0.466	0.577

Investigation: Trigonometric Ratios

Student Audience: High School/Advanced High School

Prerequisites: Use this activity at the beginning of a unit on trigonometry. Students should know or be introduced to the terms **sine**, **cosine**, and **tangent** as they apply to right triangles.

Sketchpad Proficiency: Beginner

Class Time: 40 minutes

Construction Tips

Step 4: Students should edit these measures so they can keep track of what they represent in their diagram. They may want to display and edit segment labels to correspond with point labels (e.g., side *a* opposite ∠*A*).

Investigate/Conjecture

On Macintoshes without math co-processors, students should engage the Caps Lock key so that measures will update continuously while they manipulate their triangles. While a trig chart is available in most books, and calculators will give trig values instantly, this is a relatively painless way for students to generate their own and see where the values actually come from as they create the table. (Remember this shortcut: double-click on a table to add an entry.) It will also help them see patterns so that they can make conjectures such as:

As an angle approaches 90°, its sine approaches 1, its cosine approaches 0, and its tangent approaches infinity.

As an angle approaches 0°, its sine approaches 0, its cosine approaches 1, and its tangent approaches 0.

Explore More

1. If angles are displayed with hundredths place precision, students will see they're usually unable to drag to whole number degree angles, thus values in their chart will differ from those in a textbook, though by less than 0.01. Have students print and keep their tables as they solve problems using trigonometry. You might ask them to solve a problem twice: once using values from their table and again using more precise values. Then ask them to determine the error introduced by their approximations to see if it's significant to that particular application.

3. The figure below is an example of how this construction might look.

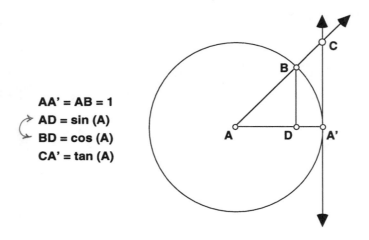

AA' = AB = 1
AD = sin (A)
BD = cos (A)
CA' = tan (A)

Investigation: Trigonometric Ratios (continued)

Conjecture: Complete the conjectures below.

As an angle approaches 90°, its sine approaches _____ , its cosine approaches_____ , and its tangent approaches _____.

As an angle approaches 0°, its sine approaches _____ , its cosine approaches_____ , and its tangent approaches _____.

Look for other patterns or interesting values in your chart and write any other conjectures you can make below.

_____

_____

_____

_____

_____

Present Your Findings

Compare and discuss your table with your partner or group.

Explore More

1. Find a trigonometry table in a book and compare it to your table. How do they compare?

2. Do research on how trigonometry ratios are used in problem solving. Would trigonometry ratios rounded to the hundredths place be accurate enough for real life applications?

3. Trigonometry ratios can be defined as quantities found in a unit circle. Do some research on this. Construct a circle with radius 1 inch and construct segments whose lengths are the sine, cosine, and tangent of a given central angle.

Exploration: A Sine Wave Tracer

In this exploration, you'll construct an animation "engine" that traces out a special curve called a **sine wave**. Variations of sine curves are the graphs of functions called **periodic functions**, functions that repeat themselves over time. The motion of a pendulum and ocean tides are examples of periodic functions.

Here are the steps of the construction:

Step 1: Construct a horizontal segment $\overline{AB}$.

Step 2: Construct a circle with center A and radius endpoint C.

Step 3: Construct point D on $\overline{AB}$ and a line perpendicular to $\overline{AB}$ through D.

Step 4: Construct $\overline{AE}$, with E on the circle.

Step 5: Construct a line parallel to $\overline{AB}$, through E.

Step 6: Construct point of intersection, F. If you consider your circle to be a unit circle, the height of point F above $\overline{AB}$ is the value of the sine of $\angle A$.

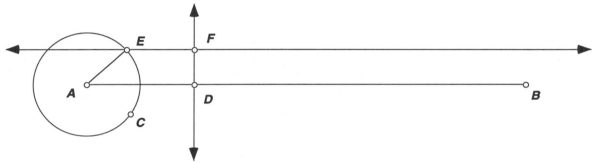

Animate the sine wave tracer:

Step 7: Move point D so that it's just to the right of the circle.

Step 8: Select point F and choose Trace Point in the Display menu.

Step 9: Select, in order, D, $\overline{AB}$, E, and the circle.

Step 10: Make an action button that animates point D on $\overline{AB}$, one-way, and animates point E on the circle, one-way.

Investigate

Try it with different size circles and with different animation options. Allow point E to travel more than once around the circle, then see if you can adjust your sketch so that the sine wave will trace over itself. On a separate piece of paper, describe the curve that your sine wave tracer creates. Be as specific as you can, and try to relate the sine wave to measurements of the circle.

Explore More

See if you can construct the locus of this curve. First hide point D, point F, and the line through them. Rather than using a random point like D, for your locus construction you need to find a point whose distance from point A is equal to the length of an arc swept out by point E as it moves around the circle. Construct an arc, measure its length, and translate point A by this measure. Proceed until you have an intersection like point F, and construct the locus of this intersection and E.

Exploration: A Sine Wave Tracer

Student Audience: Advanced High School/College/Teacher Training

Prerequisites: The activity may be more meaningful to students who've begun studying trigonometry.

Sketchpad Proficiency: Experienced User

Class Time: 30 minutes

Example Sketches: **Sin/Cos Tracer** and **Tangent Tracer** (Mac) or **9-10sim\trigtrac.gsp** and **9-10sim\tantrac.gsp** (Windows)

Construction Tips

This isn't a difficult construction, and beginners could be led through it, given time and patience. Experienced users will do the construction quickly and will be less likely to get hung up on the animation dialog.

Step 1: Hold down shift to constrain your segment to 15° intervals, making it easy to construct a horizontal segment.

Investigate/Conjecture

This activity leaves it pretty open-ended when it comes to what students are asked to describe. Students should at least notice that the maximum height (the amplitude) of the sine wave is equal to the radius of the circle. They may also make observations (in their own words) about the periodic nature of the curve and how the relationship between the circumference of the circle and the length of the segment determines whether or not the curve will retrace itself. (When the circumference and segment length are equal, the tracer will trace one period of the sine wave in one revolution of the circle, thus causing the point F to retrace its path on subsequent revolutions. Students trying this should measure the circumference and length so they can adjust them until they're approximately equal.)

If students have access to QuickTime or Video for Windows, they can make a movie of this animation. The sketch is simple enough that a movie would not take up too much memory. And students will enjoy being able to run the movie forwards and backwards and investigate when the amplitude is greatest or when the curve crosses the axis.

Explore More

(Not on activity sheet) If students try different animation speeds along the segment and circle, they can investigate how this affects the period. Challenge them to figure out what the ratios of the different speeds are (for example, the ratio of fast/medium is 5/3). Students can try constructing cosine or tangent tracers. For cosine, rotate the sine point 90° around the circle, then trace cosine and sine together to show the effect of these functions being 90° out of phase. For tangent, construct a line tangent to the circle, perpendicular to $\overline{AB}$. Construct a full line $\overleftrightarrow{AC}$ and the two points of intersection (as C rotates) with the tangent line. Proceed with these points as with sine.

     Exploring Geometry

Investigation: Modeling a Ladder Problem

Drawing diagrams is a useful method to help solve many types of realistic problems. Dynamic diagrams can be even more useful. Here's a problem that can be solved with a Sketchpad sketch:

If you lean a ladder against a wall so that the angle it makes with the floor is less than 45°, you risk having the bottom slide out from under the ladder. If the angle is more than 75°, the ladder may tip over backwards. What's the height from the ground of the lowest and highest window you can reach with a 20-foot ladder?

Sketch

Step 1: Construct vertical and horizontal segments $\overline{AB}$ and $\overline{BC}$ and edit the segment labels to say "wall" and "floor."

Step 2: Construct D on the floor. This point will be the foot of your ladder.

Step 3: Translate point D two inches in any direction. The two inches will represent the length of your ladder, so the scale of your drawing will be 1 in. = 10 ft.

Step 4: Construct circle DD'.

Step 5: Construct $\overline{DE}$, where E is the intersection of circle DD' and the wall. You may have to move D first so that the circle and wall intersect. $\overline{DE}$ represents your ladder. (Edit its label.) Its length can't change because the radius of the circle is fixed at two inches.

Step 6: Hide the circle and point D'.

Investigate

Measure $\angle EDB$ and the distance from E to B (EB represents the height up the wall that your ladder is reaching). Move point D back and forth across the floor and use your measures to find answers to the problem above. Write your answers below:

_____

Now, on a separate piece of paper, write one or more other problems that could be modeled with this sketch:

Present Your Findings

Discuss your results with your partner or group. To present your findings, you could print a captioned sketch that shows your model in the two states that solve the problem. Make sure to show the measures that represent the answers.

Explore More

1. See if you can use Sketchpad to model other real-life problems. What's the path of a can of paint at the midpoint, falling as the foot of a ladder slides along the floor? Construct the midpoint and while it's selected choose Trace Point in the Display Menu. Animate point D along $\overline{BC}$.

2. Measure the distance from the foot of the ladder to the wall (DB) and the height of the ladder (EB). Select these measures and choose Plot As (x, y) in the Measure menu. Drag the foot of the ladder. What kind of graph do you get? If you were to drag the foot of a ladder away from a wall at a constant rate, would the top of the ladder fall at a constant rate? Why or why not?

Investigation: Modeling a Ladder Problem

Student Audience: High School/Advanced High School

Prerequisites: Students should know what angles are.

Sketchpad Proficiency: Experienced User

Class Time: 30 minutes

Example Sketch: Falling Ladder (Mac) or **9-10sim\ladder.gsp** (Windows)

Construction Tips

Step 1: Construct a line perpendicular to *AB*, then construct *BC* on it. Or simply hold down the Shift key while constructing the segments to constrain them to be vertical and horizontal.

Step 2: Make sure inches are chosen in Preferences as the length units. In the example, point *D* was translated with polar coordinates of 90° by 2 inches.

Investigate/Conjecture

The approximate answers Sketchpad will give are 1.41 inches (14.1 ft.) for a 45° angle and 1.93 inches (19.3 ft.) for a 75° angle. Students should go beyond solving this one problem, though. Make sure students invent problems of their own. And encourage them to construct models for different problems.

Explore More

1. If students trace the path of a can of paint at the midpoint, they'll see it traces out a quarter circle. What if the point isn't at the midpoint?

2. The graph of the ladder's distance from the wall vs. the height on the wall is a quarter circle, centered at the origin. That means that as the foot of the ladder is pulled away from the wall, the top of the ladder starts falling slowly. But the farther away from the wall the foot of the ladder gets, the faster the top of the ladder falls.

 Exploring Geometry

Construction: Creating a Fractal

By using scripts, you can easily repeat an action again and again on the same figure. Repeatedly taking the result of a function and applying the function to that result again is called **recursion** in mathematics and is central to the creation of fractals. In this activity, you'll record a recursive script to create the first few stages of a fractal called the Sierpinski gasket. A true Sierpinski gasket, created in infinitely many stages, has dimension between one and two and has strange properties of perimeter and area.

Sketch

Step 1:   Open a new script and click Record.

Step 2:   Construct a triangle *ABC*, its interior, and midpoints of its sides.

Step 3:   Select *A*, *E*, and *F* and click Loop in your script.

Step 4:   Repeat step 3 for *EBD* and *FDC*.

Step 5:   Hide points *F*, *E*, and *D*.

Step 6:   Stop your script.

Your script constructs a triangle and the midpoints of its sides. The recursive step repeats that script in each corner of the triangle just constructed by the script.

Construct three points in a new sketch to serve as vertices of a large triangle. Play your script with a recursion depth of 3 or 4. Your script constructs a triangle, then a triangle in the corner of that triangle, then a triangle in a corner of the corner triangle, and so on, however many times you specified by your recursion depth. Then it repeats that process in each corner of your original triangle. So what you end up with is several layers of triangles, all covered by the interior of the largest, original triangle. (If the shade of that triangle is light enough, you might be able to see edges of the smaller triangles underneath.) To see successive stages of the Sierpinski gasket, you now want to hide successive layers of these triangles.

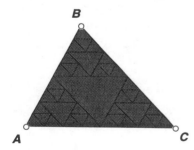 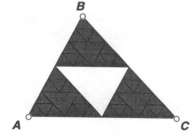 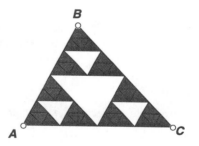

Your original triangle is a stage 0 gasket. To see a stage 1 gasket, click in the center of this figure to select the large triangle, then hide it.

This triangle with the center triangle removed is a stage 1 gasket. This gasket consists of 3 triangles, one in each corner. Hold down Shift while you click in the center of each of these 3 triangles to select them, then hide them to reveal a stage 2 gasket.

Your stage 2 gasket consists of 9 triangles. If you hide each of these triangles, you'll see a stage 3 gasket. How many triangles do you think it would have?

Construction: Creating a Fractal

Student Audience: High School/Advanced High School/College/Teacher Education

Prerequisites: It would be helpful if students were introduced to some fractal concepts and shown some examples before doing this construction. **Self-similarity, recursion, fractional dimension,** figures with **finite area** and **infinite perimeter** are all concepts encountered in this activity. You could use the activity to introduce these concepts, but some prior knowledge would probably help the construction make more sense.

Sketchpad Proficiency: Power User

Class Time: 30 minutes

Example Script: Sierpinski Δ (Mac) or **9-10sim\sierpins.gss** (Windows)

Construction Tips

This construction employs scripts and the Loop feature. Knowledge of various selection techniques is also helpful.

Step 3: It won't be obvious why students must create this interior, only to hide it in step 7. But at each level in the recursion, the triangles from the previous stage need to be hidden. At the next stage, when the script tries to construct a polygon light polygon, it will see there's already a dark one there, and will hide it instead of constructing a new one.

Steps 5 and *6:* Don't Loop on the inside triangle. The three triangles to Loop on are each comprised of midpoint-vertex-midpoint.

Students can quickly undo back to the beginning (using the menu command or keyboard shortcut), then redo one step at a time to reconstruct the initial three points. Students probably shouldn't attempt to create different triangles of different stages in the same sketch, as this will eat up memory fast.

Investigate/Conjecture

Assuming you start out with a triangle with area 1 square unit, a stage one gasket has area 3/4 square units. Think of the original triangle as having been divided into four equal smaller ones with the middle triangle taken out to create the stage one gasket. Each stage gasket, then, has 3/4 the area of the previous stage. If you assume your original triangle had perimeter 3 units, you add half again that much when you connect the midpoints, so the stage one gasket has perimeter 4 1/2 units. Each stage gasket has 1 1/2 times the perimeter of the previous stage. So with successive stages, the perimeter approaches infinity while the area approaches 0.

A stage-n Sierpinski gasket has area $A_0(3/4)^n$, where A_0 is the area of the original triangle.

A stage-n Sierpinski gasket has perimeter $P_0(3/2)^n$, where P_0 is the perimeter of the original triangle.

A stage-infinity Sierpinski gasket has zero area and infinite perimeter.

Students may write other conjectures having to do with the appearance of the gasket. Encourage them to try to define **self-similarity.**

Explore More

The areas and perimeters of successive stages can be considered as infinite geometric sequences. The area sequence converges to 0 because its constant ratio, 3/4, is less than one. The perimeter sequence diverges because its constant ratio is 3/2.

 Exploring Geometry

Construction: Creating a Fractal (continued)

Investigate

Compare your stage one gasket with your stage two and three gaskets. As you increase the number of stages, what's happening to the area of the figure (the shaded part)? What's happening to the perimeter, including the perimeter inside the figure around all the little shaded triangles? What do you think would be the area of a Sierpinski gasket at stage infinity? What about the perimeter at stage infinity?

Conjecture: Write your conjectures.

_____

_____

_____

_____

_____

_____

_____

_____

_____

_____

_____

Explore More

1. Suppose you start with a stage zero gasket (a triangle) with area 1 square unit and perimeter 2 units. Calculate the areas and perimeters of successive stage gaskets. Now suppose your original triangle has area A_0 and perimeter P_0. Can you come up with a rule for a stage-n gasket?

2. Experiment with recursive scripts to see what other figures you can create.